D1104077

WASHBURN CHILD GUIDANCE CENTER
2430 Nicollet Avenue South
Minneapolis, Minnesota 55404

PUBLICATIONS OF THE JOINT INFORMATION SERVICE

The Treatment of Drug Abuse: Programs, Problems, Prospects, by Raymond M. Glasscote, James N. Sussex, Jerome H. Jaffe, John Ball, and Leon Brill. 1972.

Eleven Indices—An Aid in Reviewing State and Local Mental Health and Hospital Programs. 1971.

Halfway Houses for the Mentally Ill: A Study of Programs and Problems, by Raymond M. Glasscote, Jon E. Gudeman, and J. Richard Elpers. 1971.

Rehabilitating the Mentally Ill in the Community: A Study of Psychosocial Rehabilitation Centers, by Raymond M. Glasscote, Elaine Cumming, Irvin D. Rutman, James N. Sussex, and Sidney M. Glassman. 1971.

Salary Ranges of Personnel Employed in State Mental Hospitals and Community Mental Health Centers—1970, prepared by Charles K. Kanno and Patricia L. Scheidemandel. 1970.

The Staff of the Mental Health Center: A Field Study, by Raymond M. Glasscote and Jon E. Gudeman. 1969.

The Treatment of Alcoholism: A Study of Programs and Problems, by Raymond M. Glasscote, Thomas F. A. Plaut, Donald W. Hammersley, Francis J. O'Neill, Morris E. Chafetz, and Elaine Cumming. 1967.

The Community Mental Health Center: An Interim Appraisal, by Raymond M. Glasscote, James N. Sussex, Elaine Cumming, and Lauren H. Smith. 1969.

Partial Hospitalization for the Mentally Ill: A Study of Programs and Problems, by Raymond M. Glasscote, Alan M. Kraft, Sidney M. Glassman, and William W. Jepson. 1969.

The Mentally Ill Offender: A Survey of Treatment Programs, by Patricia L. Scheidemandel and Charles K. Kanno. 1969.

Legal Services and Community Mental Health Centers, by Henry Weihofen. 1969.

Health Insurance for Mental Illness, by Patricia L. Scheidemandel, Charles K. Kanno, and Raymond M. Glasscote. 1968.

The Psychiatric Emergency: A Study of Patterns of Service, by Raymond M. Glasscote, Elaine Cumming, Donald W. Hammersley, Lucy D. Ozarin, and Lauren H. Smith. 1966.

General Hospital Psychiatric Units: A National Survey, by Raymond M. Glasscote and Charles K. Kanno. 1965.

Private Psychiatric Hospitals: A National Survey, by Charles K. Kanno and Raymond M. Glasscote. 1966.

OUT OF PRINT

The Community Mental Health Center: An Analysis of Existing Models, by Raymond M. Glasscote, David Sanders, H. M. Forstenzer, and A. R. Foley. 1964.

Approaches to the Care of Long-Term Mental Patients, by Helen M. Padula, with three case studies by Raymond M. Glasscote, Elaine Cumming, and Helen Padula. 1968.

CHILDREN AND MENTAL HEALTH CENTERS

Programs, Problems, Prospects

WASHBURN CHILD GUIDANCE CENTER
2430 Nicollet Avenue South
Minneapolis, Minnesota 55404

CHILDREN AND MENTAL HEALTH CENTERS
Programs, Problems, Prospects

RAYMOND M. GLASSCOTE, M.A.
Chief, Joint Information Service

MICHAEL E. FISHMAN, M.D.
Chief, Children's Services Program Area
Mental Health Services Development Branch
Division of Mental Health Service Programs
National Institute of Mental Health

MEYER SONIS, M.D.
Chief and Professor, Child Psychiatry
Western Psychiatric Institute and Clinic
Pittsburgh

in collaboration
with

LORETTA CASS, Ph.D.
Assistant Professor
Washington University
School of Medicine

PEARL SHALIT, M.S.W., R.N.
Mental Health Consultant

MICHAEL FREELUND, Ll.B.
Administrator
New York School of Psychiatry

DAVID KALLEN, Ph.D.
Associate Professor
Department of Human Development
Michigan State University

A publication of
THE JOINT INFORMATION SERVICE
of the
AMERICAN PSYCHIATRIC ASSOCIATION
and the
NATIONAL ASSOCIATION FOR MENTAL HEALTH
WASHINGTON, D.C., 1972

614.58
Gl

Copyright 1972, American Psychiatric Association
Library of Congress Card No. 77-187293

JOINT INFORMATION SERVICE
of the AMERICAN PSYCHIATRIC ASSOCIATION
and the NATIONAL ASSOCIATION FOR MENTAL HEALTH

EXECUTIVE COMMITTEE

For the
American Psychiatric Association

PAUL HUSTON, M.D.
Chairman, 1971-72

JACK R. EWALT, M.D.

LAWRENCE C. KOLB, M.D.

ROY W. MENNINGER, M.D.

WALTER E. BARTON, M.D.,
Ex-officio
(Medical Director, APA)

For the
National Association for Mental Health

CHARLES FRAZIER

MRS. JEANNETTE ROCKEFELLER

HON. LUTHER ALVERSON

HENRY WEIHOFEN, J.S.D.

BRIAN O'CONNELL,
Ex-officio
(Executive Director, NAMH)

STAFF

RAYMOND GLASSCOTE, *Chief*

CHARLES KANNO,
Research Associate

PATRICIA SCHEIDEMANDEL,
Research Associate

STEPHEN HUDDLE,
Research Assistant

MARJORIE HOLTZCLAW,
Information Specialist

Donald W. Hammersley, M.D., serves as permanent professional consultant to the Joint Information Service.

The Joint Information Service is administratively attached to the APA Division of Public Affairs, which is headed by Robert L. Robinson.

Additional copies of this publication are available from the JOINT INFORMATION SERVICE, 1700 18th Street, N.W., Washington, D.C. 20009, at $6.00, with discount for quantity purchases.

This book results from an investigation carried out as a joint undertaking of the Joint Information Service and the National Institute of Mental Health. Approximately three quarters of the funds for the project were furnished under NIMH Contract No. HSM-42-70-93; the balance came from the budget of the Joint Information Service.

ACKNOWLEDGMENTS

As always, the Joint Information Service is indebted to many persons who have helped us and participated in our work. Drs. Walter Barton, Saul Feldman, and Arthur Stein, Brian O'Connell, together with several members of his staff at NAMH, and Robert Robinson read the manuscript and made a number of useful suggestions which were incorporated. Dr. Donald Hammersley gave us continued encouragement, support, and advice throughout the project. The Joint Information Service staff during the time of the study—Charles Kanno, Patricia Scheidemandel, and Marjorie Holtzclaw—provided their usual marvelous support from the inception of the idea to the completion of the page proofs. And the directors and staff of the eight programs described herein went far beyond any obligation to provide us with a wealth of well-prepared information.

CONTENTS

I

Why and How This Study Was Done

I N 1963, ANTICIPATING that there would soon be a federal program to support community-based mental health services, the Joint Information Service undertook a field study of eleven "pioneering" comprehensive, community-based treatment facilities. Later that year the federal Community Mental Health Centers Act was passed by Congress, providing, initially, a portion of the funds for building these new services, and, in a subsequent amendment, a portion of the funds to meet the payroll.

Since then, the Joint Information Service, through a series of cost-sharing contracts with the National Institute of Mental Health, has carried out several additional studies of various aspects of community mental health centers, which led to further publications, listed on p. ii. In each case we have followed a "modelistic approach," whereby we sought to identify not typical but outstanding examples of the particular topic under study, in the hope that by disseminating information about programs that were imaginative and resourceful we might induce newer and less well developed programs to follow their lead.

A S FOR THE PRESENT STUDY, it might suffice to say that, since several facets of community mental health services had already been investigated, it was a logical next choice to look at the services the centers provide for children and adolescents. This would be true enough. But an additional impetus was the often-heard plaints of many people interested in the problems of childhood mental illness that these younger patients were of low priority in the plans of some of the mental health centers, or, to put it another way, that children and adolescents were being underserved. Certainly there have been events in recent years to give this complaint credence.

For a start, the Joint Commission on Mental Illness and Health, which did its work from 1955 through 1960, did not include young people in its study. This Commission was chartered by Congress to make an exhaustive survey of national mental health needs and to recommend a plan for action; on the grounds that it lacked both time and money, the

1

Commission did not concern itself with the mental health needs of children and adolescents.

In 1963 federal funds were made available to the states so that they might develop, over a two-year period, plans for organizing and providing comprehensive mental health services. Each state was required to submit a document setting forth the way in which it proposed to develop its plan. These proposals, called "The Plans for Planning," were analyzed by the Joint Information Service.[1] The analysis disclosed that

> nineteen of the proposals did not include services for children as a specialized area, only three mentioned public school mental health programs, and only thirteen discussed prevention of childhood mental illness as an integral part of general prevention.[2]

Alarmed by this information, the American Psychiatric Association, the American Academy of Child Psychiatry, the American Association of Psychiatric Services for Children, and the American Orthopsychiatric Association called a conference for the purpose of developing principles and guidelines for planning services for children, on the grounds that "guidance in developing plans for children's psychiatric services was clearly needed by the planning bodies, both at the state-wide and at the community level." From the proceedings was developed the publication *Planning Psychiatric Services for Children,* which discussed principles of planning, essential elements of treatment services for children, staffing, prevention, and so on. As a result some of the states which had not included children and adolescents in their mental health plans subsequently did so.

THE FIRST JOINT INFORMATION SERVICE field study, *The Community Mental Health Center: An Analysis of Existing Models,*[3] described a group of more or less comprehensive community-based mental health services that had been developed under various auspices prior to enactment of the federal support program. This study verified that even these pace-setting institutions gave relatively little emphasis to children. It said:

> We do not believe any of these eleven centers could be said to come very close to meeting the needs of all the emotionally disturbed children

---

[1] *"The Plans for Planning": A Comparative Analysis of the State Mental Health Planning Proposals.* Joint Information Service, Washington, D.C., 1963.

[2] *Planning Psychiatric Services for Children.* American Psychiatric Association, Washington, D.C., 1963.

[3] R. M. Glasscote, D. S. Sanders, H. M. Forstenzer, and A. R. Foley: *The Community Mental Health Center: An Analysis of Existing Models.* Joint Information Service, Washington, D.C., 1964.

within their catchment areas. Some of them provide hardly any service at all.

When Fort Logan [Mental Health Center], which presently accepts no children, opens its 60-bed children's unit early in 1965 it will become the first of these centers to have any sizable number of beds for children. Of the remaining ten centers, Massachusetts Mental Health Center, Albert Einstein Medical Center, and Nebraska Psychiatric Institute have inpatient units of 12, 13, and 21 beds, primarily for purposes of the teaching program. . . . [Five of the centers] do not provide inpatient service for children on any basis at all. . . . At [one center] outpatient service for children is available [elsewhere in the county. Nine other facilities] all offer outpatient treatment for children; however, there are long waiting periods at several of them, and in some cases intake is closed from time to time.

Prairie View [Mental Health Center] accepts adolescents in its day program . . . and Nebraska Psychiatric Institute accepts a few children on a day basis; otherwise there are no part-time hospitalization arrangements for children.

IN 1965 CONGRESS CREATED a second "joint commission," this time to deal specifically with the mental health problems of children and young people. This body, known as the Joint Commission on Mental Health of Children, took a different tack. Instead of focusing mainly on the mentally ill population, it addressed itself to the emotional needs and problems of all children in America. Only one of its twelve chapters is directly addressed to emotionally disturbed and mentally ill children and youth. One survey that was conducted in connection with the work of this Commission revealed that among 27 states providing data the percent of the state's mental health budget allocated to children's services ranged from less than one percent to 27 percent, averaging only ten percent.

IN 1968, ANOTHER JOINT INFORMATION SERVICE field study involved eight of the new, federally funded community mental health centers, selected on the basis of information suggesting that they were better developed and more stabilized than most others. The report of this study [4] stated:

Only two of the [eight] centers were themselves operating any services specifically for children, and only one of these provided a day-school

---

[4] R. M. Glasscote, J. N. Sussex, E. Cumming, and L. H. Smith: *The Community Mental Health Center: An Interim Appraisal.* Joint Information Service, Washington, D.C., 1969.

program. Another center was able to provide relatively long-term care for young people by housing them in its inpatient service while sending them to a day-treatment program operated by its parent institution. Three other facilities had the possibility of referring a child to a separate treatment facility with which it had an affiliation agreement, although there seemed to be no evidence on the one hand that the agreement resulted in any consideration other than what the child would have been accorded as an independent applicant, or on the other hand that the center continued to consider itself responsible for the child. At the remaining two centers children were accepted for outpatient treatment and for short-term inpatient treatment on the same basis as adults, but if residential treatment were required or if specialized child services were indicated, these two centers could only seek to arrange private care, if the child's family had the means to afford it, or else arrange for the child to be transferred to the state hospital.

One of these eight centers had indicated in its application for federal support the intention to create both inpatient and outpatient services for children; it found itself unable to do so, because of the pressures involved in developing the adult services and because of the difficulty of recruiting staff with training in treating children and adolescents.

THUS THERE WERE VARIOUS EVIDENCES that interest in developing specific services for young people is generally low and that the problems inherent in developing such services are viewed as great. It does seem clear that the National Institute of Mental Health, in administering the community mental health centers program, had not intended for children to receive less than their due. Said a 1965 NIMH publication:

> Services for children are planned as an integral part of each center's overall program; the full range of diagnostic, therapeutic, and preventive approaches to be applied to the general population will be available to children as well. . . . All presently existing services available to children will continue to be provided by community mental health centers. They will, however, be more clearly focused, intensified, and refined.[5]

But in the process of developing their programs, centers variously experienced problems in providing for younger patients, and these difficulties were officially acknowledged by the 1970 amendments to the federal legislation, which authorized specific separate sums for developing services for children.

---

[5] National Institute of Mental Health: "The Role of the Community Mental Health Center," in *Mental Health of Children*. U.S. Public Health Service Publication No. 1396, 1965.

There are various reasons for the lack of emphasis on services for children. Important among them is that many centers were disposed to concentrate their initial efforts in the area where they felt they could best demonstrate their greatest usefulness, namely with emotionally disturbed adults. Adults thought to be mentally ill are apt to be regarded as more of a threat than children thought to be mentally ill. Adults are more visible and therefore more likely to get into difficulties with policemen and other authorities. Beyond this, many of the mental health professionals working in the centers have had scant training, if any, in treating children and adolescents, and thus are wary of trying to do so. There have also been distinct problems in trying to recruit the scarce mental health professionals who do have training in treating young people. Finally, because of the need for various services, particularly educational, it is widely believed that the cost is greater in children's services.

There is no formula to tell us what percentage of mental health service should go to what age intervals, and until such time as there may be one we can judge the adequacy of service only in contrast with the age distribution of the general population. This is, of course, an altogether inadequate amount of information on which to ascertain whether present services are sufficient or to plan for the future. But on this basis, which is really all we have available to us at the present time, children and adolescents are being underserved in community mental health centers. Specifically, in calendar 1969 (the latest year for which data were available) persons 19 and under accounted for 26 percent of admissions to community mental health centers, whereas they represented a little more than 40 percent of the general population. The figure needs, however, to be cautiously viewed. Some adult patients of the centers are seen largely or mainly because of problems originating with or related to their children. Also, as we shall discuss later, a very large amount of the mental health consultation provided by the centers is directed toward agencies that focus much or all of their efforts on children. It may be, given the widely imputed shortages of personnel trained to work with children with emotional problems, and the evidently high cost of serving children, that the 26 percent figure is, at this early point in the development of the centers, a creditable one.

HAVING DECIDED TO STUDY some outstanding models of services for children and adolescents in community mental health centers, the Joint Information Service, prior to the start of our field study, surveyed the 206 centers that were operating as of early 1970, in the hope that the responses would assist us in choosing centers to visit. From these responses we were able to identify four that seemed outstanding either in the amount of service provided for young people, new and imaginative approaches, or both. In each case we consulted with mental health professionals in the locales of these programs to verify that they were suitable. To identify the remaining four it was necessary to solicit candidates from a host of mental health professionals around the country, including notably the staff of the regional offices of NIMH and various individuals who had carried out site visits for NIMH. In selecting the facilities we did not attempt to achieve diversity among particular treatment approaches and philosophies, with one exception; the Greenville, South Carolina, program was chosen precisely because its' residential and day-treatment components are modeled on the Project Re-ED program developed by Dr. Nicholas Hobbs in Tennessee. Diversity among the remaining programs was sought in terms of program components, demography (urban vs. rural vs. suburban), socioeconomic characteristics, ethnicity, auspices, and section of the country.

Each facility selected was then asked if it would be willing to complete for us a lengthy questionnaire (Appendix I) intended to provide background material, and then to receive the authors and consultants for a visit during which we would interview a representative group of staff members, some representatives of outside agencies that refer children and adolescents to the center or from whom services are obtained for these young people, and parents of the patients. Each one agreed to participate. The visits were made between September 1970 and January 1971. The authors visited all of the facilities, the consultants the following:

	Cass	Kallen	Freelund	Shalit
Western Missouri Mental Health Center, Kansas City	x	x		
Alger-Delta-Marquette Community Mental Health Center, Marquette and Escanaba, Mich.		x		x
Cambridge-Somerville Mental Health Center, Cambridge and Somerville, Mass.	x		x	
Convalescent Hospital for Children, Rochester, N.Y.	x		x	
Kedren Mental Health Center, Los Angeles	x			x
The Children's Re-Education Center, Greenville, S.C.			x	x

	Cass	Kallen	Freelund	Shalit
Arapahoe Mental Health Center, Englewood and Aurora, Colo.	x			x
Peninsula Hospital Community Mental Health Center, Burlingame, Cal.	x		x	

The interviews were recorded on tape and the tapes were transcribed. The authors and consultants also prepared trip reports. The description of each program herein is thus based on *a*) the orientation questionnaire and additional brochures, annual reports, grant applications, and so on, *b*) the transcription of the interviews, and *c*) the trip reports. Each facility was asked to review the description of its program in order to correct any misstatements or to rebut any critical comments, and each did so.

After the visits were concluded, the authors and consultants met in Washington, D.C., in February 1971, with representatives of the eight programs. During a two-day meeting, this group considered and reacted to an agenda the authors had prepared, which they felt reflected the issues and problems involved in organizing and operating mental health services for children and adolescents. This conference was recorded on tape and transcribed.

Working principally from *Psychological Abstracts, Index Medicus,* and print-outs furnished by the National Clearinghouse for Mental Health Information, the staff of the Joint Information Service concurrently carried out a search of the literature pertaining to the treatment of emotionally disturbed children and adolescents. The summary section of this volume is thus based primarily on *a*) the two-day conference with the eight center representatives, *b*) the literature search, and *c*) our own synthesis, and that of the four consultants, of all that we heard and saw during the course of our field visits.

Children in America

EARLY IN THIS CENTURY the Swedish educator Ellen Key predicted that it will go down in history as "the century of the child." In 1971, there may be many who, from their disappointing and frustrating efforts to obtain adequate services for children, would disagree. Yet a look at the historic status of children in America indicates that only in the past few decades have young people begun to come into their own. It was not until well into the present century that provisions for child welfare became uniform in the law. The twentieth century, as regards children, might most accurately be described as a time in which historic neglect, insignificance, and abuse of children were gradually but dramatically supplanted by a series of special provisions for the young, approaching, ultimately, what is very nearly an idealization of youth. It may help our perspective if we consider how recent are some of the major provisions for the well-being of children.

• *Justice*. It was not until 1899 that the first juvenile court was created in the United States, by act of the Illinois legislature. Until that time it had been commonly assumed that young children up to the age of about seven were incapable of committing crimes; those between seven and 14 were also presumed incapable of crime, "but the presumption was rebuttable upon a showing that the offender understood the nature and consequences of his conduct"; [1] those over 14 were held fully accountable. The new practice of providing distinctive procedures for juvenile offenders spread quickly; by 1909, twenty states and the District of Columbia had adopted juvenile court acts.

• *Welfare*. The provisions of the British poor law of 1601 were brought to America by the colonists. This law determined "in a large measure what was done for dependent children . . . for the next three centuries." [2] This law and its successors provided that local governments might *a*) set destitute children to work along with adult paupers if they were old enough, *b*) apprentice them to learn a trade, *c*) auction them off, if they were very young, to some person who would agree to care for them

---

[1] *Encyclopaedia Britannica*. William Benton, Chicago, 1966.
[2] *Ibid*.

in his own home, or *d*) send them to the poorhouse. While the grosser practices were shed with time, the provisions of the poor law were "not finally abandoned by some states until the passage of the Social Security Act in 1935,"[3] which provided for a modest level of financial aid to children in families that had no means of support.

● *Labor.* Efforts to limit the hours of employment of minors and to make school attendance compulsory started in the nineteenth century and gained momentum, but "it was the enactment of the Fair Labor Standards Act in 1938 that signified the beginning of the end of child labor in the United States."[4]

PROBABLY THE RIGHTS OF CHILDREN in the European and English-speaking world have moved further forward in the past century than in all the previous centuries of recorded history combined. Even if the final recognition of the special needs of children for protection came only within the lifetimes of many of us, they are at least now codified into the laws of the technologically developed nations.

---

[3] *Ibid.*

[4] *Ibid.* This same source reminds us of how greatly the status of children in highly developed countries differs from that of children in other parts of the world: "Millions of children, some as young as seven, still toil in the quarries, mines, factories, fields, and service enterprises of less industrially developed countries. They make up more than ten percent of the labor force in some countries in the Middle East and from two percent to ten percent in much of Latin America and some parts of Asia."

Disturbed Children

LOUISE DESPERT,[1] IN TRACING the history of the treatment accorded to emotionally disturbed children, states that she could not find records of the feelings, aspirations, and frustrations of children prior to the present century. However, she asserts, the relatively recent term *emotional disturbance* certainly does not stand for new forms of behavior or new symptoms, but rather represents an evolution of attitudes toward the mentally ill.

> Children affected with what we would describe today as neurotic and psychotic illness were variously labeled through the ages as "possessed," "wicked," "guilty," "insubordinate," "incorrigible," "unstable," "maladjusted," and "problem children," roughly in this order. Close as they are to us, the last three epithets do not reveal any empathy for the child. Rather they put on him the onus of guilt and accusation of his having failed society.

Given the recency of legislation providing uniform protection to children in general, perhaps we should be grateful that the awareness of mental problems in children came as early as it did. Dr. Despert cites sources suggesting that America was a particularly fertile ground for children to move "from oblivion to limelight." She quotes from the *Encyclopaedia of the Social Sciences* that "an educational journal of 1833 contains an interesting description of the new cult of childhood." She says that Old World visitors heatedly criticized the status of children in America. She cites an Englishwoman who in 1841 commented:

> The indulgence which parents in the United States permit to their children is not seen in England; the child is too early his own master; as soon as he can sit at table he chooses his own food, and as soon as he can speak argues with his parents on the propriety or impropriety of their directions.

An American writing at about the same time is quoted.

> Parents have no command over their children. . . . American children are seldom taught that profound reverence for, and strict obedience to, their

---

[1] J. L. Despert: *The Emotionally Disturbed Child—Then and Now.* Vantage Press, New York, 1965.

parents, which are at once the basis of domestic comfort and of the welfare of the children themselves.

L EO KANNER, AUTHOR of the first textbook of child psychiatry in the United States (1935), has said that

> the concept of child psychiatry as a distinct specialty did not arise—and could not have arisen—before the twentieth century.[2]

While particular individuals concerned themselves with aberrant behavior in children, they seem to have been few. Eli Rubinstein, in a review of the literature before 1900 on childhood mental disease in America,[3] came up with fewer than a score of articles and books, "beginning as late as 1812 with Benjamin Rush and ending with Brower in 1898." He concludes:

> Original research is rare and there is no discovery or theory of great fundamental importance to child psychiatry. No research of today stems directly from the work of any of these early writers. Certainly there is nothing here to refute Kanner's statement that child psychiatry did not exist as such in the nineteenth century. And yet these early writers must be considered as part of the beginning of the story. . . . Whether they inspired further progress as refutation to their own conceptions, or whether they merely helped in a small measure to bring to the attention of others the problems of childhood, they must be considered as part of the early development leading to present-day child psychiatry.[4]

Kanner says of child psychiatry prior to this century:

> The story until then is not a narrative of a practiced discipline but rather an account of the building stones that eventually formed the foundations of the present-day structure. The time is not too far in the past when children were a part of the household chattel, when Dickens' *Oliver Twist* was fiction based on stark reality, when unrestricted child labor sucked

---

[2] L. Kanner: "History of Child Psychiatry," in A. M. Freedman and H. I. Kaplan (eds.), *Comprehensive Textbook of Psychiatry*. Williams & Wilkins Co., Baltimore, 1967.

[3] E. A. Rubinstein: "Childhood Mental Disease in America," *American Journal of Orthopsychiatry* 18:314-321, April 1948.

[4] A somewhat larger number of European physicians interested themselves in emotional disturbance in children prior to 1900, according to Alexander Walk, but they do not seem to have had any interchange with their American colleagues. Dr. Walk describes their work in "The Pre-History of Child Psychiatry," *British Journal of Psychiatry* 110:754-767, November 1964.

health and spirit out of impecunious youngsters, when the Prussian police denounced the first kindergartens as hotbeds of socialism.[5]

IN ONE OF THE FEW ACCOUNTS of the history of services to emotionally disturbed children, Dr. Kanner delineates a number of the "building stones" referred to above. The principal ones[6] were these:

The introduction of psychometry. Goddard introduced the Binet-Simon test of intelligence to the United States in 1910, and Terman adapted it for use in America in 1916 as the Stanford Revision of the Binet-Simon test. Thus was spread the awareness that individuals differ in intellectual capacity and, consequently, it is reasonable to establish differential expectations on the basis of one's "native" ability.

Advent of dynamic psychiatry. "Freud abroad and Meyer in this country introduced a dynamic attitude which saw the origins of present trouble in happenings and experiences of the past. . . . The retrospective search for the meaning of childhood events as precursors of later maladjustment created an appetite for direct, immediate acquaintance with the difficulties encountered in children themselves."

Establishment of the juvenile courts, in which delinquent children were to be handled separately and differently from adult violators. With time the judges of these courts wanted to know *why* the children brought before them had committed their misdeeds; consequently, psychiatrists and psychologists were consulted and thereby obliged to concern themselves directly with the behavior of children and its motivations.

The mental hygiene movement, institutionalized in 1909 when Clifford Beers created the National Committee for Mental Hygiene (now the National Association for Mental Health). The idea of the movement was to work toward preventing "insanity and crime" in the same ways that efforts were being made to prevent smallpox and tuberculosis.

Probation for young offenders. Initially juvenile court judges could only dismiss a case or impose a sentence; when probation was added the judge could turn the child over to a probation officer "whose task it was to look after the child, to help him to avail himself of wholesome recreational facilities, to protect him from parental mismanagement. . . ."

---

[5] L. Kanner: "History of Child Psychiatry," in A. M. Freedman and H. I. Kaplan (eds.), *Comprehensive Textbook of Psychiatry.* Williams & Wilkins Co., Baltimore, 1967.

[6] The material that follows represents an amalgam of Dr. Kanner's sequential account and various additional material which is individually cited. The material appearing in quotation marks and not otherwise cited is from L. Kanner: *Child Psychiatry* (third edition), Charles C. Thomas, Springfield, Ill., 1957.

Foster home placement agencies. Although foster homes in the Midwest had been provided as early as the 1850's to homeless immigrant children who were wandering the streets of East Coast cities, it was not until about 1915 that foster homes were used for disturbed children who needed to be removed from unsuitable homes.

Special education. Between 1910 and 1920, nine states passed legislation to promote education of retarded or otherwise handicapped pupils, to be taught "by teachers who had familiarized themselves specifically with the nature of these difficulties and had developed particular methods of dealing constructively with them."

Child guidance clinics, the first of which was started in 1909 or 1911 (the date is variously reported), are discussed in detail below.

Visiting teachers. School systems began in the 1920's to add visiting teachers to secure "cooperation between the teacher and the family of a specific pupil." Initial growth was very small—from 91 in 1921 to 205 in 1927—but in more recent years the number has grown considerably.

Play therapy, an outgrowth of psychoanalysis, is discussed below.

Child guidance clinics

By 1919, there were evidently eleven outpatient clinics in existence.[7] In 1921 the Commonwealth Fund provided the financial support for eight "demonstration child guidance clinics," which, if they proved useful, were to be taken over by the communities where they were created (all but one were). Parents, schools, and social agencies were to refer or bring children with "disturbing or otherwise puzzling behavior." By 1930 there were about 500 such clinics. The nucleus of each was a "team" of psychiatrist, psychologist, and social worker, each bringing the respective specific skills of his profession to bear in each case.[8]

Because the clinics proliferated, one might assume that they were a welcome addition to the mental health professionals and to their communities. Lowrey describes the situation otherwise.

> . . . child guidance clinics were received with considerable skepticism, even open antagonism, in many quarters. Some noted psychiatrists felt,

---

[7] L. G. Lowrey: "Psychiatry for Children," *American Journal of Psychiatry* 101:375-388, November 1944.

[8] It is widely assumed that the "erosion" of the tridiscipline clinic team is an event of recent years; actually, the National Committee for Mental Hygiene, in a 1935 survey, reported that among 617 psychiatric clinics that then accepted children as patients, the "team" was utilized in less than half. (M. A. Clark: "Directory of Psychiatric Clinics in the United States—1936," *Mental Hygiene* 20:66-129, January 1936.)

and said, that this was not psychiatry at all. Pediatricians were often extremely vociferous in their opposition. Psychologists and others engaged in special projects of their own felt that their private provinces were being, or might be, invaded. Many social workers looked askance at these new-fangled "psychiatric" social workers—"They do just what we do but get more money for it." Organized medical groups feared the invasion of private practice. . . . Finally, of course, there was the inertia and ignorance of the public to be dealt with.[9]

Elsewhere Lowrey identifies an important innovation of the guidance clinics.

. . . the child guidance clinic concept included one new feature: the ideal of treating the child in his usual environments. It seems reasonably certain that the early chief aims of the clinics were a) adequate and correct diagnosis and b) manipulation of the environment in terms of the needs of the child. The chief treatment tools of the clinics were those of altering the environment and the organic approach. . . . The types of cases brought for study were such that the dynamic concept of the environment became of great importance and influenced methodology very greatly, since these children could not or should not be sent away to some new environment.[10]

In their early days it was necessary to start with staff who had no special skills in the new field, "since there was no training available. . . . The psychiatrist had his experience in a mental hospital, the psychologist was trained in academic settings, and the social worker in those early schools of social work designed to provide training to meet the needs of social agencies." [11]

With time, the clinics became major centers for training child psychiatrists and child psychologists who sought to make a career in the new field. In these settings they learned a) how to work with emotionally disturbed children, b) the nature of the disturbance "as [the child] interacted with the significant adults in his life," and c) the important place of the parent in the clinic program.[12]

The Commonwealth Fund in 1927 established an Institute for Child Guidance, to train professional personnel for the clinics, with fellowships

---

[9] Lowrey, op. cit.

[10] L. G. Lowrey: "Trends in Therapy: Evolution and Status," American Journal of Orthopsychiatry 9:669-706, October 1939.

[11] History, Development, and Current Status of Training in Child Psychiatry (Report of Preparatory Commission I, Conference on Training in Child Psychiatry). American Psychiatric Association and American Academy of Child Psychiatry, 1963.

[12] Ibid.

provided by the Fund and by the Rockefeller Foundation; terminating the Institute at the end of an originally scheduled five years, the Commonwealth Fund thereafter awarded fellowships in child psychiatry at several individual clinics.

The number of guidance clinics continued to increase, and in the 1940's, what is now the American Association of Psychiatric Services for Children was established as a membership organization of the child guidance clinics. It then began to set standards for those clinics ready to be designated as training clinics. Eventually, approval of the independent clinics for children as training centers was withdrawn; thereafter, all professionals were required to have both an inpatient and an outpatient experience.

Early on, the professionals of the clinics moved in the direction of social or community psychiatry.

> . . . opportunities were provided to learn more about the child welfare program of the community. Through conferences and visits, [trainees] learned about courts, about the functions of child placement agencies, about the opportunities of the public schools, etc.[13]

By the end of the 1930's the child guidance movement had moved remarkably far toward those persuasions and practices that in 1971 we are still inclined to think of as recent developments in the field. This is well described by Lowrey.

> The general trend [from 1931 onward] has been definitely toward a greater amount of direct work with individuals presenting personality and behavior deviations, whatever the position of the person in the total situation. Within the area of technique, the most important element seems to be the increased emphasis on present realities. It became increasingly apparent that a knowledge of the past life and of mental mechanisms was important, but not basic, for therapy. The therapeutically important point is the present situation and its management, which may be: *a*) symptomatic for environmental or personal factors or both; *b*) broadly reconstructive; or *c*) penetrative analytic-synthetic. It may be that the swing toward focusing attention on the present situation has gone too far, and that some long-range goals are thereby being interfered with; but the emphasis is, in my opinion, correct for therapeutic purposes. There seems also to be a greater awareness of the self as a therapeutic tool.[14]

---

[13] *Ibid.*

[14] L. G. Lowrey: "Trends in Therapy: Evolution and Status," *American Journal of Orthopsychiatry* 9:669-706, October 1939.

Under specific therapies Dr. Lowrey mentions:

- Psychoanalysis
- Play therapy
- Group therapy
- The "open approach," which involves open discussion by therapists with the child and parents all present, in a manner suggestive of today's family therapy
- Relationship therapy, whose major emphasis "lies in enabling the child to recognize his feelings with a person who is able to accept them and explain them, yet at the same time impose limitations and restrictions"
- Social treatment, evidently a precursor of agency consultation; it is described as involving "the use of the psychiatrist as consultant in agencies of varied function, and the integration of the psychiatric social worker into nonpsychiatric agencies"

As for those who in the 1960's were struggling with the question of "who may do therapy," Dr. Lowrey's 1939 article is significant.

> . . . the well-trained psychiatric social worker should have acquired, among other things, a definite sense of her own capacity to realize those situations in which *her skills to diagnose and treat* are adequate, and those in which she needs the more penetrating insight and more specialized technical proficiency of the psychiatrist [emphasis added].

Play therapy

Child psychiatrists in search of means "of giving their patients opportunities for self-expression" were directed first by Melanie Klein and later by Anna Freud toward utilizing play as the most natural and promising instrument. Children were given an opportunity thereby to reveal and work out insecurities, anxieties, and hostilities. An important significance of play therapy is that it represents perhaps the first involvement of the child himself in treatment. This marked an important departure from the practices of child guidance clinics in their earlier years, when

> the child did not appear [at the "team" conference]; it was not uncommon for the psychiatrist never to see the child, and the child was not always the direct recipient of the treatment program. Social diagnosis and milieu therapy were the chief concern rather than the delineation of clinical syndromes and specific individual therapy.[15]

Play therapy was the principal form in which psychoanalysis was translated into a therapeutic technique for use with children. The Conference

---

[15] L. Bender: *Child Psychiatric Techniques.* Charles C. Thomas, Springfield, Ill., 1952.

on Training in Child Psychiatry identifies Anna Freud and her pupils as having a paramount influence on child psychiatry training in the United States.

> Aside from an intangible general influence, a direct impact came through American child psychiatrists who in the 1920's and 1930's became psychoanalysts and studied with Anna Freud. . . . When they returned to this country they applied dynamic principles and taught them to child psychiatrists, psychologists, pediatricians, and social workers.[16]

American analysts brought psychoanalytic methods into child psychiatry. These influences were strong in Chicago, Boston, New Haven, New York, Philadelphia, and Topeka. "Intensification and a wider field of penetration began in the late 1930's with the immigration of European child analysts [who] have trained a large segment of the present generation of child psychiatrists and social workers." [17]

Inpatient services

Inpatient services for severely disturbed children began to be established in the 1920's. Probably the first was the children's psychiatric service at New York's Bellevue Hospital, established in 1923; shortly afterwards children's services were established at Kings Park (N.Y.) State Hospital and Allentown (Pa.) State Hospital, for the purpose of treating children who could no longer live in the community.[18]

In 1930 a full-time psychiatric unit for children was established as an integral part of the pediatric clinic at the Johns Hopkins Hospital, and similar services were inaugurated subsequently at Columbia, Cornell, Yale, Stanford, and Minnesota.[19]

The 1940's

In 1946 three events occurred that favorably influenced the development of services for children.

• The Social Security Act was amended to provide earmarked funds for mental hygiene.

• The Mental Health Act, creating the National Institute of Mental Health, directed the development of training in the professions essential

---

[16] *History, Development, and Current Status of Training in Child Psychiatry* (Report of Preparatory Commission I, Conference on Training in Child Psychiatry). American Psychiatric Association and American Academy of Child Psychiatry, 1963.

[17] *Ibid.*

[18] *Ibid.*

[19] L. Kanner: "The Origins and Growth of Child Psychiatry," *American Journal of Psychiatry* 100:139-143, April 1944.

to programs caring for mentally ill persons; early attention was given to training child psychiatrists. In 1947 the first eight trainees entered Massachusetts General Hospital and the Philadelphia Child Guidance Clinic. By 1961, 33 centers had 88 trainees.

• The Group for the Advancement of Psychiatry was established. This influential organization from the outset showed a strong interest in services for children and issued a number of reports on various aspects of services to children.[20]

IT IS LESS SIMPLE TO IDENTIFY the most significant developments of the recent past, not because they seem less consequential but simply because it is always difficult for one to ascertain what the lasting effects will be of well-regarded contemporary formulations and practices. In any case, since World War II important work has been done to yield information about the characteristics and needs of young people. René Spitz published studies showing the tremendous impact of love and mothering on normal human development. In 1967 Eleanor Pavenstedt's book *The Drifters, Children of Disorganized Lower-Class Families* attest the deleterious effects of love deprivation, with its resulting lack of purpose and goal, and the difficulty of restoring children so affected into normal interaction. Erik Erikson moved forward theoretical formulations about the particular qualities and needs of young people, particularly in adolescence.

During this time new developments and refocusing of therapeutic activities were also taking place. There was an evident growth of interest in group methods, particularly with adolescents, not merely as a substitute for individual treatment resulting from shortages of staff time, but as an approach with distinct merits of its own, sometimes to be combined with individual treatment, but in some cases preferred as the sole therapeutic involvement.

Perhaps inevitably treatment moved toward family therapy. Just as earlier the child came to be seen directly, eventually efforts were made to effect desired change by involving the family as a unit or system. Sometimes this has included both parents and the identified child patient, sometimes these persons plus all the siblings who agree to participate. Figures on the present extent of family treatment are not available, but there is much evidence that interest in it is growing, largely as a result of

---

[20] *History, Development, and Current Status of Training in Child Psychiatry* (Report of Preparatory Commission I, Conference on Training in Child Psychiatry). American Psychiatric Association and American Academy of Child Psychiatry, 1963.

the influence of Nathan Ackerman, who pioneered in this treatment approach. Training programs for mental health professionals now commonly offer courses in family therapy, although in many programs they are elective rather than required.

Operant conditioning, a variant and refinement of behavior modification, adopted in various programs, is particularly exemplified in this study by the "Re-ED" program at the Marshall I. Pickens Hospital Mental Health Center (p. 193). It involves a programmed arrangement for reinforcing desired behavior by rewards. Although some programs describe the use of operant conditioning with outpatients, it is difficult for us to conceive how this could work very well, since the child's exposure to the therapist is limited to an hour or two a week. However, it appears to be a sufficiently promising approach in day treatment and inpatient treatment that it should be researched. It is also possible, as the Greenville program has done, to train parents to utilize this approach with the child while he is at home.

While many colleges and universities still do not have formal programs for responding to the needs of emotionally disturbed students, there has been considerable expansion in this area, attesting an awareness that vulnerability to the stresses of growing up does not end with high school. A variety of experimental approaches have been introduced with college students in recent years, one of considerable interest being the encounter and sensitivity groups in which troubled young people explore their feelings and increase their understanding of their behavior and needs.

A S TO THE CONCERN OF PRACTITIONERS in mental health services for children and adolescents that these age groups have been underserved, statistics are sketchy. An interesting early report on clinics operated by state hospitals shows that, in 1935, among 281 such clinics that reported statistics by age:

- 76 percent had a patient load of which 40 percent or more were children
- 64 percent had a patient load of which 60 percent or more were children[21]

Moving far ahead to the latest statistics available, we find the National Institute of Mental Health reports for 1967 indicate that young people, proportional to their numbers in the general population, were slightly

---

[21] H. L. Witmer: *Psychiatric Clinics for Children.* The Commonwealth Fund, New York, 1940.

overserved in outpatient clinics but considerably underserved in inpatient services. Specifically:

- 1561 outpatient clinics terminated 192,400 patients that year who were 19 and under, representing 41.6 percent of the total number terminated; during that year those 19 and under represented 39.3 percent of total population.
- Among first admissions to 279 reporting state and county mental hospitals in that year, there were 18,234 patients 19 and under, representing 11.9 percent of all first admissions.
- Among discharges from 903 reporting general hospital psychiatric units and services, there were 36,662 patients who were 19 and under, representing 9.6 percent of the total.

As we have said, there is no verified formula to indicate the "correct" percentage of the caseload that young people should comprise. We suspect that the relatively low proportion of inpatients in this age range results from both positive and negative factors; on the one hand, some facilities have been known to lack enthusiasm for developing services for younger people, on the grounds that they are expensive to operate and difficult to staff; on the other hand, there is a pervasive tendency to try to avoid hospitalization of younger patients except as a last resort.

It is interesting to note that even in outpatient services there are few patients under the age of five. In 1967 there were 7560 terminations, representing 1.6 percent of the total. There were considerably fewer in inpatient services: 2685 discharges from reporting general hospital psychiatric units and services, representing 0.7 percent of all discharges, and only 116 first admissions to state and county mental hospitals, representing 0.1 percent of all such admissions.

PERHAPS THE MOST SERIOUS PROBLEM in regard to the services available for emotionally disturbed children and adolescents has been and continues to be the fragmentation of such services. Health services in general in this country have frequently been characterized as fragmented, and mental health services even more so. Within mental health services, the fragmentation of services for children may go even a step further. Said the report of the Committee on Clinical Issues of the Joint Commission on Mental Health of Children:

> . . . if a child case needs at once certain drugs, individual therapy, and casework with the family, there may be three different agencies involved to provide the three services. If, in addition, some remedial education were necessary, yet a fourth agency might have to be turned to and this involves the parents in endless running about, repetitious giving of his-

tory, fees going four different ways, paper work, appointments, phone calls, and ultimately confusion. The child is also at the focus of ministrations of several pairs of hands during the week over and above that of the school, and the problem for him of relating himself to so many people can be overwhelming.[22]

This same report states elsewhere:

... we have seen in our communities the spotty and uneven provision of services so that here a residential center has been asked to take cases where some other placement should have been made, but no other placement was available; there a clinic was called upon to treat a case that needed residential care, only no funds were available, or no beds could be found. In many areas there has been an almost systematic misuse of facilities and the resultant dissatisfactions with the outcome have cast their shadows over the real worth that is in fact inherent in the several methods [of treatment].

The final report of the Joint Commission asserts that

even at present there is no community in the United States which has all the facilities for the care, education, guidance, and treatment of [emotionally disturbed or mentally ill] children. The few services which are available are poorly coordinated and are usually unavailable to poor and near-poor children.[23]

---

[22] Joint Commission on Mental Health of Children: *The Mental Health of Children: Services, Research, and Manpower.* Harper & Row, New York, in press.
[23] Joint Commission on Mental Health of Children: *Crisis in Child Mental Health: Challenge for the 1970's.* Harper & Row, New York, 1970.

The Numbers and Kinds of Emotionally
Disturbed Children

THE EXACT NUMBER of emotionally disturbed and mentally ill children in this country is not known," states the report of the Joint Commission on Mental Health of Children. We would disagree only with the word *exact,* on the grounds that we suspect not even the *approximate* number is known. Up to now there has been no national·epidemiological study. However, there have been many evidences that a great gap exists between demand and supply, evidenced by a) waiting lists, which are common at many, perhaps most, treatment services for children; b) exclusionary policies which facilities have set to keep the caseload within bounds; and c) chronic difficulties in recruiting professional staff. While we do not know the ultimate need, certainly it is much greater than is now being met.

WHILE IT WOULD BE USEFUL for long-range planning to know the numbers of children and adolescents needing treatment for various kinds of emotional problems, the matter of more immediate concern is one of *how much mental health service* there should be for young people in a particular locality.

The approach would be complicated. Probably one should presume on the one hand that services will be provided to some children, and their parents, who are not formally diagnosable as mentally ill but who are in fact experiencing pain and distress in the course of a warranted response to some actual catastrophe in living. One should presume on the other hand that it will probably not be possible to induce all those who need help to apply for it, because of stigma, lethargy, denial of need, and so on; further, of those who do apply, some will quickly drop out of treatment for a variety of reasons.

Beyond this, there are differences of perception from one professional to another, one agency to another, and one subculture to another, concerning the bounds of "normal" and "disturbed" behavior.

It may be of interest to consider the few statistical studies that were identified in our search of the literature.

- In Wisconsin a five-year study was undertaken of all cases of children diagnosed at any of the large number of facilities in the state as having infantile autism or childhood schizophrenia. The author, in working up his statistics, appears to assume that almost all such children with a condition of this extreme gravity would have come to the attention of some health facility, and one suspects that he is correct. He found 280 unduplicated cases in a five-year period, amounting to a rate of 3.1 cases per 10,000 children, or one autistic or schizophrenic child per 3,220 of the general child population.[1]

- A survey of the need for children's mental health facilities was carried out in San Diego, where all licensed and registered psychiatrists, pediatricians, psychologists, and social workers with 25 agencies having some contact with disturbed children were asked to indicate how many would have been benefited by day treatment, inpatient treatment, or a residential center, if these had been available. Although only 41 percent responded, they indicated that they would have recommended such placements during a one-year period for 109 preschool children, 310 in the six- to twelve-year-old group, and 1061 in the 13-18 range.[2]

- In 1959 the University of Indiana did a state-wide survey of emotionally disturbed children. It estimated that about 29,300 of 1,407,000 children required professional services for emotional disturbances. This represents two percent of the child population.[3]

- In twelve Chicago schools first-grade teachers were asked to rate their students in terms of state of adjustment. They rated 70 percent of the children as having some degree of maladaptation.[4]

THE JOINT COMMISSION ON MENTAL HEALTH OF CHILDREN attempted to illustrate the magnitude of effort that would be involved if mental health services were to be made available to all the young people who need them. To do so, it took what it considered a quite conservative figure of one half of one percent as seriously disturbed. This would amount to more than 450,000 young people. If all were being treated in residential centers or on day status, using a team approach with quite

[1] D. A. Treffert: "Epidemiology of Infantile Autism," *Archives of General Psychiatry* 22:431-438, May 1970.

[2] J. M. Sattler and B. W. Leppla: "A Survey of the Need for Children's Mental Health Facilities," *Mental Hygiene* 53:643-645, October 1969.

[3] Indiana Department of Mental Health: *Treatment Centers for Mentally Ill Children.* (Mimeograph, 1964.)

[4] S. K. Schiff and S. G. Kellam: "A Community-Wide Mental Health Program of Prevention and Early Treatment in First Grade," in M. Greenblatt, P. E. Emery, and B. C. Glueck, Jr. (eds.), *Poverty and Mental Health.* American Psychiatric Association, Washington, D.C., 1967.

large caseloads of fifty children, this arrangement, for these children alone, would require six times the present number of child psychiatrists, more than the entire number of clinical psychologists, plus 18,000 social workers and 27,000 psychiatric nurses.

The Commission, on the basis of various statements of the numbers of children needing service, estimates that 0.6 percent of young people are psychotic; that another two to three percent are severely disturbed; that an additional eight to ten percent are in need of some kind of help from knowledgeable persons. In actual numbers, these translate into many millions of young people—and many times the number who at present are receiving any treatment for emotional problems.

The State of the Art

WHILE THERE HAVE BEEN over the past several decades a multitude of descriptions of programs, case studies, and theoretical articles, controlled studies of the outcome of clinical efforts with children and adolescents have been very few. As the Joint Commission on Mental Health of Children aptly put it:

> Very little systematic research has been devoted to evaluating the effectiveness of the various treatment theories and methods [discussed in this volume]. This is also true of the program strategies which were recommended. Many more well-designed studies are needed. . . .

One reason for the dearth of controlled studies has been the unwillingness of treatment programs to deliberately deny service to some of the children needing it simply for the purpose of having a control group. A different kind of reason is very probably the traditionally greater concern of the mental health professional with *process* than with *outcome*. "How we do it" has loomed large in the minds of clinicians who have rarely attempted systematic investigations which would indicate how much better the treated population fares than the untreated population, either as of the time of discharge or at some later point.

Beyond this, there have been some historic, quite real impediments to engaging in research. Funding bodies and agencies allocate money primarily for *service*. When research funds become available, they are frequently too inadequate to pay for definitive studies; and typically, when tight money dictates a cutback in program, research is one of the first efforts to be dispensed with. There is the further fact that most clinicians other than psychologists are not trained in research method and consequently are uneasy when given the task of identifying and recruiting well-trained research people.

FOR OUR PRESENT PURPOSES, we need to consider the state of the art in a quite broad sense, to include not only actual clinical interventions but the entire interplay between mental health center and catchment area. This would include the efforts of the center to acquaint the community both with its capabilities and with its limitations. We can draw some

25

conclusions about the present state of the art by considering a series of steps whereby an applicant becomes a patient and then an ex-patient. These might be termed: attraction, assessment, prognosis, placement, retention, improvement, consolidation. Beyond this comes a further effort which one might prefer to place at the beginning rather than at the end, namely, prevention.

If the state of the art were perfected, or quite highly developed, the center should be able to operate in these particulars somewhat as follows:

Attraction. By having educated the community to the purposes and capabilities of the mental health center, on the one hand it would attract substantially all of the people who have a mental disorder that would benefit from any of the interventions that the center is capable of making; on the other hand, it would not attract those whose problems fall outside the capabilities of the center.

Assessment. The clinical staff would be able to determine quickly and accurately the degree of impairment and whether the basis of the need for help is primarily psychological, social, educational, or some combination of the three. If the behavior which impelled the parents, the school-teacher, or whatever other referring source to seek help for the young person is simply some age-appropriate but aggravating behavior, this would be explained to the parents and service would be terminated.

Prognosis. Rather than making a trial-and-error effort to contain the child or adolescent at progressively more intense levels of treatment, the clinician would determine at the outset the probable required intensity of care.

Placement. By having a range of services available, either directly or by affiliation or both, the patient would be placed in the setting of choice, rather than having to be handled by default in some substitute service or locus.

Retention. By means of rapidly building a positive relationship with the parents, the clinician would ensure that substantially all families remain in treatment until there is mutual agreement that maximum benefit has been derived.

Improvement. Because the assessment, prognosis, and placement were expertly done and the child remained in treatment, with time the behavior or handicap that brought him to the center would show improvement.

Consolidation. When treatment has been terminated, the patient would retain and consolidate his improved status and consequently function at a higher level for some considerable further period.

Prevention. By developing positive relationships with many community agencies which would provide an opportunity to bring to bear knowledge and skill about attitudes, opportunities, and behavior that constitute a positive milieu for optimal growth and development, the staff of the center would reduce the extent of emotional problems, at least those of situational origin.

Now we need to consider some of the problems and pitfalls that exist in the face of a limited state of the art.

We know of community mental health centers that have expertly developed cooperative programs with community agencies and have skillfully presented their resources and capabilities to the general public. Some others have had problems, not necessarily of their own making. Their offer of service has resulted sometimes in a welfare department or a juvenile court sending wholesale numbers of young people who were troublesome to them but not in need of the services of a community mental health center; the center's subsequent efforts to educate the referring agency about its proper role and function have sometimes resulted either in that agency's taking offense, or "writing off" the center as a useful resource.

By contrast, some community mental health centers state that they have deliberately avoided publicity, for fear that this might produce a greater number of applicants than their limited facilities and staffs could serve. This is a very real consideration. Mental health centers are likely to have from fifty to one hundred staff members performing many other activities in addition to caring for children and adolescents. If we take the Joint Commission on Mental Health of Children's figure of one half of one percent of young people as having serious emotional disorder, we are speaking, in a catchment area of 200,000, of about four hundred cases—plus, of course, the considerably larger number who have milder degrees of emotional disorder. Most present mental health centers would require considerably augmented professional staff in order to be able to serve at one time all the children who might benefit from their help.

Because many teachers and parents have a less than perfect understanding of what constitutes mental illness or emotional disturbance in a young person, the mental health center can expect to receive a certain number of inappropriate referrals. Most of these probably cannot be screened out without at least one personal interview, except in such unusual cases as, for example, when a clinic does not accept those with less-than-average intelligence and the referring agent already knows that the child has subnormal intelligence. It seems likely that most centers will need to schedule an appraisal interview in most cases. Said Dr. Koret of the Convalescent Hospital for Children:

> We like to feel that we can offer something to everyone who has a felt problem. Consequently, anyone who shows up, we see. The question of what we can do about a particular problem is, of course, a different matter.

Dr. Katf stated that at the Western Missouri Mental Health Center

> quite often we say to the parents, "Your child is behaving as he should behave and doesn't need what we have to offer here." Sometimes in the first session it is possible to give the parents some simple advice about how to handle the child.

Thus we approach the rationale for setting quite brief limits, as several of these centers do, on the initial treatment process. At Convalescent Hospital, for example, the initial therapeutic transaction is set at three sessions at two-week intervals. After this short time, it will have become evident in some cases that the parents have misjudged the child's need for treatment, while in other cases a real but transient and situational problem will have taken care of itself. But in all of these centers, if the problem should continue, arrangements will be made for treatment to continue.

What we seem to have here is a short-term treatment plan which is, in effect, an extended diagnostic procedure which at least in part is successor to the more formal diagnostic procedure of earlier days, wherein the clinical team all participated in the process, a battery of psychological tests was administered, and physical and neurological examinations were called for when there was an indication of need. (The present limitations of diagnosis may be symbolized in the considerable fall-off in the use of psychological tests, which for many years were considered essential to diagnosis and treatment planning. We do not have comparative data, of course, from which one might judge whether the outcome of treatment was better in those cases where psychological tests are routinely used in formulating a treatment plan. In the meantime, many psychologists lament what they perceive as a present-day overly casual attitude toward testing. One may at least hope that the person doing the solo intake which has by now become widespread will be acquainted with the various tests available and alert to indications that particular ones might yield information that would lead, in the particular case, to a more informed treatment plan.)

There appears, in fact, to be relatively little interest in formal diagnosis. This stems in part from a deliberate desire to avoid giving the child a stigmatizing label that may do him a disservice for the rest of his life. At several of the centers we were told, in so many words, that the diagnoses of record were not accurate in many cases, precisely in the interest of protecting the child. An even more important reason for playing down diagnosis is the persuasion of the clinical staff that what matters is the *behavior* of the child; the diagnostic approach was viewed as static, in contrast with the desire to formulate a dynamic approach that had as its goal the remediation of particular habits and deeds that caused distress or handicap to the child or his parents.

PROGNOSIS COMES INTO PLAY mainly in the form of exclusions. Some centers, having decided that they can provide only a certain length or intensity of care, have set exclusions of particular categories of disorders, on the grounds that the prognosis, at best, calls for a longer period of treatment of a more intensive nature than the resources of the facility will permit.

One of the few longitudinal studies of disturbed children indicates that the prognosis for them, if they are untreated, is quite poor. Several hundred young patients who in the late 1920's were diagnosed but, with rare exceptions, received no treatment, were followed up about 30 years later. Among this group, 27 percent were judged to be neurotic, 18 percent psychotic, 15 percent sociopathic personalities, and three percent alcoholic; among a control group, there was approximately the same proportion of neurotic reactions (23 percent) and alcoholics (three percent), but only three percent psychotic and no sociopathic personalities. The authors observe that "the former patients produce many more psychiatrically ill adults than does a group of normal controls, and the increment is in the more seriously incapacitating psychiatric diseases."[1]

RETENTION IS A PROBLEM that seems always to have plagued outpatient mental health services. A survey of all psychiatric clinic outpatients in the country revealed that among adolescents who were offered treatment, about forty percent dropped out shortly thereafter,[2] and we suspect from our own impressions that this figure is low. It is possible, of course, that the patient drops out because he is disaffected

[1] P. O'Neal and L. N. Robins: "The Relation of Childhood Behavior Problems to Adult Psychiatric Status: A 30-Year Follow-Up Study of 150 Subjects," *American Journal of Psychiatry* 114:961-969, May 1958.

[2] L. D. Hankoff: "Introduction," in S. Nichtern (ed.), *Mental Health Services for Adolescents: Proceedings of the Second Hillside Hospital Conference.* Frederick A. Praeger, New York, 1968.

with what goes on in the treatment process. Some studies of dropouts to ascertain the reason for their doing so are badly needed.

PUBLISHED OUTCOME STUDIES *of any kind* are rare. Typical of those that tell us only part of what we need to know are these:

• Forty-seven adolescent psychiatric patients were contacted one to five years after discharge from a small, intensive-treatment hospital with a special program for adolescents. Sixty-two percent showed significant improvement in social adjustment. . . . Of those patients who received individual psychotherapy following discharge from the hospital, 80 percent were improved. These data are compared to follow-up studies of adolescents discharged from other hospitals with different types of treatment environments.[3]

• A study of 1656 cases in planned short-term treatment in 54 family agencies and 44 child guidance clinics showed that, in the opinion of the clinicians, two thirds showed improvement.[4]

What is missing is a control group. As Wellner *et al.* have put it,

Changes in desired directions on postintervention measures, if they occur, are not sufficient tests of effectiveness. It is possible that these same changes could result from just the passage of time. It is therefore necessary to include comparisons with groups receiving no intervention.[5]

The only controlled study identified in our literature search is one that was done in the late 1950's at the Illinois Institute for Juvenile Research. The investigators compared on 26 variables several hundred cases of children who had received at least five hours of treatment with several hundred children who terminated contact with the clinic without ever having received any treatment interviews. It found that "the data of this study indicate that there is no difference at follow-up between the adjustments made by treated and untreated child patients."[6] The authors

---

[3] W. R. Beavers and S. Blumberg: "A Follow-Up Study of Adolescents Treated in an Inpatient Setting," *Diseases of the Nervous System* 27:606-612, September 1968.

[4] H. J. Parad and L. G. Parad: "A Study of Crisis-Oriented Planned Short-Term Treatment," *Social Casework* 49:6:346-355, 1968.

[5] A. M. Wellner, L. M. Garmize, and G. Helweg: "Program Evaluation: A Proposed Model for Mental Health Services," *Mental Hygiene* 54:530-534, October 1970.

[6] E. E. Levitt, H. R. Beiser, and R. E. Robertson: "A Follow-Up Evaluation of Cases Treated at a Community Child Guidance Clinic," *American Journal of Orthopsychiatry* 29:337-349, April 1959.

emphasize that about half of the therapy was rendered by trainees and young therapists with less than one year of experience. (The study has also been challenged on the grounds of the nature of the control group, incomplete reporting, heterogeneous case material, and so on.[7])

Of the eight programs visited in this survey, only two had developed a plan to do a follow-up study on the status of discharged patients; both of these studies were still in process.

[7] L. Eisenberg and E. M. Gruenberg: "The Current Status of Secondary Prevention in Child Psychiatry," *American Journal of Orthopsychiatry* 31:355-367, April 1961.

Prevention

CLEARLY IT IS PREFERABLE to prevent the development of disorders than to try to eliminate or control them after they have developed. To simplify somewhat, the effort to eliminate or at least reduce the frequency of new cases of particular disorders is the main purpose of what is known as the "public health approach." The process is one of identifying the contaminating agent and doing away with it or rendering it inert, or, when this can be done only partially or not at all, by developing prophylactic measures. In some disease categories, the results have been splendid, as in the control of malaria through eliminating the breeding places of the mosquitoes that transmit it, or in the prevention of various contagious diseases by rendering the individual immune by giving him vaccines before he has contracted the illness.

Understandably, there is a great interest in preventing emotional disorders. In a relatively few of the organic categories of those illnesses classed as "mental," prevention is not only possible but has been largely realized; for example, psychoses resulting from dietary deficiencies and from central nervous system syphilis, once widespread, are now almost nonexistent. Preventing some of the other organic illnesses such as senile psychosis resulting from hardening of the arteries is beyond present capabilities. But it is in the evidently much larger category of functional emotional disorders that prevention becomes a much more ambiguous matter.

While there are many theories about the causes of functional disturbances, there are scarcely any data that would withstand the demands of exact controlled scientific analysis. Indeed, among the theorists there are areas of marked disagreement, with some holding that schizophrenia, to cite an important example, will ultimately be proved to be organic after all—the result of imbalances or defects in the body chemistry; others who hold that it is clearly the result of one's life experiences including particularly the way in which he was treated during his first few years of life; and others—perhaps the considerable majority—that it is in some way the result of certain interplays between the internal characteristics of a susceptible individual and the particular external stresses that he encounters. Perhaps it will suffice for our present purpose to observe that scarcely anyone denies that some life circumstances are more conducive to an individual's well-being than others, even if there are differences of opinion about what circumstances are best.

One can endorse the interest in encouraging and creating influences and conditions that will promote emotional well-being, while at the same time acknowledging that our knowledge of how to do so is at present quite limited. We need not concern ourselves with a consideration of the extent to which mental illness might be eliminated by incorporating mental health professionals in the planning of housing projects, recreational programs, and similar activities. Rather, we can focus at a simpler level on the belief that it does make a difference to the emotional health of a child how he is treated by his parents, his schoolteachers, and, if he is poor, his welfare worker, and, if he gets into trouble, his probation officer.

There are such diverse opinions about such matters, however, that it is difficult to come up even with general principles. Whether it is better, for example, for a child to be reared "permissively," with much latitude to make his own decisions and to be granted his requests, or "authoritatively," where decisions are made for him and the rules are many and strictly observed, is a matter of debate. Not only do opinions vary at a given time from one parent or teacher to another, but also with the persuasions of the moment (as for example the changes of attitude back and forth on the matter of scheduled vs. demand feeding of infants). To put it another way, the practices believed to encourage healthy development are largely culturally determined, and they change from time to time. The practice becomes a matter of the individual parent's or teacher's understanding of what is approved and his acceptance or rejection of these values.

But at minimum there is substantial agreement about certain physical and emotional needs of children, and a belief that if these needs are appropriately met the child will have a better chance to develop into an adequate adult. We have mentioned already the considerable evidence that children need love and affection if they are to enjoy healthy emotional development. We know that they require a certain amount of sensory stimulation in order for their intellect to develop and, in cases of severe deprivation, will become functionally retarded even though born with average intellectual potential. We are persuaded that children need reliable and consistent relationships with adults so that they can learn to trust people. On these and a number of other matters there is something approaching a consensus among people who have studied child development, and they are persuaded that the prospects for a child's optimal development will be enhanced if these needs are suitably provided for.

In this respect, the eight centers we visited were doing a variety of things, although it is probably accurate to say that none of them, with their limited resources, were as yet meeting more than a small portion of the need in their catchment areas. Such activities may be divided into two categories, called *education* and *consultation*. While there is some overlap, in general education is directed toward the "general" public, parents, and children, while consultation is directed toward the personnel of various service agencies that are involved with the lives of children, most importantly the schools, and also the welfare department, the juvenile and domestic relations courts, the recreation department, clergymen, and so on.

The activities of these centers in the education area consisted of various lectures, seminars, speeches, and counseling groups for such "normative" groups as expectant parents and such "high risk" groups as pregnant unwed teen-agers. These various activities are detailed in the descriptions of the individual programs.

A greater amount of time was being spent in consultation, the greater part of it with schoolteachers. While such efforts have various purposes, a particularly important goal of the mental health professional is to help the schoolteacher better understand the process of child development, including the emotional needs of children at particular ages, and to be alert to any indications that a particular child is experiencing some undue difficulty in growing up that might be helped either by a special approach on the part of the teacher or by her recommending that his parents apply to a mental health facility to ascertain whether the child might benefit from the kind of help it is equipped to furnish.

These efforts, as far as they go, are commendable, but we have said elsewhere that the magnitude of trying to provide an optimum opportunity for every child to develop to his greatest potential is far too great to be accomplished by such small facilities as mental health services. Such services are in a good position to develop principles and techniques that might be widely applied, but perhaps the most promising approaches lie in the area of providing family-life education to young people, through the schools, and to increasing the information, competence, and comfort of the people whose work involves children.

The present state of the art in prevention is generally acknowledged to be limited. Whether present efforts "work" in the sense of eventuating in emotionally healthier young people and a reduced incidence of emotional casualty is not known, since systematic studies of education and consultation programs have not yet been carried out, and the methodological problems of doing so would be gigantic. Interest and belief in consultation is great among many mental health professionals, for which reason we will consider this activity further in the following chapter.

Consultation

M ENTAL HEALTH CONSULTATION is one process through which mental health professionals attempt to enhance the mental health of the people living in the area which the center serves by means of enhancing the mental health skills of a large variety of persons in agencies and institutions that bear upon the lives of the community. It is an "essential service" required of all federally supported community mental health centers. It is not new; one bibliography of mental health consultation for children lists several articles published in the 1940's and one that goes back to 1936.[1] It is posited on the assumption that the mental health professional by dint of his training and experience has information about and an understanding of human behavior, interactions, and problems that exceeds that of the personnel working in other helping agencies, but can be imparted to them, thus enabling them to serve their clients in ways that will promote emotional well-being.

Consultation efforts may have any or all of several purposes. At the simplest, a mental health professional may make periodic visits to other agencies, such as the welfare department, the courts, and, particularly in the case of children, the schools, simply to encourage these agencies to refer clients who appear to be dysfunctional or at least impaired by some form of emotional problem or illness that might respond to treatment at the mental health center. For the most part, present-day consultation efforts seem to have moved a long way beyond this simple purpose, and now have more complex and intricate goals. These would include increasing the knowledge of the "consultee" about mental illness to such extent that the consultee gradually assumes the capability of dealing with some of the less severe emotional problems among his or her clients. Beyond this, the consultation may concern itself not even indirectly with a client but rather with the workings of the agency, in the belief that an improved quality of relationships within the agency will create a climate conducive to positive mental health, which in turn will enhance the likelihood that the clients will be benefited from their contacts with the agency.

---

[1] National Institute of Mental Health: *Mental Health Consultation to Programs for Children.* U.S. Public Health Service Publication No. 2006, 1970.

One of the grounds on which consultation efforts are justified is the fact that such agency personnel as welfare workers and probation officers frequently have no training for their work. The need for consultation within the schools is seen as particularly great, on the basis that schoolteachers often have limited training in classroom management and developmental psychology.

The community mental health center that sets out to establish a consultation service is likely to face a multitude of problems, which may be grouped under the headings of *a*) staff selection, *b*) agency acceptance, and *c*) financing.

The person directing the consultation program will be lucky if he finds, in the mental health center, staff members who have been trained in mental health consultation and therefore know something of the structure, function, problems, and needs of the agencies they will be consulting to. If he does not, he will need to establish an inservice training program that will probably include reading assignments in the literature of consultation. In the usual case, the consultant will be a clinician who spends some part of his time with the consultee agencies while continuing to spend the rest of his time in clinical activities; with rare exceptions, mental health centers do not consider it a good idea to have a separate staff devoted exclusively to consultation. At the same time, a successful and harmonious consultation program seems to require that members of the clinical staff be given the *option* of devoting a part of their time to consultation; it seems self-defeating to make it mandatory for staff members who are shy or for other reasons disinclined to visit agencies to do so. It is important to try to ascertain whether the agencies being consulted to will accept those without professional training as consultants; some centers that have attempted to use particularly capable "paraprofessionals" have found that the agencies were interested only in services from doctors.

Next, and perhaps most important, is the problem of resistance. It is not universal, and in fact some courts, welfare departments, school systems, police departments, and clergymen appear to welcome the efforts of the mental health consultant. But in many cases the proffer of help will be turned down, for any of a variety of reasons, including an unwillingness to acknowledge that any mental health problems exist, a fear that accepting help will cause one to look weak, a concern about invasion of privacy, and so on. Ordinarily the effort will begin by seeking the approval of the administrators and officials; for example, in school consultation, one would first attempt to gain the approval of the superintendent of schools. When this has been done, one must then approach the principal of a particular school. If he agrees for his school to participate in mental health consultation, it will then be necessary to win the confidence and collaboration of the individual classroom teachers. In some cases the administration has mandated participation, usually with limited success.

A common tack in establishing relationships has been "to earn one's way in." Many agencies will have some one or two clients who are disturbed in particularly distressing and aggravating ways; if the consultant agrees to arrange treatment for these clients at the mental health center, and if the treatment effects an improvement, it is highly likely that the agency personnel will then be disposed to accept and learn from the consultant, who can then move on to other aspects of consultation which attempt to upgrade the mental health capabilities of the consultees and to improve the internal operations of the agency.

As for meeting the cost of the consultation, many mental health centers have found the consultee agencies either unable or unwilling to pay. This is not uniform, of course; certain school districts in the catchment area of the Arapahoe Mental Health Center actually put up the matching funds necessary to obtain a federal mental health center grant. But all too often the school district faces such a stringent budget that it cannot arrange to pay for the consultation. Federally supported community mental health centers have had considerable capabilities in their early years, while the federal share of their operating expenses remained high, to provide the consultation without charge. It remains to be seen what will happen as the federal grants continue to phase down and then are terminated.

BEYOND FINANCIAL CONSIDERATIONS, there are two important problems inherent in mental health consultation. The first is that of *scope*. The second is that the consultation seeks to do remedially what it might be better to do before the fact.

By scope, we refer to the fact that to provide consultation to all the personnel of all the helping agencies would be manifestly beyond the resources and capabilities of any present mental health center. Consultation programs in these still early days of community mental health centers have been feeling their way along, extending into the more receptive agencies and dealing with the more "psychologically minded" personnel. Should the time come that all the agencies of any catchment area recognize the need for and request mental health consultation, the dimensions would have to be vastly greater than at any present program. For example, in a catchment area of 200,000 there are approximately two thousand classroom teachers. Even if they were seen for only one hour a week, in groups of five, by a consultant from the mental health center who spent fully 30 hours a week in actual consultation sessions, this would still require about fifteen full-time equivalencies for the schools alone.

By referring to consultation as a "remedial approach," we mean that it attempts to provide after the fact an understanding of human behavior and problems that might better have been imparted before the fact. When mental health professionals are outnumbered by schoolteachers in a ratio of perhaps twenty to one, it seems evident that the longer-term goal should be one of augmenting the education of the schoolteacher—with a practicum if necessary—so that he or she will have an adequate understanding of children, their problems, and their development. Until such (unforeseeable?) time as this may happen, it seems desirable for mental health resources to continue to attempt to do as much as they can in the way of remediation.

Services for Children in Community Mental Health Centers

EARLY IN 1970, preliminary to the field study, the Joint Information Service sent a brief questionnaire (Appendix II) to all of the 206 federally assisted community mental health centers then operating, in the interest of ascertaining the nature of their services to children and adolescents. Responses were received from 70 percent. We have no information to suggest that respondents and nonrespondents differ in any important respects.

The centers were asked to indicate the month and year in which they became operational "within the federal definition of a program offering at least the five 'essential services.' " Of 135 who gave this information, a little more than half (52 percent) had been operating for two years or less, and the substantial majority (84 percent) had been operating for three years or less.

Without respect to whether services for children and adolescents were separately organized, the centers were asked to "indicate the administrative categories you use to subdivide your services to clients or patients under the age of 21, and specify the age limits for each category." One hundred and twenty-seven did so. Thirty-nine of these, or 31 percent, indicated a single category that combines children and adolescents. More than half of these (21) set age limits of zero to 18, and another 13 set even lower maximum age limits (16 and 17); only five indicated an upper age limit higher than 18. Three gave age limits indicating that they provide services to adolescents but not to children.

Another 48 respondents indicated two administrative categories, these being in substantially all cases "children" and "adolescents." Another 27 divided their young clients into three administrative categories, in almost all cases "preschool," "children" or "elementary," and "adolescence." Another ten divided those under 21 into a varying number of groups with a variety of alternate and variant terms, such as "preadolescents," "latency age," "late latency," and "young adults." Six of these centers divided their under-21 patients into four categories, mostly by means of dividing the elementary school age group into "latency age" and "preadolescents"; one included a separate category (zero to 2.5 years old) for infants.

There is considerable variation in the upper age limit specified for the three principal groups: the upper limit for "preschool" ranges from four through six; for "children" from ten through 18; for "adolescents" from 16 through 22, as follows:

	Upper age limit	*Number of facilities*
Preschool	4	2
	5	9
	6	17
Children	10	2
	11	14
	12	38
	13	6
	14	8
	15	1
	16	2
	17	0
	18	1
Adolescents	16	5
	17	12
	18	46
	19	8
	20	4
	21	7
	22	1

Despite the variations, a pattern does emerge. By a good margin, the modal upper limits are, for preschool, six years old; for children, 12 years old; for adolescents, 18 years old.

In summary, the administrative divisions by age were:

Only one category—children	31%
Only one category—adolescents	2
Two categories (children and adolescents)	38
Three categories (preschool, children, and adolescents)	21
Unusual categories	8

Federal regulations concerning eligibility for financial support for community mental health centers stipulate that the center must provide at least five services defined as "essential"; these are inpatient service, outpatient service, emergency service, partial hospitalization service consisting at least of day care, and consultation and education. No program applying for federal support ever requested a dispensation from providing all five of the essential services for children, and there was no supposition that any center receiving federal support would deliberately exclude children from any of the essential services. Nonetheless, it became evident with time that not all centers were finding it possible to provide all five essential services for children and adolescents. At the same time, substantially all centers have been providing at least some service for these younger groups; only three of our respondents indicated that they do not provide any service at all to children, and all indicated that they provide at least some service for adolescents. In mid-1971, NIMH clarified this matter by stating that henceforth all applications for federal community mental health center funds must provide all five services for children and adolescents.

Under the federal regulations, the agency designated as the mental health center need not itself furnish all services; some, particularly specialty services, may be provided through an affiliation agreement with other agencies within the catchment area. But to obtain some idea of the extent to which provision is made for children and adolescents, we tabulated the responses regarding the essential services *without regard to* whether particular services are provided directly by the center through a separate department, directly by the center as part of its general service, or outside the center through an affiliation agreement. The responses were as follows:

	Children (N=143)	Adolescents (N=143)
Provide all five essential services	90 (63%)	113 (79%)
Provide four of the essential services	25 (17%)	20 (14%)
Provide three of the essential services	18 (13%)	7 (5%)
Provide two of the essential services	4 (3%)	2 (1%)
Provide one of the essential services	3 (2%)	1 (1%)
Provide none of the essential services	3 (2%)	0

As for which particular services are provided, again without differentiation between those provided by the center itself in a separate department, those provided by the center itself as part of its general service, and those provided outside the center through an affiliation agreement, the responses were:

	Children (N=143)	Adolescents (N=143)
Outpatient service	138 (97%)	143 (100%)
Inpatient service	113 (79%)	132 (92%)
Emergency service	128 (90%)	136 (95%)
Partial hospitalization service	99 (69%)	120 (84%)
Consultation and education service	137 (96%)	140 (98%)

The most significant missing elements are clearly partial hospitalization and inpatient service for children, which in 31 percent and 21 percent of cases respectively are not available on any basis at all. This undoubtedly reflects, in the case of inpatient treatment, both the expense and difficulty of mounting an inpatient service for a relatively few young patients who cannot be otherwise managed, and the widespread reluctance to hospitalize children for psychiatric disorders. We suspect that the low percentage for partial hospitalization reflects the feeling that such a service for children requires a special education program, which requires establishing a school, however small it might be; such an arrangement is quite expensive, and many mental health personnel appear to feel that the responsibility of such a service properly lies with the school system.

Adolescents appear to be generally well served, although it seems probable from our personal knowledge that some of the inpatient service indicated may consist simply of admitting the adolescent to the adult service. The one fairly deficient area is partial hospitalization, here again suggesting the reluctance of some mental health centers to get into the business of special education.

The centers were asked to indicate whether particular services were provided within the center as a part of its general service, within the center in a separate department, or outside the center through an affiliation agreement. In a number of cases the respondents indicated that particular services were provided in two or all three of these arrangements; consequently some rows add up to more than one hundred percent.

Children	Separate service within center (N=143)	General service within center (N=143)	Outside by affiliation agreement (N=143)
Outpatient service	34%	66%	10%
Inpatient service	13	35	34
Emergency service	19	71	16
Partial hospitalization service	18	34	22
Consultation and education service	29	71	13
Adolescents			
Outpatient service	28	76	11
Inpatient service	8	60	31
Emergency service	14	81	15
Partial hospitalization service	11	62	15
Consultation and education service	24	77	13

The centers were asked to indicate the percentages children and adolescents represented of the total active caseload as of the time of responding to the questionnaire. The responses were as follows:

Percentage of caseload	Outpatient service No.	%	Inpatient service No.	%	Emergency service No.	%	Partial hospitalization service No.	%	Consultation and education service No.	%
Children										
0	3	3	64	67	44	52	65	68	9	11
1- 5	16	16	17	18	28	33	9	9	2	2
6-10	17	17	9	9	12	14	4	4	8	10
11-15	17	17	3	3	1	1	5	5	5	6
16-20	15	15	0	0	0	0	1	1	8	10
21-25	15	15	2	2	0	0	1	1	8	10
26-35	13	13	1	1	0	0	5	5	19	23
36-50	5	5	0	0	0	0	2	2	18	21
51+	1	1	0	0	0	0	4	4	7	8
Adolescents										
0	1	1	13	13	9	11	29	30	3	4
1- 5	5	5	20	21	16	19	22	22	1	1
6-10	19	18	21	22	16	19	18	18	8	10
11-15	18	17	13	13	10	12	9	9	5	6
16-20	25	24	13	13	9	11	5	5	6	7
21-25	13	13	7	7	8	9	2	2	7	8
26-35	16	16	6	6	10	12	4	4	26	31
36-50	5	5	4	4	5	6	4	4	22	26
51+	1	1	0	0	2	2	5	5	6	7

An interesting cutting point is at the 15 percent level. The following percentages of the respondents had child and adolescent patient loads that represented *15 percent or less* of their entire patient load:

	Children	*Adolescents*
Outpatient service	52%	42%
Inpatient service	97	69
Emergency service	100	60
Partial hospitalization service	86	80
Consultation and education	29	20

Three things are clear from these figures: *a*) the only service in which children and adolescents are served to a greater degree than their proportion of the general population is consultation and education, *b*) in all other areas, children and adolescents are considerably *under*served in terms of their proportion of the general population; *c*) adolescents as a proportion of total patient load are considerably better served than children in all respects.

One further means of considering these figures is to examine the median interval for each of the services.

	Median interval	
	Children	*Adolescents*
Outpatient service	11-15%	16-20%
Inpatient service	0	6-10
Emergency service	0	11-15
Partial hospitalization service	0	1- 5
Consultation and education	26-35	26-35

This tells us that at least half (in fact, considerably more than half) of respondents were, as of the time of responding to the questionnaire, serving *no* children as inpatients, in the emergency service, or in a partial hospitalization program.

The centers were asked to indicate the staff members assigned to services for children and adolescents, in terms of job title, highest degree, and hours per week spent with children, adolescents, or collaterals. Only 88 did so, and in many cases the job titles listed were of such nature that one could not translate them into the basic occupational categories associated with mental health services. It is interesting, in any case, to note that 56 percent of respondents did not indicate a child psychiatrist on the staff; 53 percent did not indicate any kind of physician in the service for children and adolescents; 80 percent did not indicate any teachers; 65 percent did not indicate any nurses. All but 14 percent indicated at least one psychologist and all but 16 percent indicated at least one social worker. Many of these professionals were part time.

For those centers that did indicate any child psychiatrists, the average was 2.35 persons per facility, putting in a total average of 55 hours per week per facility. For those indicating Ph.D. psychologists, the average was 1.87 persons working a total average of 39 hours per week per facility. Those indicating master's-level social workers had an average of 3.8 per program, providing a total average of 88 hours per week.

THE CENTERS WERE ASKED to describe "the extent and nature of your relationships" with a variety of agencies. A number of the responses were so perfunctory as to be useless, and some others were so vague and diffuse as not to convey what their activities really were. (For example: "We collaborate with two classes for emotionally disturbed children," or, "Our children's day treatment is directly related to the schools via an educational-clinical relationship with the teacher and principal.") Among the others there were various interesting activities described, such as the following:

• One center solicited the support both of the state department of education and the local school administration to set up its own "therapeutic day school."

• A center in Arkansas provides a screening service for children in Headstart programs as a means of identifying those who, when they enter school, will have special educational needs.

• A center in San Francisco arranged to have the board of education assign teachers trained in special education to teach on its children's and adolescents' inpatient service.

• A center in Southern California operates a school for mentally retarded, disadvantaged, multihandicapped children and children with severe learning disabilities, who have been excluded from the public schools.

• A Colorado center in collaboration with the county school system operates a "therapeutic educational center" for sixteen emotionally disturbed children who could not be maintained in normal classrooms.

• A center in Florida introduced a program of "precision teaching techniques" in several schools "in an effort to manage academic and behavioral problems in the school, without requiring referral to the center."

• A Boston center operates a class for emotionally disturbed children from four to seven years old, and another for children from nine to eleven.

- A center in Massachusetts developed two "mental health nursing clinics" in local parochial schools; these clinics also function as "drop-in centers for anyone with a problem."

- A North Dakota center sees students both individually and in groups at the schools, during regular school hours.

- A center in Maine conducts formal courses entitled "The Troubled Child in the Classroom Setting" and "The Exceptional Child" as in-service training for schoolteachers. The courses are approved for credit for recertification by the state board of education.

- A Baltimore center conducts, in one of the high schools, group therapy sessions for students referred by administrative and counseling staff.

- A San Francisco center reported that "court hearings are sometimes held on our premises, with the judge in attendance, to facilitate the presentation and discussion of recommendations by all professional personnel involved on the case."

- A center in Maine provides eight hours of training for new police officers.

- A Michigan center set up group therapy and individual therapy in a "children's village" for the patients from their catchment area who were waiting there to be admitted to the community mental health center.

- A center in San Antonio entered into a contract with the local juvenile court to screen new cases, do psychological and psychiatric evaluations and mental assessments, "alone or as part of a complete evaluation which is generally provided by an interdisciplinary team."

- Fourteen centers indicated some type of formal and continuing relationship with pediatric services or pediatricians. Several were involved in the training of pediatric residents.

- A Florida center provides a full-time "mental health consultant" for the county health department.

- A center in Michigan which has limited psychiatric time available utilizes pediatricians for prescribing medication.

- An Ohio center uses local pediatricians to give physical examinations for younger patients whose problems suggest the suitability of such an examination.

- A Washington State center requires that each of its residential children be under the care of a pediatrician for general health care and medications.

• At an Oregon center, public health nurses serve as cotherapists in a number of therapy groups, and they serve as the staff making home visits to patients.

• A Colorado center provides inservice training for three groups of welfare staff of approximately 15 persons each.

• A center in Maine has a contract with the welfare department to provide home-care services to its clients.

• A New York State center provides a weekly half-day seminar to welfare employees. These are either case problems, or, at the request of the welfare staff, didactic material on child development and special problems.

THE CENTERS WERE ASKED to "describe any preventive activities such as educational programs for parents, expectant mothers, mothers of newborn babies, etc." What we had in mind were those activities that would be defined within the public health framework as *primary* prevention, but beyond listing three examples, we deliberately did not provide any definition of prevention. We were interested in learning to what extent the activities named by the centers would correspond to our own conception of *prevention* as an activity distinguished from *treatment*.

Three responses were not usable for technical reasons. Among the remaining 142, there were 12 (eight percent) that provided no answer to this particular question; one cannot know whether this was oversight or lack of interest, or whether it meant that these centers were providing nothing that they considered to be preventive activities. Another 11 (also eight percent) wrote "none," "very little," or equivalent comments. The remaining 119 (84 percent) listed one or more activities, with a number listing several. Very few of the specific activities named seemed to us to constitute *treatment* efforts as distinguished from *prevention* efforts.[1]

The responses were highly individual in language, but it was possible to sort them into 26 categories, only five of which were specified by more than ten centers. In a few cases it was difficult to distinguish between categories; for example, "parents groups" may in some cases have had

---

[1] An example of such a response would be: "Our program for adolescents in the day hospital stresses self-awareness." It would be our view that an adolescent appropriately attending a day hospital had already attained *patient* status, meaning that he had been identified as having an emotional disorder for which he was receiving treatment.

essentially the same content and purposes as "child rearing" and "family life" programs. The responses were as follows:

Lectures, seminars, courses, group discussions regarding child rearing and development, family life, sex education, "marital enrichment," etc. 24

Parents groups (some for parents of disturbed children, others for parents of normal children) 15

Speakers for a broad variety of groups, such as the Parent-Teachers Association, service clubs, church groups, child-study clubs, etc., on a broad variety of topics 15

Consultations to teachers and other school personnel 14

Drug education programs, mostly for students 13

Seminars and courses for expectant mothers 9

Seminars and courses for mothers of newborn children 8

Consultation to Headstart programs 5

Screening programs for preschool children for speech, hearing, and other deficits 5

Seminars and courses for unmarried mothers 4

Groups for single parents ("Parents Without Partners") 3

Family planning, birth control education 3

Operating a preschool nursery, play school, etc. 3

Consulting to nursery schools 3

Group activities, "coffeehouse," etc., for teen-agers 3

"Normative crisis" groups, "worry clinics," etc. 3

Alcoholism education 2

Training for ministers to act as counselors 2

Tutorial programs 2

Radio broadcasts on mental health topics 2

Summer program stressing readiness for school 2

"Hot line" telephone for teen-agers 1

Operating social and recreation program for children 1

Consultation to OEO program 1

Group sessions for parents of retarded children 1

Baby-sitting course "to help baby sitters anticipate and avoid problems, handle crises, discipline children, and one day be better parents for having been provided with some skills in dealing with young children" 1

THE CENTERS WERE ASKED, "In what ways do you feel that your services to children and adolescents need to be intensified or augmented, in order to meet the needs of your catchment area?" Many of the responses were fragmentary, so that it was difficult to tell what the respondent had in mind, but even so there are some general clues to what the centers feel they need most.

Three of the responses were unusable for technical reasons. Of the remaining 142, five did not answer the question and three indicated that they were satisfied with their services to children and adolescents. The remaining 134 indicated one or more deficiencies, coming to a total of 327. Forty centers named only one deficiency; 38 named two; 25 named three; 21 named four; eight named five; and two named six. It was possible to codify the responses into 61 categories, many of which were indicated by only one or two centers.

It was somewhat difficult to differentiate between responses having to do with *services* in the sense of a *capability* and *facilities* in the sense of a *locus* and a *plant*. However, interpreting the best we could, we found that by far the most common deficiency expressed by the centers had to do with facilities; there were 89 responses in this category. The most frequent (20 responses) was the expressed need for facilities to provide partial care, usually in the form of a day program; next came the need for a residential treatment center (18 responses); and the same number expressed the need for an inpatient service. Eleven indicated the need for group homes and/or foster homes, and six mentioned short-term emergency beds.

Forty-eight centers indicated that consultation and education services should be more extensive and/or of better quality, and of this group 23 specifically singled out their relationships with the schools. Only three mentioned the courts, and no other specific community agency was indicated. Seven expressed the need to provide enhanced educational programs for parents and/or teachers.

There were 57 responses indicating a need to provide additional services. Thirteen stated their desire for additional programs to deal with (unspecified) special problem groups, and almost as many (twelve) indicated the need for a special service for drug abusers. Nine said they wanted to be able to establish satellite services within their catchment areas.

Thirty-seven centers stated that their services for children and adolescents suffered from a lack of staff, and four others indicated a specific need for staff members trained in consultation and education activities.

There were two other responses that involved a considerable number of the centers: seventeen said they should be making a greater effort to prevent mental illness, and another seventeen indicated that they needed to expand their services for children and adolescents in unspecified ways.

F INALLY, THE CENTERS WERE ASKED to indicate the most significant problems that confronted them in attempting to provide adequate services to children and adolescents. Ten responses were not usable for technical reasons, and another six centers did not reply to the question. The remaining 129 listed a total of 247 problems. Among these, 57 centers indicated a single problem; 42, two problems; 17, three problems; 10, four problems; and three, five problems. In terms of the types of problems that the centers said confronted them, the responses were as follows:

Financial	57%
Staff availability	44
Interagency coordination and cooperation	17
Inadequate physical facilities	15
Inadequate community resources	12
Community's perception of the center	8
Difficulty with parents	7

From two to four percent of respondents indicated additional problems that fell into nine other categories.

II

EIGHT PROGRAM DESCRIPTIONS

Cambridge-Somerville Mental Health Center
Cambridge and Somerville, Mass.

C AMBRIDGE AND SOMERVILLE are contiguous incorporated towns in the metropolitan Boston area. Although having no significant ties except proximity, they were paired by the state as a catchment area for mental health services, and as such applied for and received a federal grant to help meet the cost of staffing various new services that each now provides. These two communities collaborate in an adult inpatient service and an emergency service located at Cambridge City Hospital and in a day-treatment program for preschool children. By far the largest portion of services for children and adolescents in each community consists of outpatient treatment and consultation to a variety of community agencies, and these are provided in an essentially separate manner in the two communities. Thus, it will present a more comprehensible picture of the operation to describe the two operations separately.

Cambridge

The area served

Cambridge is a long, narrow city, separated from Boston on the south by the Charles River; on the north it has a five-mile common border with Somerville.

The image of Cambridge outside the Boston area is principally that of the home of two great universities, Harvard and the Massachusetts Institute of Technology. In actuality, it is a diverse small city, whose 100,000 population provides considerable contrast. Despite its affluent Brattle Street area, Cambridge, overall, has considerable poverty and a generous share of urban problems. Indeed, it has come to be considered a part of the "inner city" of Boston. Between 1960 and 1970 it lost about seven percent of its population. It has the country's highest rate for certain categories of crime, such as breaking and entering, among cities in the 50,000-100,000 range. It has the highest proportion of people over 65 of any city in Massachusetts.

We can best understand the diversity of this city by comparing West Cambridge—the Harvard area, with high income, low population density,

53

and minimal social problems—and East Cambridge, which, although it houses M.I.T., is characterized by high population density, low income, and a variety of social problems. Between East and West Cambridge, the average annual rate of juvenile delinquency varies from 45 to zero cases per thousand. Adult crime varies from 144 to two cases per thousand. Truancy varies from 55 cases to none. Aid to Families of Dependent Children varies from 183 cases per thousand to none. Old-age assistance varies from 513 to 23 cases per thousand. The rate of dilapidated housing varies from 19 percent to none. Housing with deficiencies (for example, no central heating) varies from 60 percent to none. In some East Cambridge neighborhoods, the housing is one hundred percent tenant occupied; in some parts of West Cambridge, 95 percent is owner occupied. The average number of children per family varies from 2.85 in East Cambridge to 0.44 in West Cambridge. The population concentration varies from 233 per acre to 21 per acre. The percentage of adults not completing high school varies from 82 percent to 17 percent. Median family income in West Cambridge is $11,000, in East Cambridge, $3,700. Seven percent of Cambridge is black, varying from more than fifty percent in some neighborhoods to none in others.

There are many internists and psychiatrists and a few pediatricians serving the Harvard community, but these practitioners have scarcely any contact with the poor people living in the eastern part of the city.

Cambridge has two hospitals. One of these, Cambridge City Hospital, has historically served the poor; since 1966 it has been affiliated with Harvard Medical School, as a demonstration facility for the practice of community medicine, in transition toward becoming a regional community-oriented hospital intended to serve not just the poor of Cambridge but the entire population of Cambridge plus some of Somerville. The process of change has been slow. It is at this hospital that most of the adult services of the Cambridge part of the mental health center are located. The other Cambridge hospital is Mount Auburn, a voluntary hospital in the Harvard area, serving mainly the affluent parts of Cambridge and some well-to-do suburbs. There is one staff psychiatrist but psychiatric service is limited.

Drug abuse has been a special problem in Cambridge. Starting in the mid-1960's, the city began to attract many "hippies" around the university; they have largely developed their own community with their own informal institutions, and avoid using the Cambridge hospital, which they see as part of "the establishment."

The community mental health center identifies, in addition to private practitioners for those who are able to pay, the following mental health resources, among others: Avon Home, an adoption agency; a family counseling service; the Bureau of Pupil Services of the local school department; the Catholic Charitable Bureau; and a service for retarded children.

Origins

Because of the dearth of mental health resources in Cambridge, other than private practitioners, a group of concerned citizens began in the early 1950's to express interest in creating a local mental health association that would serve as a mechanism for promoting treatment services. Thus, in 1954 the Cambridge Mental Health Association came into being. The directors decided to give first priority to children's services, "because of public demand and in the belief that preventive work should start at a young age." With financial support from the Division of Mental Hygiene of the Massachusetts Department of Mental Health, the mental health association in 1955 established the Cambridge Guidance Center, in a tenement in Harvard Square. One of the initial staff members was Dr. Robert Reid, then a child psychiatry resident, who has been the director from the beginning.

Services in those early years were limited to outpatient treatment and consultation to community agencies. The first consultation efforts were directed to the settlement houses and community centers. During this same period, other agencies dealing with children who have problems were being separately established, notably a Children's Developmental Clinic to serve mentally retarded children, with part of the funds from the federal Children's Bureau, and a clinic attached to the juvenile court, started by the state as a pilot project involving the court and staff from the Judge Baker Guidance Clinic.

A day program was started by the Cambridge Guidance Center in 1962 which served the preschool retarded, for whom there were no related services available.

In 1965 the state's new mental health act, under which Cambridge and Somerville were combined as a catchment area, provided impetus to combine existing Massachusetts Department of Mental Health services in the two communities and develop others to provide comprehensive services for children and adults in both communities. The Cambridge Guidance Center consulted a great number of community agencies about their needs, among them the staff of the Model Cities program, the director of the local OEO-funded agency, the director of the Cambridge and Somerville Settlement House Alliance, and a variety of physicians. Cambridge City Hospital was enlisted as the proposed locus of much of the adult service; the Somerville children's clinic, which the Cambridge clinic helped to start, proposed to mount new services for its community.

These efforts led in 1968 to an application for federal staffing funds that would permit expansion of the program, including the development of services not theretofore available. The expanded program came into effect in late 1969.

In the interim, in 1964, the Cambridge clinic had moved from its Harvard Square location to its present facility, an attractive old house with 20 rooms, providing offices for clinicians and administrative staff, a nursery room, and a large conference room. The building is owned by Harvard, which charges a rent well below the prevailing rate. Much of the Cambridge children's staff is based there, and it is the central facility for clinical services. However, center staff are deployed in many outside programs, including Headstart, Follow Through, and the Neighborhood Family Care Center. In addition, about forty percent of the time of the staff housed in this building is spent outside in community consultation and collaboration. The staff grew in size over the years as the Department of Mental Health budgeted new positions for it and as personnel were added to serve on special projects. Accordingly the number of trainees in all disciplines was expanded, and volunteers working under supervision were added as well.

Philosophy, purposes, and policy

An attractive brochure describes the children's service as "an outpatient community organization designed and staffed to help children who experience more than the usual difficulty in growing up." In explaining why the service exists, the brochure states that

> a good start is the first essential step toward a good life. Parents, sometimes on their own, often on the advice of a school, family doctor, or other interested party, may recognize that their child needs more help than they are able to give him. Danger signals such as persistent excessive fears, unusual resistance to discipline, academic performance far below potential, and lack of friends often indicate that a child needs professional help. Time and again, a skilled team at the center, working together with the child and his parents, have turned confusion into confidence and fear into happiness.

The staff is pervaded with the philosophy that the center owes service to the entire community, not just to particular families who are highly motivated to come and apply. "It is incumbent upon us to extend ourselves where possible to provide service," said Dr. Charles Hersch, the assistant director and chief psychologist.

We have a fair number of families [he continued] that don't know what helping services are all about, and therefore don't know how to get to us, and others that wouldn't accept what we have to offer even if they did know about us. But in philosophy we've always felt that we're responsible for everybody out there. Every child in town is to one degree or another our responsibility, for whatever kind of problem he may be experiencing. One can't always translate this concern into clinical activities, but the viewpoint is reflected in our thousands of hours of consultation to agencies in the community and the considerable investment we've made in community planning.

The program is not divided into separate components for children and adolescents but rather provides a unitary service to any child up through the age of 17. In the caseload adolescents are underrepresented, perhaps for several reasons. One is their imputed distrust of "establishment" services, another is the possible reluctance to come to "a children's clinic." Another is the fact that disturbed adolescents oftentimes have some kind of charge against them and in this particular community are therefore brought to the attention of the court clinic.

Dr. Reid feels strongly that most of the children who are prospects for the services of a mental health facility can be successfully served on an outpatient basis. "I hope that this community never builds an inpatient center for children," he said. "We have only six or seven children a year that truly require placement for more than a short time in a residential facility, and we would rather have these seriously disturbed children go to a topnotch specialty facility which should serve an area larger than ours." He did, however, express the need for a nonmedical, homelike local facility where children could be placed for a short time until an emergency can be resolved. But he is persuaded that, for almost all children, outpatient treatment, while they remain with their family, is the preferable, and feasible, course.

After the intake interview, the case is reviewed with senior personnel at the team meeting. From this point what is to be done and what assignments will be made are determined by the needs of the case. Some will go through the typical sequential diagnosis; others will have a shorter diagnostic evaluation of selected aspects; some will move promptly into crisis intervention; and so on. In any case, the staff is less concerned about nosology than about function. "The reservoir that we draw from," said Dr. Samuel Braun, a child psychiatrist who is clinical director of the Preschool Program, "is dysfunction. As a result, we intermix kinds of children that others tend to separate. Our treatment groups often include both severely disturbed and mentally retarded children, because we are concerned not with diagnosis but with intervening in the lives of these children in ways that will help them to function better."

The sense of responsibility to the community is evidenced in the welcome that the clinic provides to all applicants. This is reflected in the fact that the clinic caseload has more than twice the percentage of Negro children as in the community (fourteen percent vs. seven percent), and a disproportionate percentage of families who are welfare clients under the Aid to the Families of Dependent Children category.

The staff quite deliberately directs itself toward short-term treatment, in the belief that an effective and appropriate allocation of resources is toward helping individuals successfully negotiate points of particular stress. The staff accepts, at the same time, that particular children and their parents have problems and circumstances that call for a longer-term involvement, and thus there is no formal limit on service. With many families, the major service is the clarification of issues to aid in planning. An important aspect here is working toward appropriate referrals, such as school placement, or to other agencies for group work or family counseling, for example.

Administration and staffing

Ultimate authority for the total Cambridge-Somerville Mental Health Center lies with a 21-man area board, whose members include representatives from the local mental health associations and mental retardation associations, plus citizens drawn from a range of occupational groups, including both labor and management, selected so as to represent consumers of public mental health services. The area director is Dr. Reid, who, while retaining his job as director of the Cambridge Guidance Center, took on this new responsibility when the mental health center was established. He spends about 80 percent of his time as director of the overall Cambridge-Somerville program (which provides services for both children and adults), the remaining 20 percent as director of the children's service in Cambridge. The Cambridge Mental Health Association is the local sponsor of the Cambridge Guidance Center. Authority is vested in a 39-member board of directors.

The assignment of staff at the guidance center in terms of accountability to the director is as follows:

• Three teams of clinicians, each headed by a child psychiatrist, dividing their time between outpatient services provided there and in community settings, and consultation to a variety of community agencies.

• Directors of certain special programs, namely the Preschool Program, a special community satellite known as the Neighborhood Family Care Center, community services (meaning consultation), and a research institute whose relationship with the mental health center is more one of administrative convenience than one of direct involvement in researching the center's program.

• The chiefs of psychiatry, psychology, social work, and preschool education.

• The training director.

Thus, a social worker member of a particular team might have as many as four lines of accountability: to the head of the team for clinical services; to the chief social worker; to the assistant director in his responsibility as head of the consultation program; and, if she is supervising trainees, to the training director. This potentially formidable spread of accountability had in fact rarely posed a problem, because *a*) responsibilities are well defined, *b*) supervisory arrangements are systematic, and *c*) highly qualified staff interact with one another in an atmosphere of good will, confidence, and enthusiasm.

The total staff based at the Cambridge Guidance Center include the equivalent of just under three full-time child psychiatrists, all fully trained, plus a half-time resident in child psychiatry; the equivalent of three full-time psychologists trained at the doctoral level plus five trained at the master's level, all with extensive background in working with children; and six master's-level social workers, all trained in child guidance centers. There are also nine psychology interns for amounts of time varying from one day a week to full time; five half-time social work students; about 20 college students who serve as volunteer tutors for clinic patients; about ten other volunteers working in a nursery program; two work-study students; and office staff. Additional to these is the large staff of the Preschool Program.

Each team and the special service units hold weekly meetings to keep abreast of case management and flow of patients. The staff members of each discipline meet together every other week to discuss developments having particular relevance to their discipline. The heads of each discipline meet every week for similar purposes. And the chiefs of the three primary clinical teams meet once a month "to discuss problems of overlapping service and possibilities of children getting 'lost.'" There are regular meetings with school adjustment counselors and other child-caring agencies "to attempt to avoid inadequacies of service."

Dr. Reid said that there have been no problems in recruiting well-qualified staff, despite a remarkably low salary scale. Most staff members were recommended by staff members already in the agency or came by unsolicited application for positions. Dr. Reid believes that professional staff have been readily available for these reasons: *a*) Cambridge is considered an attractive and exciting place to work; *b*) many faculty members at local universities have wives who are well-trained social workers; and *c*) Boston institutions have trained many people in child guidance who are reluctant to leave the area, despite attractive offers from other parts of the country.

The clinical services

The outpatient service. Most of the outpatient service is provided at the principal locale described above. There all clinical personnel are assigned to three "team units" which "function like small clinics," with a good deal of autonomy. For many years, when the staff was smaller, it operated as one team serving all of Cambridge. With growth in staff size, teams were introduced in 1966, largely as an administrative necessity, and without geographic assignment. With the growth of a more vigorous attempt for the clinical personnel also to be involved with schools and other agencies, each team was subsequently given a particular portion of the city of Cambridge. In the interest of having each team's area of responsibility include all socioeconomic levels, the districting was somewhat gerrymandered; but even so one team has more low-income multiproblem families and another has a higher proportion of stable, low- to middle-income families.

Inevitably the teams vary in their orientation and their practices. Staff members from the team serving the poorest neighborhoods described themselves as more traditional than the other two. They had largely maintained disciplinary specialties, with all intake being done by social workers and with a traditional diagnostic sequence. Psychological tests were done on most children assigned to this team, each was interviewed by a psychiatrist, there was a conference between the staff and the parents, and finally a formal diagnostic conference. With the other teams a good deal of "role blurring" had come about, with any professional available for assignment to intake duty, with psychological testing taking place only in the face of the evident need for specific kinds of data. One team has attempted considerable variation in the use of paraprofessionals and volunteers, in concentrated (including one-day) diagnostic evaluations, in focusing on short-term goals, and in working collaboratively with other community agencies. Neither the "traditionalists" nor the more experimental teams seemed to question the prerogatives of the other to operate as they saw fit, and it appeared to do credit to the director that this freedom to pursue individual persuasions could exist with an evident harmony throughout the staff.

Each team holds a weekly meeting to hear brief reports of new applications, to decide whether to accept the case or to refer it to some more appropriate agency, and, if it is accepted, to assign it to a particular staff member for principal clinical responsibility. At the same time a conference is held on any formal diagnostic procedures that have been completed during the previous week. These include summaries of interviews with parents, with the child, and the result of any psychological tests that were done; thereupon the team formulates a diagnosis and makes recommendations for a treatment plan. Other management issues, case closings, community service, and program philosophy are discussed.

During 1970, a total of 201 inquiries about service were received, and 185 of these were seen at least for an intake interview. The largest single source of referrals was the schools, including parochial, public, private, and preschool programs, accounting for 31 percent. Next came medical services, such as hospitals and community retardation services, 20 percent; self-referrals, 11 percent; the welfare department, ten percent; family physicians, nine percent; social service agencies, eight percent; family and friends, eight percent; and the courts, three percent. The active caseload during 1970 was about 500 families, including 160 new applications, approximately evenly divided among the three teams.

Most inquiries are made by telephone. The receptionist asks for the street address, determines to which of the three teams the applicant should be assigned, then calls the particular staff member on intake duty at that time. If it appears from the information provided during the telephone call that the problem has been longstanding, the intake worker attempts to find out what earlier efforts have been made to obtain a diagnostic work-up or treatment. If the caller has reached the clinic through some misunderstanding of its services and purposes, the intake worker attempts to recommend some other resource that will be more appropriate.

If it appears, as in most cases, that a personal interview is indicated, the intake worker makes an appointment, usually within one week. Both parents are asked to attend, and, whenever possible, the child as well. During this initial interview, the intake worker obtains written permission from the parents to contact the family physician, the school, and any other community resources with which the family has been in contact. If it appears that the family will be seen at least for diagnostic study, the intake worker discusses the fees that would apply. She then completes a "face sheet" that is sent to the office to establish a case record.

The application is then presented at the team's next weekly meeting, when any subsequent steps are planned. If the "diagnostic sequence" seems indicated, usually the child is assigned to one staff member and the parents to another, although occasionally, when the trouble may be more in terms of interactional than internalized problems, the entire family is assigned to a single staff member. Psychological tests may be requested. In almost all cases the staff worker will visit the school to talk with the teacher and sometimes to observe the child. When all of the material required for the diagnostic procedure is in hand, the case is presented to the team, which then decides whether or not to recommend treatment on the basis of

> whether we have a service program suited to that family, and one which is not more readily or adequately available elsewhere in the community. Since we cannot offer treatment in all cases, and since service here is not the treament of choice in many cases, arrangements for service by other facilities are often made.

Once a family has been seen in the clinic, a form letter is sent to the Director of Pupil Services of the local school department, notifying her of the nature of the clinic's contact.

The chief social worker told us that while some families fail to appear for the initial interview, once that interview has been held relatively few drop out. She believed that the early attrition is mostly in the case of welfare clients who are urged by their caseworker to apply to the clinic but soon decide that they do not want to carry through.

The clinic has provided for staff use a "diagnostic summary" outline which is particularly comprehensive. In such terminology as "superego development," "libido," and so on, it is considerably more psychoanalytic than that of several of the other programs we visited. It is used more as a didactic device than on a case-by-case basis.

The range of treatment is comprehensive. All parents are seen, many as couples and a few in groups. About half of the children are seen in individual psychotherapy. Some families are seen in family therapy. There is group psychotherapy for parents, a group for mothers alone, a "couples group," a special group for parents of nursery school children, a little girls' group, four after-school boys' clubs, and a tutoring program. Home visits are frequently made. A particular child and his parents can be assigned to whatever combination of individual or group activities seems most to promise a beneficial effect.

Medication is conservatively used. At the time of our visit only about 15 of 160 children in treatment were receiving drugs, the considerable majority of these for hyperactivity and aggressiveness. Dr. Reid told us that

> at times I think we use too little medication, which reflects the period when most of our staff were trained, namely, prior to 1960.

We were furnished a report of the diagnoses of one hundred consecutively closed cases during late 1970. (Each team meets periodically to effect closing of cases that have become inactive but have not been formally closed.) Among these, the diagnostic process was not completed for 22 children. Among the remaining 78, more than half of the diagnoses were adjustment reactions of childhood and adolescence and behavior disorders of childhood and adolescence. Specifically, the percentages were as follows:

Adjustment reactions of childhood and adolescence	38%
Mental retardation	18
Behavior disorders of childhood and adolescence	14
Personality disorders	12
Special symptom reactions	5
No mental disorder	5
Neuroses	3
Psychoses not attributed to physical condition	3
Psychosis associated with brain syndrome	1
Nonpsychotic organic brain syndrome	1

Among these hundred cases, the disposition, in three broad categories, was as follows: patient withdrew "unilaterally" by declining further service, 25 percent (a low figure compared to most clinics); case terminated by the clinic without need for referral elsewhere, 42 percent; case terminated by the clinic with recommendation that psychiatric or other kinds of services be sought, 33 percent.

Of those who were treated, 69 percent were considered to be improved, 30 percent to be unchanged, and one percent worse.

The size of the caseload is related to the school year. In the fall there is rarely a delay for diagnosis or treatment. As the school year progresses and more troubled children are identified, the caseload grows; by late in the school year there may be a wait for treatment of several weeks or longer.

Emergency service. Dealing with such emergency behavior in children and adolescents as fire setting, self-destruction, and school phobia is divided between the Cambridge clinic and the emergency room at Cambridge City Hospital.

All children brought to the hospital's emergency room are seen by the pediatric house officer. Should he feel that the problem is psychiatric, he can send for the psychiatrist on emergency call. This general psychiatrist is in turn backed up by a child psychiatrist.

Grossly disturbed or destructive children (although not more than one or two at a time) can then be temporarily placed on the pediatric ward. There are fewer than ten such admissions per year.

Younger adolescents who have attempted suicide or have otherwise behaved in a destructive way that seems to call for the protection of a hospital ward can be admitted to the adult psychiatric service. There have never been more than one or two such patients at a time, and there are perhaps a dozen in the course of a year. Should their behavior remain seriously destructive, it would be necessary to try to arrange for transfer to the state hospital.

Older adolescents (over 17) are simply admitted to the adult psychiatric ward as regular patients.

When the Cambridge Guidance Center receives an inquiry that seems to involve seriously disturbed behavior that might best be characterized as "urgent" rather than "emergent," the intake worker makes an appointment for the parents and child to come in within 24 hours. Examples of such behavior would be torturing animals or seriously hurting another child; such behavior is seen as suggestive of psychosis.

If the parent fails to keep the emergency appointment, the staff member arranges a home visit to be made within the next 24 hours.

Partial hospitalization. Realizing the need of certain children for a more extensive therapeutic experience than could be provided on an outpatient basis, the Cambridge clinic in 1963 started a "nursery clinic" for retarded children; a similar clinic for emotionally disturbed children was begun in 1966 for children who could not be dealt with in Headstart classes. From this small beginning has developed under the federally funded program the separate Preschool Program that serves both Cambridge and Somerville. While the patients in this program are mostly from three to five years old, its duration nonetheless is related to the school year, and at the time of our visit in early fall the 1970-71 program was still under development. Eleven groups were either already operating or about to start; they were to range in size from five to twelve children. (During the previous year a total of one hundred children had been served.) They meet at four different locations, including two churches, the Cambridge clinic, and the nearby building that houses the research unit affiliated with the mental health center.

The staff of the Preschool Program consists of a child psychiatrist as clinical director, a special educator as education supervisor, an R.N., and an administrative assistant, plus five full-time and three half-time teachers, the majority with master's degrees, several part-time teachers' aides, and 13 college student volunteers devoting from one to two days a week each.

The children in these programs are those who have serious developmental problems that appear to reflect mental retardation or emotional illness or a combination of the two. Very few, perhaps no more than five percent, in the view of the clinical director, could be called psychotic, either autistic or symbiotic. The majority are children whose behavior is so destructive or disorganized that they have proved more than their families or a variety of agencies could tolerate. A considerable number are children who had been evicted from Headstart preschool programs. The behavior of the parents often calls for intervention as well. Many parents are asked to attend group meetings and attendance is quite good. Fathers are involved in activities which take place in the evening, such as toy building. Home visits are frequently made; each teacher tries to make a weekly visit to the home of each of her students.

Each group of children meets at least twice a week, and most meet either three or five times, for sessions of two and a half hours. The interaction between the teacher and the children might be described as one of educationally oriented play designed to provide a corrective emotional experience with an appropriate adult. There was some discussion of a behavior modification philosophy, but this did not seem to have been formalized beyond the verbal approval of desired behavior.

This program was too new to have any definitive outcome data. However, Dr. Braun indicated that about ninety percent of the children who had been in the program in the preceding year had been able to move on satisfactorily to regular day-care programs and to special classes in the schools.

> The kind of children we're successful with [he told us] are the kind everybody else is successful with—the ones that have families you can make a dent on.

Without the program, these children would be at home requiring 24-hour, seven-day-a-week care, at great personal cost to the mother and the rest of the family. One or two of these children might be institutionalized if space were available; however, there is currently a several-year wait for admission to residential institutions.

The summer program mentioned above had an enrollment of 45 children between three and seven years old, most of whom were retarded.

Held five days a week, for three hours a day, it was staffed largely with college-student volunteers. Most of these children were in the Preschool Program during the regular school year. They were placed in the program because no other resource was available except the home. Through the program, relief was provided for the mothers, and the children could develop skills in motor activity, interaction with other children, and so on. It was essentially a continuation of the winter program and served to facilitate the child's entry into subsequent schooling.

Inpatient service. The only provision for hospitalizing children or adolescents within the catchment area is on the very occasional emergency basis described above. (In the planning stage with the Avon Home, an adoption agency in Cambridge, was a 24-hour-care arrangement for brief periods while some family crisis is being worked out, possibly to be staffed by a divinity student and his wife.)

For children requiring longer-term treatment, inpatient resources are limited to a particular state hospital that receives children from a substantial portion of the state. This unit often has a waiting list, and it proves a complicated and aggravating process to get a child accepted. However, only six or seven children each year from Cambridge require such placement. It is because of this limited need, plus the availability of emergency admission at the Cambridge hospital, that Dr. Reid expresses the hope that "we never build a children's inpatient service in Cambridge-Somerville."

Massachusetts law provides for private placement of children who are not learning in school as an evident result of severe emotional disturbance. These placements are also often not easy to arrange. During early 1971, a significant number of children from Cambridge and Somerville were at private out-of-state facilities under this provision.

Consultation and community services

As we have mentioned, Dr. Hersch, who is both assistant director and chief psychologist, is also in charge of consultation activities. The focus of consultation is often on the children and families that the other agency is serving; some deals with organizational problems; and at times advice from a mental health viewpoint is offered on projects the agency is undertaking. By mid-1971, the Guidance Center staff was working with more than 30 other community programs. These include social service agencies, community schools, preschool and day-care programs, public and parochial schools, and community planning activities.

All of the consultation, whatever its focus and goal, is done by clinicians. That is to say, the clinic deliberately does not assign any staff member to full-time consultation activities, on the grounds that it is a more effective arrangement for each professional to combine clinical activities with consultation. Furthermore, no staff member is hired with any advance stipulation that he will split his time in some particular ratio between directly clinical and consultative activities. Rather, the basic commitment is to one's geographic team, and thereafter an allocation is sought that the particular clinician will feel comfortable with. Indeed, some who feel shy about, for example, conducting group sessions with teachers do not do any consultative work at all of this sort. The time spent in consultation would thus range from none, for an occasional staff member, to a maximum of about 75 percent. All of the staff engaged in consultation meet with Dr. Hersch twice a month in a kind of all-purpose meeting which reviews problems with particular clients or agencies and the general progress of the consultation program. Consultation is defined by the clinic as "a means of primary and secondary prevention." A further purpose is "to share with other agencies in the planning and development of new projects in response to community needs."

Dr. Hersch, with two years of formal training in mental health consultation and an additional thirteen years of experience in this area, feels that the members of the staff have individually evolved their own particular styles of consultation. "There is no one overriding consultation 'system' used," Dr. Hersch said, "but rather approaches that are more eclectic and pragmatic. There is case-centered and system-centered consultation and often an interweaving between the two. Some of the consultation works within an 'interference' model, working through the emotional intrusions of the consultee; other aspects operate on a 'deficit' model, attempting to provide knowledge and technique in areas where the consultee is deficient. The staff learn from one another through sharing experiences at the consultation meetings. Students sit in on these meetings as well, although the major part of their learning is on an apprenticeship basis with one of the senior staff." Asked why agencies show an interest in having consultation from the clinic, Dr. Hersch said that

> they think we have a lot of expertise about children—that we know a very great deal about them—and that we can translate what we know into advice for them that will be useful in their own work with children. The first assumption is easy for us to accept; I wish that we could always feel as confident about the second. In any case, we strive to take what we know and render it discernible, usable, and suitable to other people who are involved in the lives of children. It is almost explicitly understood that we start to work with particular agencies on a "case-directed" basis, focused on specific children that they're having trouble with.

Activities with the schools. For many years the public school system of Cambridge was isolated from mental health facilities and resources and the academic community because the superintendent denied the need for such services. (Indeed, the school of education at Harvard was not even allowed to place trainees in the public schools.) With a new administration in 1968, the situation changed dramatically. Although the clinic's consultation for a number of years had involved an interview with the schoolteacher and classroom observation for each child being considered for treatment, it still had not, as of late 1970, developed a program whereby regularly scheduled "program consultation" was being provided to groups of classroom teachers or guidance counselors and other "pupil personnel." The center hopes that this can be developed over time.

Perhaps the most impressive of the contacts with the public schools was that with the Headstart and Follow Through programs. Both of these federally supported programs for children from poor families are operated by the public schools in Cambridge, and the schools in turn contract for mental health services from the Cambridge clinic. The Headstart program involves about 200 children aged three to five from low-income families, who are provided a half-day's "enrichment" program designed to help them overcome the lack of stimuli from their impoverished backgrounds. During 1969-70, the Cambridge clinic assigned a half-time doctoral-level staff psychologist *a*) to observe all the children in the program, *b*) to consult with teachers, teachers' aides, and social service aides, *c*) to see parents when indicated, and *d*) to collaborate with other Headstart personnel, particularly social service, in working with particular families. In the course of the year, the psychologist interviewed 21 of these children in class. She arranged for the clinic to do diagnostic testing for two children, initiated referrals of four children to the clinic for treatment, and arranged referrals of 13 children to other kinds of agencies for other kinds of services.

The Follow Through program serves low-income children, many of whom were in the Headstart program, in the first three regular grades of school. With the intention of maintaining any gains realized from Headstart, Follow Through provides smaller classes, teachers' aides, a flexible structure, and specialized programs to meet the special needs of groups of children. To this program the clinic assigned one three-quarter-time and one half-time psychologist, a psychiatric consultant, two psychological consultants, a "psychological assistant," two activity group leaders, a "perceptual tutor," a "therapeutic tutor," and four attention trainers. Of the 255 children in this program, psychological screenings were done in the schools for 68. The clinic staff held regular consultations and policy conferences with teachers and met with parents in indicated cases. Ten children were referred to the clinic for diagnostic testing, seven were referred for treatment, six were referred to the boys activity group at the clinic, 13 were referred for therapeutic tutoring. Thirty-seven children were seen in the schools for interviews with the psychologists.

In addition to these activities with the public schools, the clinic is involved in regularly scheduled consultations with seven nursery schools, five community schools (after-school programs sponsored by the community using school facilities), five day-care programs, and four parochial schools. Examples of the nature of these contacts are these:

• A psychologist visits a nursery school a half day each week to observe children in the classroom and discuss with the director and staff of the school how best to meet the needs of particular children.

• A social worker from the clinic participates in a community school program for teen-agers, in which topical films are shown on such issues as drug abuse and racial conflict, followed by group discussion.

• A psychiatrist meets every other week with the full staff of a day-care center to offer assistance in their work with individual children and at times to consult on aspects of their program.

The courts. Since about 1950 Massachusetts has had a separate network of clinics attached to the juvenile courts throughout the state. Established and financed by the Department of Mental Health, they have operated on an essentially independent basis, with relatively little collaboration or contact with other agencies in the community. Occasional cases of neglected children are referred by the court to the Cambridge clinic, but by and large it provides its own direct service or disposition for the majority of its clients, specifically, teen-agers with a charge against them.

During a three-month period early in 1970, ten children were referred by the court to its own clinic. All were within the 13-to-16 age range, and they were variously diagnosed as having anxiety reaction, depressive reaction, passive-aggressive personality, and adjustment reaction of adolescence. Two were treated at the court clinic, three were placed on probation, one was placed in a residential treatment facility, and the others were referred to various other agencies.

With an impending reorganization of the state's mental health department, there was some anticipation that the court clinics might be brought into closer contact with the community mental health centers.

The welfare department. Because almost half of the clinic's patients come from families that are on welfare, the collaboration between the two agencies is close. The clinic's chief social worker for several years has conducted weekly training seminars with welfare department case-workers; the seminars "seem to be appreciated because most of the workers are untrained." During the year prior to our visit, a psychiatrist who was an advanced trainee in community mental health had spent a day each week with welfare workers, occasionally going with them to make home visits.

Services to other agencies. The clinic has provided various forms of consultation to a considerable variety of other kinds of agencies in the community. Some of these have been deliberately time limited, others have been continuous. An example of a consultation relationship that has been sustained for several years is that of the clinic's chief social worker with the local YWCA. She goes there each week to meet with the residence director to discuss any problems that have arisen among the women living there, to help make referrals to other agencies where this seems indicated, and to review applications from prospective residents.

One of the psychiatrists meets one evening each week with the director and staff of DARE House, a community residence for predelinquent and delinquent adolescents, to discuss problems of the children living there, to review applications for admission, and to consider any problems that have arisen. A staff psychologist consults to the Cambridge Community Center, which serves mostly black clients, concerning program development and problem children; another staff psychologist helps out with the tutoring program that the center provides. A staff social worker consults regularly with the staff of the Neighborhood Youth Corps concerning adolescents who have a difficult time finding or adjusting to work.

Mental retardation services

Since 1956 Cambridge has had a Children's Development Clinic, funded by the U.S. Children's Bureau, with major responsibility for retarded children. At the same time, the community mental health center has provided a number of specific services for retarded children. About half of the one hundred children in the preschool day program are retarded. Dr. Reid has a specific "assistant for mental retardation" on the staff. Herself the mother of a retarded child, she told us that

> in my view the integration of services for disturbed children and retarded children has often been considered by the parents of both to be a shotgun wedding—an arrangement forced upon them that does not work out happily for either. But in the Cambridge-Somerville area, things have evolved differently. This mental health program seems to be looking for

children who need service and trying to find service for them, rather than concerning themselves with which category the child belongs in.

Her own job she described as principally one of "getting to know programs by observing them and interpreting back to the parent groups what is really going on."

For many years prior to its becoming a component of the mental health center, the Cambridge clinic accepted retarded children for diagnostic evaluation, for treatment if indicated and available, and "if we had nothing further to offer we made every effort to find a proper placement."

The summer recreation program for preschool retarded children mentioned earlier was started in 1968. During the summer of 1970, it served forty such children. The "camp" is held at the same sites as the regular-year preschool classes and is staffed by public service interns from Massachusetts' Commonwealth Service Corps (VISTA), by volunteers, and by trainees who join the program as a field placement.

At the Cambridge Infirmary, in 1969, a daytime program for about 16 severely retarded children of school age was started. These children had been entirely excluded from school.

Research

A component of the mental health center is a large research program known as the Research Institute for Educational Problems. As we have mentioned, its affiliation with the center is largely one of administrative convenience, since this Institute is not and has not been involved in any research relating specifically to the program of the Cambridge-Somerville center. Its staff of thirty, with funds from several federal agencies, is performing some interesting work regarding the learning capabilities of retarded children. The research includes experimental projects in learning potential and a large program involving about ten special classrooms in Boston public schools. Another principal project is to establish a learning center designed to provide a means by which specialized remedial services can be made available to children at risk of failing academically, "such that each child has the opportunity to profit from individually designed educational programs."

Within the mental health center, three evaluation studies were going on at the time of our visit. One, a part of a research methods course at Emmanuel College, involved twelve students who, under the direction of a staff psychologist, were doing a follow-up study of 150 families to evaluate the effectiveness of the center's clinical service as perceived by its clients. In another, two students from Harvard's new program in

Clinical Psychology and Public Practice were working within one of the center's clinical teams in an effort to devise a model for evaluating clinical services which could be used throughout the center. In the third, the social service staff was doing a follow-up study of children who had been referred by the center for placement outside their own homes. A fourth project had been proposed to the Commonwealth of Massachusetts for funding,[1] a "cross-age" tutoring program that would involve disturbed adolescents as tutors for disturbed young children, on the hypothesis that the tutoring could prove an effective therapeutic device both for the tutors and for their pupils.

Training

The clinic is involved in a variety of training programs, including a placement for the child psychiatry rotation for residents from Metropolitan State Hospital. In 1970 there were two residents at a time. While the clinic was approved as a two-year training facility for fellows in child psychiatry, as of 1971 the program had not been funded. It is anticipated to begin in 1972, and these fellows will spend their full time at the Cambridge clinic in its clinical and community programs.

Nine graduate students in psychology come for specialized training programs from Harvard, Boston University, and Boston College. They come not only from clinical, counseling, and educational psychology programs but also from human relations, community mental health, and community psychology.[2]

In recent years there have been five student social workers each year, from Simmons College and Boston College.

Within the preschool unit placements are available for approximately ten student teachers from Harvard, Tufts, and Boston Universities, and Simmons and Lesley Colleges. Their training includes classroom work, home visits, individual tutoring, and contacts with the community.

From time to time the clinic has provided training for student nurses, who typically are assigned to a particular clinical team to work with families that have problems of a medical nature. This includes home visiting.

Starting in 1970-71, the center provided six placements for students from the Harvard Divinity School, who each spend about thirteen hours per week working with the boys' club groups and as companion-tutors.

---

[1] Which it subsequently received.

[2] Subsequently an NIMH grant was awarded for a joint clinical psychology training program between the Guidance Center and the Harvard University Health Services.

They are supervised by clinical staff who are working with the families of the children they are involved with. Each trainee is assigned to one of the clinical teams, and the program is coordinated by a staff psychologist.

Financing

The children's service in the Cambridge center is budgeted during 1971 at $486,000, which comes from a variety of sources including research grants. Very little is from the NIMH staffing grant, since the funds from this grant were used mainly to develop new services in Somerville and adult services in Cambridge; specifically, within the Cambridge children's services, only the preschool program is paid from the federal grant. The largest single source of income is a payment of $192,000 from the state to cover professional salaries. The next largest item comes from the city government, as a block grant of about $32,000 for services rendered. Patients' fees and health insurance are minor categories of income; in 1970 the fees came to about $5000 and health insurance to only $1500. The Cambridge Mental Health Association, through the contributions of its membership and by United Fund monies, provides about $17,000 per year in overhead expense.

Fees are set according to a sliding scale that takes into account both family size and income. A family of four with an income of $4900 per year would pay $1.25 per week, and a family of the same size with an income of $8500 would pay $7.00 per week. This fee would apply irrespective of the amount of service; every member of the family could be in treatment, and the fee would remain the same.

The clinic did not have a complete breakdown of the cost of its various services; an indicative figure which it had computed was $25 per hour for individual outpatient treatment.

Somerville

Dr. William Ackerly, a child psychiatrist who is director of the Somerville program, describes Somerville as "extraordinarily different" from Cambridge. It is much more homogeneous, with a population that is 99 percent white and 85 percent Catholic. Only four percent of the 100,000 Somerville residents have completed college, contrasted with eleven percent for the Boston metropolitan area. By occupation it is very largely blue-collar, with scarcely any upper-middle-class sections but also without the extreme poverty of certain Cambridge neighborhoods.

With a population of 23,000 per square mile, Somerville is the most densely populated city in all of New England. The median income is slightly below that for the entire state and a good bit lower than that for the Boston metropolitan area; only 13 percent of Somerville families have incomes of $10,000 or more, compared with 21 percent in the metropolitan area. More Somerville residents rent than own their homes. The housing is old, with 93 percent of dwellings existing in 1960 having been built before 1930.

There are approximately 35 physicians practicing in Somerville, but no pediatricians and, except for the staff of the mental health service, no psychiatrists. The average age of physicians is above sixty, and no general practitioner has moved into the city for more than twenty years. Somerville is characterized by a poverty of resources and of leadership. Its economic base is small and weak and the tax structure is poor. There are few social agencies.

The advent of mental health services in Somerville is strikingly similar to that of Cambridge. Citizen concern about the lack of any local treatment resources for children and adolescents led to the establishment of a local mental health association, as a facilitator toward the creation of a child guidance clinic. The mental health association relied heavily on advice and support from the Cambridge clinic in getting started, recruiting staff, and program planning, and when the Somerville service was established in 1964, its first staff member was Dr. Ackerly, who was at that time on the staff of the Cambridge service and for a year divided his workweek between the two facilities. Dr. Ackerly provided an interesting account of how the clinic was created.

> The center was established with a unitary purpose of "service for Somerville children." There was particular emphasis by the Somerville public schools, which had long felt the urgent need for mental health services and referrals that previously had to go outside the city for help. Because community people had been so discouraged by long delays in getting appointments in Boston clinics for their children, the first policy set was one of "no waiting list" for a diagnostic evaluation and treatment. Because of the great need for service the second priority was that the focus should be on short-term treatment and crisis intervention so that we would be able to see larger numbers of children. Due to the virtual absence of mental health services in the city, we very quickly became the focus and center for referrals. The third priority which was established quite early was working closely in liaison with community leaders. Principals, teachers, adjustment counselors and guidance counselors, the juvenile court, Headstart, the mayor, political leaders, doctors, priests, ministers, and hospitals were introduced to the clinic and made aware of its services. Because the director met and knew these leaders, the clinic became very responsive to community needs. We did emergency

evaluations for the court, home visits for those who could not come to the clinic, and saw cases in collaboration with welfare workers, family doctors, settlement house staff, and school personnel. . . . Also, the clinic began to evolve programs in response to demands for service; for example, many grammar school children were without fathers and had inadequate socialization so that college volunteers were recruited. They proved extremely helpful both for brief treatment as well as for evaluating the total needs of the family.

During its first several years, the staff of the clinic grew from three to ten. Dr. Ackerly states that with this growth the philosophy moved toward that of general practice.

We found that our availability to the community was crucial and perhaps the most important of our functions. Families would drop in for service, community people would ask for help and consultation. We also found that staff people could no longer continue with their traditional roles, but had to become multiskilled individuals, as they might be called on for many tasks. We were also aware that psychiatrists, psychologists, and social workers could not always deliver the most adequate service, so that other staff disciplines were added—a nursery school teacher, then a psychiatric nurse, and following that a mother's aide or child-care worker who had special knowledge from her advantage of living in the community. . . . With time we were asked to help out in many ways in community consultation programs such as Headstart, the public schools, a settlement house, a tenants association, family physicians, and so on.

Thus, as Dr. Ackerly describes it, the clinic moved more and more towards a "public health model with increasing emphasis on preventing problems as well as developing neighborhood satellite clinics." A part-time pediatrician was added to the mental health service staff "so that we could give more complete service." The support of two neighborhood groups was sought in developing satellite mental health services. The satellite clinics began operating together with well-baby clinics as a nucleus for two new neighborhood health centers.

In 1969 the Somerville clinic became part of the Cambridge-Somerville Mental Health Center. The federal funds thus awarded made possible the creation of outpatient services for adults and the collaboration with Cambridge in the preschool unit previously described. In addition, the federal funds considerably augmented (by fifty percent) the services already developed for children and adolescents.

The staff as of early 1971 consisted of two child psychiatrists; four Ph.D. psychologists; three full-time and two half-time social workers, all with master's degrees; three R.N.'s; six "special service assistants" (indigenous workers and postgraduate case aides); two nursery school teachers; and an occupational therapist. Most of the professional staff have had special training in working with children and see clients of all age ranges; two psychologists, however, see only children and adolescents.

About sixty percent of the caseload consists of children and their families and about 34 percent are adolescents, with or without their families. Adolescents represent a much larger portion of the caseload in Somerville than in Cambridge, in part because there is no court clinic in Somerville and in part because more emphasis has been laid on developing services for the teen-ager. For example, because many adolescents were walking in seeking help with problems related to drug use, Dr. Ackerly started a twice-weekly open group therapy program for them, to which they can and do bring their friends, their girl friends, and their parents. At the time of our visit, arrangements were just being completed for a "hot line" telephone service specifically designed for adolescents.

Dr. Ackerly describes the first five years of operation as "dominated by the development of clinical services and community collaboration . . . accompanied by an emerging philosophy of community mental health in order to accomplish our commitment of 'service to Somerville children.' " The future, he believes, lies in two directions: a) training and research and b) prevention of illness and disability. He describes the clinic as "in the process of exploring with the Harvard School of Public Health ways of implementing better school health programs, and consulting and collaborating with community groups around the concept of preventing illness and strengthening capacities and capabilities for coping with life. The importance of 'total health' for families and comprehensive care will be the guidelines of the future."

Convalescent Hospital for Children
Rochester, New York

The area served

The area of responsibility for Convalescent Hospital for Children varies from one service to another. Its residential treatment program, the only one for Monroe County children other than that at Rochester State Hospital, serves the entire county. It provides day treatment for the county conjointly with another federally assisted community mental health center located in the northern part of the county. Its outpatient service and prevention and consultation programs are limited to the catchment area designated under the provisions of the federal program: a portion of the southern half of the county with a population of 180,000, which includes seven school districts, part of the city of Rochester, and a number of subdivisions, villages, and towns.

Each of these three overlapping "catchments" covers a broad socio-economic and demographic spread, including rural areas, a number of middle-class suburbs of varying characteristics, the inner-city slums of Rochester, and an area in transition. The clientele includes the families of top executives and professionals, well-to-do and poor farmers, small-town dwellers, storekeepers, and "the turbulent, deprived citizens of the city streets."

The hospital is located on the outskirts of Rochester, just outside the city limits, about a 25-minute drive from the furthermost point of the "federal catchment"; no point in Monroe County is more than 45 minutes away by private transportation. Bus service is infrequent and generally unsatisfactory, but most of the population have access to private means of transportation. The Convalescent Hospital supplements public transportation by providing its own system of "courtesy cars" to the end of the city bus line. In addition they have set up several "satellite clinics" in the inner city, thus placing service within walking distance of those least able or least motivated to provide their own transportation.

Origins

In 1885 a tent colony known as the Infant's Summer Hospital was created on the shores of Lake Ontario to treat children from the slums of

Rochester who were suffering from "infant summer fever." Within a few years this illness disappeared, and the facility redirected itself toward providing long-term convalescent care for children with rheumatic hearts, polio, and orthopedic problems. Still later (1913) permanent buildings near the lake were erected. As the decades passed, the need for hospitalization for such children waned, and by the early 1950's Convalescent Hospital was faced with the need to identify some new form of service.

A committee of the Council of Social Agencies, appointed in 1950 to study the needs of children in Monroe County, identified one unmet need as that of a residential treatment center for emotionally disturbed children. It involved the board of directors of Convalescent Hospital in assuming responsibility for this service "after much soul searching, self-evaluation, and refocusing."[1] The first such children were admitted to the old hospital building late in 1958. During this time a 45-acre plot had been acquired in the town of Chili, just outside the city of Rochester. Fifteen of these acres were donated by a philanthropist and the other 30 were purchased from unrestricted endowment funds. Since then another five acres were acquired to protect the property from commercial encroachments, making a total of 50 acres. By mid-1960 the first patients were admitted to the first two cottages of the Residential Treatment Center. This population of 16 was increased less than two years later to 24, when a third cottage was added.

In 1963, because of the need to provide aftercare for children being discharged, a small outpatient clinic was added; it soon began to serve families other than those whose children had been inpatients. At about the same time, because of an increasing number of referrals of children who were significantly disturbed but did not seem to require 24-hour care, a pilot day-treatment program was opened for three to five children. And in the same year a consultation service was started for day-care centers and private nurseries, and training programs were begun for social caseworkers and group workers, psychiatric residents, clinical psychologists, teachers, nurses, and pediatricians.

With the advent of the federal program for helping to meet the expenses of building and staffing new community mental health centers, the board of Convalescent Hospital decided to apply for such funds. With prior approval of the State of New York, the application became the first and thus far the only one to be approved as a community mental health center solely for children. This unusual procedure was accomplished by

---

[1] Because of considerations of endowments and legacies, the name was not changed to something that would more accurately describe the new purpose.

arranging an affiliation agreement with the University of Rochester Mental Health Center, which would provide adult services for the same catchment area and emergency services for all ages.

Construction funds were used to build a new school serving the children in residential and day treatment. This building includes a reception, recreation, and eating area for children in day treatment, separate school wings for residential and day-treatment children, and a recreation wing. In addition, the Cutler Building, which includes both administrative and clinic facilities, was doubled in size, providing more offices, play-therapy and group-therapy rooms, conference rooms, and a library.

Staffing funds were used to establish a day-treatment program, moving from the pilot group of three to five children to the current 36. The outpatient services were expanded greatly with emphasis on a thrust into the inner city. A research department was established to provide ongoing research and evaluation. The education department was expanded and enriched. A consultation and prevention service was established as "an equal partner in the mosaic of services."

Thus, by the end of its first decade as a facility for emotionally disturbed children, Convalescent Hospital had grown to a capacity of 27 in residential treatment, plus seven others in "extended residential treatment" (described below), 36 in day treatment, 450 families being seen in the outpatient department, and an extensive program of consultation to many schools and to a broad variety of other community agencies.

Philosophy, purposes, and policy

The director of Convalescent Hospital, Dr. Sydney Koret, a psychologist, feels strongly that children's services ought to be separate from adult services, both administratively and financially. "When one simply incorporates younger patients into a generic treatment facility," he said, "it is likely that the children and adolescents will get less than their due, particularly when money gets tight. Furthermore, I'm convinced that a children's service, to be effective, must have a staff trained to work with children, a staff that understands the developmental process and appreciates the importance of the age gap between therapist and young patient."

As for the·"catchment area" concept developed for generic mental health centers, he feels it is in one respect too broad and in another too narrow to serve as an effective and efficient model for the needs of children. On the one hand, the indicated maximum population unit of 200,000 may not produce enough children who are so seriously disturbed as to require residential treatment, and thus the inpatient service would be prohibitively expensive. Consequently, a center such as his own, he feels, might provide a single inpatient program for a fairly large region—for example, several catchment areas consisting of several counties with a population of a half million or more. Conversely, he feels that a population of 200,000 may in many areas contain *more* children and families in need of outpatient service than can be effectively served from a single locus; thus, Convalescent Hospital, like some other federally assisted community mental health centers, has begun to establish "satellite clinics" serving a subsection of the catchment area, so that services will be more readily accessible.

The broad range of service at Convalescent Hospital has been developed out of a philosophy of "rendering effective services parsimoniously." The intensity is seen as starting with the consultation program, moving on to outpatient treatment, to day treatment, and to residential treatment.

As the facility has had more operating experience, it has moved more and more toward "prevention and early treatment." The prevention program of consultative services to schools and other agencies that are in touch with children "reflects our very strong conviction," its director told us, "that the most appropriate initial agents or carriers of mental health prior to the onset of serious pathology are not mental health professionals, but those persons who ordinarily come into extended contact with the children for some other purpose—for example, parents, teachers, pediatricians, clergymen, policemen, scout leaders. . . . The consultation program seeks to promote the enhancement of a climate or atmosphere whereby each child can learn and grow to the fullest extent of his or her potential. Such an atmosphere would minimize the likelihood of the development of the children being interfered with by emotional problems." Dr. Koret anticipated that as this approach took root it would mean "increased work with expectant and new mothers, with all families, and educational work in the community." Such a program for new and expectant mothers was initiated in 1971.

The priorities in mental health consultation programs are "determined for each program individually in response to needs identified by the consultee," with the general aim of enabling the consultees:

- To be more aware of mental health principles and concepts
- To understand children and child development
- To be cognizant of feelings and the ways they are expressed
- To be helpful to children who are encountering emotional difficulties
- To build positive approaches for coping with problem children

- To accurately and speedily identify the child in need of more intensive psychotherapeutic treatment, and to refer such children to appropriate resources
- To be aware of themselves "as feeling people" and of the effect that their personalities have upon the children they work with

The content and structure of consultation programs vary. Some are didactic, others involve discussions. Some are child oriented, others program oriented, and still others consultee oriented. Some focus on content, others on feelings. Some are "targeted toward improving communication," others toward improving program, still others toward self-understanding.

The hope—and belief—is that a definitive consultation program will thus result in a service to many children who might, if the program did not exist, eventually be referred for clinical services. At the same time, Dr. Koret feels that a complete range of clinical services is called for, but that it should operate on the philosophy that each child and family should be served at the lowest intensity of care consistent with their circumstances and needs, both because it is preferable to retain children insofar as possible in their ordinary, everyday environments, and second, because the more intensive the clinical service, the greater the financial and emotional cost. "There is no need to shoot howitzers at sparrows."

It is easy, in reviewing the sequence in which services were added at Convalescent Hospital, to trace the emphasis away from exclusive attention to the severe, manifest casualty toward an effort to prevent the development of pathology. By the time of our visit, Convalescent Hospital was clearly one of the most comprehensive children's services in the country. At the same time, Dr. Koret was able to identify some gaps in service that impede it. One is the lack of transitional homes for children who have been in the residential program, "who can utilize public school and enjoy community facilities but who are not yet ready to cope with the intimacies of a more tightly knit family." He believes that such homes would not only enhance the outcome for particular children but would also shorten the stay in the residential service. Another would be the creation of therapeutic foster homes operated directly by Convalescent Hospital, "for children who either do not have homes to return to or whose homes are unsuitable." These homes might also be used to protect the child awaiting admission to residential treatment and as a measure of the impact of separation from the family.

The other two major gaps in service are on either end of the age range. There is an urgent need for residential and day-treatment facilities for adolescents in the total community. The extension of the Convalescent

Hospital for Children program in this direction would be a natural and essential move to rounding out the service. A program was funded for implementation in the fall of 1971 for the establishment of classes in the inner city for children who have been psychiatrically exempted from public school. This will provide some of the desired service.

The other limitation was the lack of a program, other than outpatient, for preschool children. Staff were hired and funds secured for a therapeutic nursery for at least ten children between the ages of three and five, which started in September 1971.

Administration and staffing

Convalescent Hospital has a 36-member board of trustees who represent a variety of middle-class and upper-middle-class segments of the community. Among them are lawyers, bankers, and educators. While there is no professional advisory committee, the board itself has several physician members. The board members are assigned to fourteen committees, five of which relate themselves to specific functions and services of the hospital, while the others are concerned with such matters as financing, physical plant, and so on. The board appears to have been active and effective, with an excellent relationship with Dr. Koret.

The activities of the center are divided into departments, as follows: outpatient (known as the Child Guidance Clinic), day treatment, inpatient (known as Residential Treatment), research, and prevention and consultation. Each has its own director with whom Dr. Koret meets weekly. At the time of our visit there were department heads for the various disciplines—psychiatry, social work, psychology, education, pediatrics, and sociotherapy (described below). These were subsequently replaced by "coordinators" for each department, responsible for communication, inservice training, and community liaison. There is also an administrative council, composed of all service heads and department coordinators. It considers and recommends policy to the director based on the needs and concerns of the various services and departments, and it serves as the staff long-range planning committee.

The total staff includes 109 full-time persons in addition to the summer-camp staff. Two categories are of particular interest—psychiatrists, because there are so few, and sociotherapists, because there are so many. At the time of our visit, there was, in fact, only one psychiatrist, although there were newly authorized positions for one and a half additional. (Dr. Koret said that child psychiatrists were the only personnel that the center had ever had any trouble recruiting—a familiar story.)

Like much of the rest of the professional staff, the one psychiatrist, Dr. Lewis B. Ward, did part of his training at Convalescent Hospital and then decided to join the staff. He spends substantially all of his time in two particular ways that appear to utilize his competence most appropriately —evaluating and diagnosing prospective patients, and educating and training the staff. By way of the administrative council, he is involved in determining policy of the treatment program. As a clinician, he sees, at least twice, every child who is a potential admission for the day-treatment or residential-treatment program. Beyond this, he sees in the outpatient service any child, or his parents, or both, where there are complications that seem to call for psychiatric intervention. He directly supervises all use of psychoactive medication. In addition to his assignment as Chief of Psychiatry (his "Indians" are limited to three psychiatric residents on three-month rotations), he is designated Director of Psychotherapy and therefore has considerable influence in shaping the nature of the clinical program.

Dr. Ward told us that he feels both confident and comfortable as the only psychiatrist in a large treatment program, in part because of the checks and balances built into the clinical activities, but perhaps even more because he believes that both the professional staff and the sociotherapists are highly capable people, who either through formal academic training or within the center have acquired both the requisite skills to deal with children effectively and a realistic awareness of the limits of their capabilities.

In terms of formal credentials, the sociotherapists are at the other end of the scale. There are 37, comprising about a third of the entire staff and outnumbering the mental health professionals. Most of them are assigned to the residential cottages, but there are several each in day treatment and in the outpatient program, particularly in the new satellite clinics in the urban slums. They are an impressive group. All are required to have at least a high school education; several have completed college, and a larger number have had one or two years of college work. During earlier times, they were recruited mainly through classified advertisements in local newspapers, but more recently, as word of the program has spread, most openings have been filled by people who have applied on their own. For this category of personnel, the turnover rate is low; more than half of the sociotherapists have been on the staff for at least five years, and several have been there close to ten years.

They are carefully chosen. First comes an interview with the director and the coordinator of sociotherapy, following which, if the applicant seems promising, an appointment is scheduled for psychological testing.

The prospect of the tests causes some to withdraw. The tests themselves are not as precise as the center would like, but at least serve to eliminate "the grossly unsuitable." Those who are hired are given two weeks of classroom training, as part of which they read the records of a number of children then in treatment. Subsequently they are assigned to a particular cottage as observers for two weeks, largely with the same children whose records they have been acquainted with. Then they go to work, under careful monitoring. As long as they remain with the program, they meet weekly with a supervising sociotherapist and with a member of the professional staff for a discussion of their interpersonal relationships with children and staff "to understand and deal with countertransference phenomena," including any problems or concerns they have experienced.

The coordinator of sociotherapy told us that by and large the sociotherapists have relationships with the children that fall somewhere between parent-surrogate and big brother or sister.

> It's a type of relationship that the kids enjoy, and it's very trusting [he told us]. The sociotherapists are absolutely free to show affection to the children, by holding them on the lap, for instance. Or if a kid is having some little problem, the sociotherapist may walk up and put his arm around him, which can make all the difference in the world. These people give themselves to the children all the time. They enable the child to understand the inadequacies of his methods of coping with the environment and offer substitute techniques or defenses. They deal with behavior and inner feelings and turmoil in a special and uniquely prescribed fashion. They complement the professional who deals directly in psychotherapy with the children's problems, which are not the province of the sociotherapist.

The use of these "paraprofessionals" at Convalescent Hospital may be one of the more outstanding examples of the suitable augmentation of professional time with ancillary personnel. In respect of recruiting, screening, preparatory education, continuing education, supervision, and delineation of capabilities and limitations, the process makes excellent sense and is much in contrast with the anti-intellectualism and "anybody-can-do-anything" manifestation that have sometimes occurred in some mental health facilities in recent years.

Much the largest category of professional staff is social work, with 21 full-time master's-level social workers. Both day treatment and the Child Guidance Clinic are headed up by social workers. There are four assigned to residential treatment, six to day treatment, ten to the Child Guidance Clinic, and one to the new nursery school. There are ten full-time doctoral-level psychologists, plus another who spends part time in the program as research consultant. There are also three psychology interns. The education program for the day- and residential-treatment children has a director of education and nine academic teachers, all with college degrees, plus four others teaching music, art, speech, and arts and crafts. The remaining 25 staff members are in such support positions as clerical and bookkeeping, the kitchen, the maintenance department, and housekeeping.

The part-time staff consists of three pediatricians who come regularly to check on the health of the children in residential treatment and are otherwise available on call, plus a neurologist on call.

The clinical services

Every family in the service area who applies to the center is offered an initial interview, although there are some age limits operating in particular services which would limit the possible assignment of the child and his family. While outpatient and consultation services are provided up through the age of eighteen, residential treatment is limited to children from six through twelve and day treatment to children from six through fourteen. But whatever the assignment of the child may be, the path of entry for the considerable majority of children is the outpatient service. The total annual treatment capability at the time of our visit was about 575 children, of whom about 450 were on outpatient status. (By September 1971 the capacity had grown to about 900 per year, with about 750 anticipated to be outpatients.) If a given child is evaluated as needing day treatment or residential treatment, a waiting period is usually involved. In such circumstances, the family would be offered outpatient service, since, as Dr. Koret puts it, "We always offer something as a holding device; we don't abandon anyone." A review of the applications indicated that more than ninety percent do in fact become active cases, and those who do not are mostly families that either refused the particular kind of service offered or failed to show up for the initial interview. Children are taken into treatment on either an informal or voluntary basis or as the result of agency referral, but not on commitment from the court. (The outpatient service does, however, do about sixty diagnostic evaluations for the juvenile court each year.)

During the first half of 1970, 188 new cases were opened. Forty-two of these were not diagnosed. Of the remaining 146, almost half (49 percent) were diagnosed as having a personality disorder, and 21 percent were diagnosed as having transient situational disturbances of childhood.

Almost a third (31 percent) were diagnosed as having schizophrenia, a remarkably high percentage for any children's service.

Dr. Koret felt that several factors operated to "inflate" this figure. The early history of this center as the only residential program in the area led to the continuous referral of the most profoundly disturbed children and the establishment of a reputation of offering a specialized service for this type of child. As a result, as community referral decisions are made, the more seriously disturbed tend still to be channeled toward Convalescent Hospital when there is even a prospect that an inpatient service may eventually be required. "Working with families of psychotic children also tends to unearth others within the same constellation who are also seriously disturbed," Dr. Koret said. He also feels that many organizations tend to shy away from this diagnostic classification for children for fear of stigmatizing the child or raising feelings of hopelessness in community agencies and/or staff.

The outpatient service. Most of the outpatient service is provided at the hospital itself, by a staff of ten social workers, three psychologists, four sociotherapists, a case aide, and about half a psychiatrist's time. The Child Guidance Clinic, as the outpatient service is known, is headed by one of the social workers.

The process of entry is a simple and prompt one. A telephone call to the social work secretary results in an appointment within a week, plotted from a master schedule. If the case concerns a child, only the parents are seen in the initial interview; if it concerns an adolescent, he may be included as well. The staff member attempts in this first interview to ascertain whether there is a problem of such magnitude as to indicate a clear need for a complete diagnostic evaluation or the probability that day treatment or residential treatment will be required—as for example in the case of obvious psychosis. Such situations are rare, and when they occur the case is discussed at the next staff conference; if it should then be decided that day or residential treatment, intermediate-term outpatient individual psychotherapy, or a formal diagnostic work-up is indicated, a wait is likely to be involved. Meanwhile, the case is assigned to some staff member of the service for which it is ultimately destined, who must make some interim arrangements.

But in the majority of cases, the parents are simply offered a series of three interviews involving the entire family. The first of these is ordinarily scheduled for a week or two after the initial appointment, and the next two at no more than two-week intervals. The purpose of these three interviews is to get the family working together, with the therapist as catalyst, to overcome the problem that led to the application for treatment. In a given case the therapist is free to extend the sequence by one or two visits, but ordinarily would be expected to bring the case before the staff after no more than about five visits. After this brief intervention, an appointment is usually made for the entire family to return in three months for a series of three more family sessions. This approach has virtually eliminated the waiting list. The parents are instructed to call the clinic at once if an emergency should arise. During 1970 about 250 families were seen in this "initial family treatment" process. About eighty percent of those families seen for the initial interview completed the three-visit sequence. The considerable majority of these were not seen for any further service; on inquiry, it was found that the problem that had caused them to seek help had ameliorated.

In about 15 percent of cases, a formal diagnostic process was completed, and most of these children were then assigned either to individual or group treatment; the majority of the parents were seen either in individual or group psychotherapy or for social casework. Of all children seen in the clinic during a recent year, 18 percent were seen in individual therapy, 14 percent in family therapy, 44 percent in group therapy, and 24 percent in combinations of these modalities. The continued utilization of initial family treatment will continue to shift these figures in the direction of short-term family therapy. To put it another way, during 1970, 199 families made up of 868 individuals were seen in family therapy, including the three-interview sequence; 95 children were seen in individual psychotherapy; 108 children were seen in 13 groups (57 adolescents in six groups and 51 children in seven activity groups); 98 parents were seen in nine parents groups; and 142 parents were provided social casework. Thus, 402 children were offered various types of treatment, together with their families, during the year. An outcome study is now in progress to assess the impact of these efforts, not only upon referred patients, but also on siblings involved in family therapy. In addition, diagnostic studies were done for 108 other children including those for the family court. A rather extensive lay and professional community-education program is also conducted. The outpatient service also provides consultation and clinical services for the fifty children in the summer camp and their parents.

By age, the clinic caseload runs approximately as follows:

Under 6 years old	10%
6- 7 years old	15
8-10 years old	27
11-13 years old	28
14-16 years old	17
17 years old and over	3

For the adolescents there is some duplication of service between Convalescent Hospital and the mental health center at the University of Rochester, which also accepts adolescents as outpatients. In general there are more self-referrals at the University of Rochester, and they tend to be older than the adolescents seen at Convalescent Hospital. As of the time of our visit this duplication had not created any problems, and consequently there had been no need to establish any formal criteria for acceptance or exclusion.

Shortly before our visit the outpatient service had begun to be extended to several locations in the poor black sections of Rochester. By mid-1970 treatment facilities were in operation in a neighborhood settlement house, a day-care center, a church, a YMCA, and in the local OEO office. "This work out of established community organizations has eliminated or markedly reduced the expected community reticence toward or suspicion of a new mental health facility (and its stigma)," Dr. Koret said.

"Intensive treatment." Intensive treatment is the generic term used to indicate both the day-treatment and residential programs. Certainly even the day program, with its thirty hours a week of contact with the child, is a great deal more intensive than anything available on an outpatient basis. If it is determined that a particular child requires this intensity of treatment, the decision whether to schedule him for day or for residential treatment depends largely on his family environment. Even if the child is grossly disturbed, the decision will be for day treatment provided he has a home where his behavior can be tolerated, where the parents are eager to cooperate in the treatment plan, and where his illness will not exact an intolerable price from his siblings and the community. Diagnosis itself "has minor significance," we were told. "Rather we look to the criteria of the child's daily living situation at home and the nature of symptoms and problems."

Referrals may come to intensive services either from the clinic or directly from other agencies. First, the parents are seen by the director of social services, who discusses with them the implications of placement and secures their signed application. Then the total family is seen by Dr. Koret for one session. Next, the child has two interviews with the psychiatrist and two or three with a psychologist for a battery of tests. During this same time the parents are seen by a social worker. If neurological or specialized medical material is needed, it is obtained at this time.

Then an intake conference headed by Dr. Koret is held. All who have been involved in the intake process attend, as well as the directors and supervising social workers of residential treatment, day treatment, and the clinic, the director of education, the coordinator of sociotherapy, and a representative of the referring agency. If the child is considered appropriate for either day or residential treatment, the director of the designated service assumes responsibility and, if no vacancy exists, arranges some interim plan.

Children with a primary problem of mental retardation are not accepted in either day or residential treatment. Indeed, hypothetically, children with a less-than-average I.Q. are not accepted, although increasingly there has been a trend to view the low I.Q. as "functional" rather than "actual"—that is, depressed as a result of the illness, and consequently if there is not actual brain damage a child with a less-than-average I.Q. score might well be accepted.

There is no limit on stay, other than the upper age limit of 12 for residential treatment and 14 for day treatment.

The residential program. With a capacity of 27 and an average stay of about two years, the residential program has always had a waiting list. At the time of our visit, early in the school year, 14 children were waiting for an opening. "Since admissions and discharges usually occur during the summer," Dr. Koret told us, "this means that the wait will probably be at least another nine months for children who have already been waiting a considerable period of time. Considering that another twenty children will probably accrue by the time those now waiting are admitted, plus the 'hidden waiting list' that would surface if beds were immediately available, we have a situation that could be depressing. In the meantime, we provide as much as we can for these children and their families on an outpatient basis."

Because of the age limitations and long wait children discharged from the program who then deteriorate usually cannot be readmitted. As soon as one child leaves, another takes his place.

The children in the residential program can be roughly divided into three categories: grossly psychotic, bizarre children; borderline psychotic children who appear very normal at times but break down under stress into psychotic behavior; and those with hyperaggressive, delinquent behavior.

The children are housed in three attractive cottages, adjacent to each other and to the main building where the offices and outpatient service are located. Each cottage accommodates nine children; boys and girls are intermixed in two, while the third is for boys only. Each cottage, in addition to the bedrooms, has a living, dining, and play area. Throughout, the furnishings are simple and pleasant.

The director of residential treatment is Dr. Armin Klein, a psychologist. His staff consists of a fellow psychologist and four social workers, who spend much of their time with the children in individual psychotherapy, and 25 sociotherapists who staff the cottages. A minimum of one male and one female sociotherapist are on duty in each cottage for each of the day and evening shifts, and one female for the night shift. Within each cottage a particular sociotherapist is designated "cottage head." In addition each cottage has a professional consultant—a psychologist, the psychiatrist, or one of the social workers—who follow all the children in the cottage "to make sure things are all together, to make sure people get to talk to each other."

Children are initially assigned from the waiting list to the cottages on an "extended" or day basis. Criteria for placement in a particular one of the cottages are predicated on the need to maintain an adequate sex balance, an appropriate age distribution, patient needs which "will make the optimum group process operable and present symptom combinations which the staff can deal with." This "extended treatment" status for a period of months usually indicates whether the assigned cottage has been the correct one or whether the child should move to another cottage when actual admission time arrives.

The philosophy of treatment in the residential program was described to us as an eclectic application of methods based on psychoanalytic personality theory, the work of Erik Erikson, and the work of Dr. Koret in sociotherapy and psychotherapy. "Thus, there is room to incorporate psychotherapy, behavior modification, and learning theory within the framework of one basic philosophy which is consistent with the total treatment facility." There has been a strong tendency to feel that every child must have an individual therapist, and each one does.

The entire day is highly structured for the residential children. "We found," said Dr. Klein, "that the more structure we offered, the more freedom of feeling the children seemed to have. With complete freedom of behavior they seem to get uptight, to the point that they can't handle their feelings at all."

Thus, the children are awakened at seven thirty by the sociotherapists, who encourage them to dress and clean themselves but help each child as necessary. Breakfast is served in each cottage, at about eight o'clock. The sociotherapists then go with the children to the nearby school building, where they spend the morning participating in the school program. At noon the sociotherapists accompany the children back to their cottages for lunch, followed by a play period. Then they return to the school building for activities until three o'clock. Then the children are brought back to their cottages for snacks, followed by sports, indoors or out according to the weather, involving all 27 children from all three cottages. They eat dinner at five o'clock and then engage in programmed activities in small groups, intermixed among the cottages. There are snacks again at eight o'clock, following which the sociotherapists help the children get ready for bed. The night sociotherapist makes herself available to any child who has night fears "or who in other ways is particularly open to therapeutic intervention at that time."

Each child is seen two or more times a week in individual psychotherapy. The psychotic child "who has difficulty carrying over from one day to another" may be seen as frequently as five times a week in brief interviews. The borderline and hyperactive children are usually seen twice a week for 45-minute interviews. Because of the young age of many of the children, much of the therapy is in the playroom. These sessions are scheduled during the day, and each child simply leaves the classroom to come to the administration building to see his therapist.

All parents of residential children are involved in treatment, usually a weekly casework session with a social worker other than the child's therapist. Some parents are in group therapy. Toward the latter part of a child's stay, family therapy may be utilized. Home visits are made when indicated or when a parent cannot come to the office. For other parents, combinations of all of these approaches may be used.

While an occasional residential child may have seizures for which he is given anticonvulsant medication, none are given any drugs that alter mood or reduce hyperactivity. This is quite deliberate. Said Dr. Klein:

> Our children have already been ejected from the community, but we feel we can take their behavior better than the community can, so we do not feel the need to use drugs to contain them. Furthermore, we feel that it interferes with both psychotherapy and sociotherapy. We want everybody to treat these children psychologically. The drugs are too easy to fall back on and remove responsibility for internalizing control from the child.

When it seems appropriate, residential children go home for holidays or weekends. Otherwise, visiting hours are limited to Saturday and Sunday afternoons, although of course special arrangements are made in special situations. Most of the parents visit regularly. As a child approaches discharge, he spends days, then weekends, and then prolonged holidays at home.

"Extended residential treatment." A few children who are candidates for residential treatment—seven at the time of our visit—are placed in a special category called "extended residential treatment." It has already

been decided that these children need very much to be removed from their homes, but they continue to live there while coming into the hospital during the day until an inpatient vacancy occurs. Because of the ultimate intention of placing them in residential status, they are considered a separate group from the day-treatment children, and in the educational program described below they are placed with the residential children. They come to their respective designated cottages each morning, where they become associated with the particular children and sociotherapists, have their snacks and lunch, and are generally involved in the same way as the residential children except that they go home in the afternoon and stay at home on weekends. "This gets intensive treatment started early and provides a marvelous transition for the children," said Dr. Klein. He added that an occasional "extended residential" child had made dramatic improvement in this status and then did not need to become an inpatient.

The educational program. Serving both the residential children and the day-treatment children is a school located in a very pleasant building near the cottages and the administration building. The space is adequate, providing not only bright and cheerful classrooms but also special rooms for arts and crafts, a gymnasium, a lounge for teachers, and two group rooms for the children.

The new director of the school, when asked whether any of the children in this school might be satisfactorily contained in the regular schools if they had better psychological services, pointed out that the schools in the area do have superior psychological services through their own rather sophisticated mental health services and the Boards of Cooperative Educational Services. Despite this, they have found it necessary to refer and to make psychiatric exemptions. "Further, our approach is a treatment one; theirs is strictly educational."

The nine academic teachers, all with training in special education, are divided among separate classes for the residential and the day-treatment children. The classes vary from two to five children each. The curriculum corresponds as far as possible to that of the public schools.

An important aspect of these classes is that each child is expected to monitor his own behavior. If he feels that he is losing control, he asks for permission to leave the classroom, to go and spend some time at a "mental health station" manned by a selected sociotherapist. Almost invariably the permission is given. In other cases, when the teacher detects that a child is losing control, she will suggest to him that he go to the mental health station. Some children do not go at all in the course of a day, or several days, while others may ask to go out during virtually every class period. The average is about one visit per day per child.

While at the mental health station the child may talk with the socio-therapist or decide to work on his school assignments, and he may stay a very short time or for the rest of the class period. Whenever it appears that his anxiety, restlessness, or other troubling behavior has subsided, he returns to the classroom. Children who have stayed in the classroom and completed their work before the end of the scheduled time may go to the mental health station as a sort of reward.

A particular sociotherapist is designated the "read and feed" teacher. She has cookies and other snacks always available for children whose behavior is too primitive for academic materials, and she monitors them in a variety of play activities. "The association technique, equating a basic satisfied need (eating) with learning, has been most successful in making school palatable," we were told.

The residential and day-treatment children are intermixed in gym, art, and other nonacademic activities.

Day treatment. The day-treatment program had grown by the time of our visit to a capacity of 31, and plans were under way to expand it to accommodate several more. Because it was relatively new (having been initiated in 1967), there was less pressure for admission than to the residential program, and only a small waiting list had developed.

Day treatment is under the direction of a social worker, and it is staffed by a psychologist, five other social workers, and six sociotherapists. Since the intake and diagnostic process precedes the decision of whether a child should be assigned to residential or day treatment, the entry process is the same for these children. Some of the staff members we talked with were inclined to think that the day children had somewhat less severe pathology than the residential children, but certainly there is a large degree of overlap, and the fact of the child's having an appropriate family to live with seemed a more important determinant than the pathology. About twenty percent of the day children are diagnosed as psychotic.

These children are brought to the hospital by school bus and in taxis provided by their local school districts. When they arrive between eight thirty and nine, their sociotherapists meet them and help them to settle down for the school day. If any do not arrive, the sociotherapist tele-phones the family and also notifies the family's social worker. The children gather around the tables in their dining room and play games or talk.

In the morning and the afternoon there is a mix of academic classes and activities. The academic classes of one hour each are conducted by the academic teachers specifically assigned to the day children. There is a midmorning snack period of twenty minutes, served by sociotherapists, while the teachers have a break. The children have lunch with their sociotherapists. In the afternoon they join the residential children for arts and crafts, physical education, and domestic science. These children, like the residential children, have a "mental health station" that they may ask to go to when they sense difficulty in maintaining control.

Shortly before three in the afternoon, the sociotherapists meet again with the children and prepare them for the trip home.

Each day child has an individual therapist, whom he sees, typically, once a week. In addition, all the parents are seen either conjointly or in family therapy. There has been a pronounced swing toward family therapy, and at the time of our visit ten of the 31 families were being seen in this manner. Psychoactive medications are used with some day children, on the grounds that they may need this chemical intervention to help them function adequately outside the center.

The staff of the day-treatment program considers the demands, the rationale, and the philosophy of day treatment to be different in quality from that of residential treatment. A paper prepared by Avel Goldsmith interestingly denotes some of the differences.

> . . . day treatment is not simply [identical to residential treatment] except that the children go home at night. Rather, this very fact of living at home calls for a new dimension of treatment with unique features and implications of which we should all be aware. We must remember that the life of the day-treatment child is *not* circumscribed by our setting, as is that of the child in residence. . . . There are 168 hours in a week, and day children are programmed with us generally for about 30 of these. . . . From this basic fact we derive two considerations: one is to shape the time he is with us to obtain the maximum therapeutic effectiveness that will carry him through the intervening periods, and second to maintain a close and planful intervention in his experience at home and in the community when away from our program. . . .
>
> The cycle of daily rotation between the day center and the community calls for building certain expectations into that culture of the program that may not necessarily be appropriate or desirable in residential treatment. Often children must be reconstituted quickly when they arrive in the morning before they are ready for class, and they must be helped to attain a fair degree of control before they are ready to undertake the trip home. . . . Limits must be placed on both aggressive and regressive behavior which may not follow the model of the residence milieu. Furthermore, a greater degree of socialized and conforming behavior is expected in the community and the models for this that the child gains in day treatment cannot be too far out of line.

The average length of stay in the day program is about two years, just slightly less than the average stay in the residential program.

Outcome of treatment. A follow-up study was made of children who had been discharged from residential treatment between the time the program was begun, in 1958, and the end of 1964. The subjects were limited to those who, after follow-up, had not been seen in any other form of treatment, and who could be located. These 42 children were felt not to be representative of the subsequent patients, "since these early admissions tended to represent a backlog of children for whom adequate inpatient facilities had not been available" and were "in large part referred by agencies that had been involved in the planning of the residential treatment center." In general they were of lower socioeconomic level than children admitted in later years. Most were seen about four years after they had been discharged. It was found that

> the majority of these children displayed many symptoms similar to those that had characterized them at the time they had been referred. The striking change now in evidence, however, was that these symptoms and these characteristics were now under sufficient control so that they, as well as the rest of the child's behavior, were allowing him to function tolerably well in the environment which earlier had been forced to reject him as uncontrolled.

Sixty percent of the children were judged to be "functioning acceptably in their environment." They rated "very good" to "excellent" on the Astor Home Adjustment Scale. The report of the evaluation candidly concludes that

> we cannot . . . maintain that this result and change have any necessary relationship to residential treatment because of various methodological problems inherent in the study, including the lack of an adequate control group. We are, however, encouraged by these findings and hopeful that their tenability may be subjected to analysis in future studies which can measure such effects appropriately and more generalizably.

The day-treatment program had not discharged a sufficient number of children to carry out a follow-up study. Of the children seen as outpatients during a recent year, ninety percent were judged at point of discharge to be significantly improved; ten percent were unchanged and for the most part were those who had not remained long in the program.

Emergency service. Convalescent Hospital does not have an emergency service as such. While it is often possible for a family with an urgent problem to be scheduled for an initial interview within a day or two, the formal emergency service for this catchment area is provided by the University of Rochester Mental Health Center.

The summer camp. In 1967 an eight-week summer day camp was instituted for sixteen children, with Community Chest funds. The camp in 1971 had fifty children, more than half of them from the inner city. Referrals are accepted from all agencies for children six through twelve years of age.

There are eight counselors administered by the coordinator of sociotherapy and assisted by the group worker and a social worker. Eight teen-agers from the inner city are provided as aides and paid for by the city youth opportunity agency.

Children are assigned to groups of six or seven. The aim is "to make relationships acceptable with adults and peers and to establish an ego-building, confidence-inspiring program." Children build many of their own facilities, prepare their menus, and cook their own meals. The program includes fishing, boating, archery, miniature golf, swimming, hiking, overnight trips, arts and crafts, weekly outings, and various athletic events. There are group therapy sessions twice a week and parents are seen in educational and therapeutic groups unless they are already in individual casework.

Consultation and other community services

Convalescent Hospital has provided consultation to community agencies since the early 1960's, but it established a separate consultation and prevention department only in 1969. Known as the Preventive and Consultative Service, it is described as having a mandate

> to provide for the mental health needs of all those children in the catchment area served by Convalescent Hospital who do not require psychotherapeutic treatment.

This is, of course, a very large and ambitious responsibility for any mental health facility to take on, and while many agencies were being regularly visited at the time of our visit, this new service had made only a beginning toward this stipulated goal. In any case it is rather bolder than many other mental health facilities in attaching the term "preventive" to its efforts with community agencies. A description of the program speaks to this point.

> "Preventive" implies efforts geared to avoid the onset or increase of emotional problems or psychopathology, as well as efforts geared to avoid situations conducive to the development of emotional problems in children. Speaking positively, it refers to the promotion of mental health, to efforts at creating a climate or atmosphere which will maximize the likelihood of healthy growth and development of children and promote the expression and expansion of each child's talents and capabilities.

The primary goals of the service, this description continues, are "to facilitate the agents becoming more understanding of children and their behavior, the interaction between child and agent, and interaction between child and institution."

Elsewhere Dr. Koret describes the service as "an attempt to provide an economical service by training teachers and other lay people to deal with minor deviations in children and avoid more expensive treatment later."

At the time of our visit, the service was being provided to 22 private and cooperative nursery schools, three public school systems, six day-care centers, two residential centers, and two schools for disturbed children.

During 1970, the Preventive and Consultative Service theoretically reached 15,145 children. This figure was arrived at by calculating the number of children who were the direct responsibility of consultees in mental health consultation programs. In addition, this service operates a speakers bureau which provides speakers and/or programs for lay and professional groups upon request. During 1970, the service averaged two such engagements per month.

"In spite of its accomplishments, the service is constantly faced with the fact that its efforts are still skimming the surface," Dr. Koret said. "The consensus is that programs ought to be targeted toward younger children as well as toward specific current concerns in our society." Examples cited of efforts currently under way to implement the former direction are:

1. Working with nurses who teach prenatal classes to expectant parents with the aim of elevating mental health in the parents, siblings, and newborn.

2. Offering structured discussion groups for parents on a "no-referral basis" around issues of child rearing.

Two specific pressing concerns in the community currently are *a*) the numerous attempts to reorganize school districts to achieve racial balance and *b*) the nonmedicinal use of drugs. One example of consultative intervention in the former area is a program for suburban districts which are busing inner-city children, primarily black, into their schools. This program aims at enhancing the teachers' understanding of the cultural and environmental background of these children, hence obtaining a greater awareness of their needs and becoming able to deal constructively with them.

One approach to the drug problem involves a telephone communication system called GAP-LINE, organized in conjunction with a local narcotics council to respond to community concerns about nonmedicinal drug use. The telephones are manned by young volunteers who are screened, trained, and supervised by the Convalescent Hospital, which also provides backup consultation to them. Its aims are to provide accurate information, support in crisis situations, and appropriate referrals when necessary.

There are three full-time staff members of the Preventive and Consultative Service, whose director, Dr. Matthew Perlman, is a psychologist. Each member of the professional staff is slated to spend one half day per week in consultation activities.

The schools. The consultation service has not been overly involved with any of the public schools from that part of the city of Rochester that falls in its catchment area, because the Rochester school system, with its own mental health services, tends to rely on its own staff and use the Convalescent Hospital for service referrals. Recently a liaison committee with representatives from the city school district and the center was formed to coordinate their services.

Initially resistance was met with from some of the schools in the outlying townships of the catchment area. Said Dr. Perlman:

> I was treated as if I were a traveling salesman, so I stopped knocking on doors; instead we waited for the schools to send us a referral. We would accept the referral and would call at the school to establish a treatment plan. If the clinical staff did a good job, then the school would feel good about the help they received. Our caseworker would then propose that it would be very nice if we could have some kind of continuing relationship where perhaps we could head off problems before they become so severe. Usually the answer has been favorable, and has led to some regularly scheduled contacts.

Three of the seven outlying school districts were involved in the consultation program as of the time of our visit. The center had proposed to each school that participation by individual teachers be voluntary; "voluntary" in some cases was tantamount to a directive, and in these schools most of the teachers have participated. In others it has ranged from fifty percent participation upward.

An arrangement of particular interest is that whereby Convalescent Hospital provides a local school district with a consultant to meet with six "master teachers," especially talented and experienced teachers who have been elevated to leadership of a group of six or seven teachers in the same grade, providing supervision and "classroom trouble shooting." The purpose is "to increase sensitivity to the emotional needs of individual children." Psychological consultation is also now provided for the school system. In exchange the school district provides to Convalescent

Hospital a part-time music teacher, a part-time art teacher, and a remedial-reading teacher.

At several of the schools, at the request of the teachers, the mental health staff run "semisensitivity groups." Said Dr. Perlman:

> We feel that if we can get the teachers to be more tuned in to themselves as people, and more tuned in to others and their interactions with others, it will affect them on the job.

The programs in the nursery schools are much the same in nature as those in the public schools. A representative relationship is that with the Rochester Children's Nursery, where a consultant from the center meets with teachers in a group to discuss the differences between normal and abnormal behavior at various ages. The director of this nursery school reports that as a result the teachers sometimes find that they can themselves deal with the child's behavior rather than referring him to a clinic. She says that the consultations have helped the teachers to accept the fact that there are poor parents, to understand parents' feelings and attitudes, and to support those whose children are in treatment. She said that

> there has been a real sharing. The staff who have come here from the mental health center have helped our teachers to value their knowledge of normal child development. This has helped them to define their own roles as teachers. In the past, every time a child was acting out the teacher felt he needed to be referred.

The welfare department. While there are no regularly scheduled consultations between the center and the welfare department, the relationship has been a positive one. The welfare department refers about twenty children a year as potential patients. For those in the residential and day-treatment programs, it pays a substantial amount of the cost of treatment. It has also been making an increasing number of referrals to the outpatient clinic.

The courts. A program of consultation for the family court and diagnostic service is provided at the court's request. In a recent year sixty children referred by the court were evaluated. Some of these were placed in residential and day treatment, although on the basis of a referral to a social agency rather than as a commitment. Case consultation and inservice training are provided by the diagnostic team to family court probation officers.

Mental retardation services

Convalescent Hospital does not accept in its inpatient and day program children with brain damage nor those whose I.Q. is below average, unless it is believed that the low test score is a result of a functional disorder and will improve with treatment. Monroe County has, in the Al Sigl Center, a treatment facility for retarded children, to which Convalescent Hospital refers those children whom it believes to have a primary problem of retardation. The outpatient clinic does accept retarded and brain-damaged children with emotional problems.

Research

The program has a separate research department, headed by a social psychologist with a master's degree. Dr. Koret is sympathetic to research efforts and encourages the staff, within the limits of the time available after their clinical and consultative responsibilities, to undertake research projects. A research psychologist from the University of Rochester spends about ten hours a week with the center, reviewing projects proposed by individual staff members and advising those who have projects in progress.

We have mentioned the follow-up study of children who were in residential treatment between 1958 and 1964. This study used tape-recorded interviews with the children, parents, and school personnel, as well as telephone and mail inquiries. Data on 43 variables were gathered to describe the children at points of intake, discharge, and follow-up. The children were rated on the seven-point Astor Home Adjustment Scale in respect of adjustment to home, school, and community.

Four projects were under way at the time of our visit. One was an effort to ascertain, through administering the Bristol Social Adjustment Guides, how much benefit those children who participated in a summer camp had received from this experience. Both counselors and parents were involved in the evaluation. It was hoped that the results would make it possible to arrive at conclusions about the "cost-benefit effectiveness" of the camp.

A second study was intended to determine what happens to children who, while awaiting a vacancy in residential treatment, are placed in outpatient treatment as an expediency. This, too, has considerable financial implications, since children can be seen as outpatients for a small fraction of the cost of residential treatment.

The third study was designed to determine whether those children with below-average I.Q.'s who had been admitted in the belief that the low test score was a function of the psychopathology had, by the time of discharge, exhibited a rise in I.Q. score.

The fourth project deals with parents expecting their first child, who meet in groups "at strategic times of anticipated psychological crisis."

The study hopes to determine whether such intervention can substantially reduce the incidence of emotional disturbance.

Several other studies were under consideration, and proposals for four had been submitted to prospective funding agencies. The limited amount of research is primarily a result of lack of funds. The comprehensiveness of the program and the exhaustive data it has available make it a particularly apt locus for an extensive research program.

Training

Inservice. One of the consultants described the inservice training program at Convalescent Hospital as one "that might well serve as a model for many mental health centers."

We have described the thorough process of recruiting and training the sociotherapists.

The professional staff spend two hours each week in "staff development seminars." These are divided into three sections each year, and two are offered concurrently; thus, a given staff member may choose from several different seminars in the course of the year, on such subjects as child psychotherapy, family therapy, administration, activity groups, behavior modification, and group therapy. For new professionals, there are orientation seminars, the major one in the fall, consisting of three two-hour sessions, during which the director and department heads acquaint the new people with treatment philosophy and administrative matters. There are also several two-day workshops in the course of the year, conducted by such noted figures as Bruno Bettelheim and Fritz Redl.

Each September all except inpatient services cease operating while an institute is held for three days. During that time the total program undergoes "a complete analysis and critical evaluation."

Formal academic training. Convalescent Hospital participates in formal training of all the mental health disciplines, pediatrics, and special education.

At the time of our visit, there were three psychology interns from the Universities of Waterloo (Ontario), Massachusetts, and Indiana, all on NIMH training grants. They spend full time for eleven months at Convalescent Hospital, working in residential and day treatment and the outpatient service, with opportunities to participate in group therapy, family therapy, crisis therapy, consultation, and diagnosis.

There are usually three social work trainees per year, from the University of Buffalo, Syracuse University, and Smith College. About twelve psychiatric residents from the University of Rochester spend a portion of their six-months' rotation in child psychiatry; at the time of our visit, there were, however, no fellows in child psychiatry training.

Each year there is a pediatric resident assigned for a full year. He spends one half day a week in conferences, plus such time as is needed to provide direct medical service.

Convalescent Hospital participates in the Cleveland International Programs for Youth Leaders and Social Workers. This special organization, with the aid of the U.S. Department of State, recruits talented candidates from all over the world. They participate, train, and contribute to programs, for periods of three to twelve months. There are from three to six per year, and they have come from Japan, Malaysia, India, Liberia, Finland, Norway, France, Germany, Czechoslovakia, South Africa, and South American countries.

Teacher trainees from Monroe Community College, Syracuse University, and from the State University of New York at Brockport, usually about two at a time, come to Convalescent Hospital for their field placements with emotionally disturbed children. Training is also offered to graduate students in physical education from the State University at Brockport.

Recreation workers and mental health aides are offered field placement in conjunction with Monroe Community College. There are usually one or two at a time.

Fees and financing

Charges are made for all services on a sliding scale adapted from that utilized by the County Department of Social Services and approved by the New York State Department of Social Services. All family expenses for any legitimate purpose, such as other medical care, are included in the basic budget allowance. Surplus of income over necessary expenses is the figure used to determine payment for service. There is a single fee for service no matter how many members of a family are seen, unless the income is such that the family can afford to pay for each at the established hourly or daily cost. Fees are all-inclusive with no supplementary charges such as special services or medications. A family of four with two children between six and 15 and a gross income of $10,000 per year would be expected to pay $1.75 per week, regardless of the number of sessions, the number of family members being seen, or the modality of treatment utilized. A family of the same size with an income of $16,500 would be expected to pay $30 per week. Below $9,000 there would be a charge of $1 or less, depending upon other factors.

Since residential or day treatment involves an extremely high daily cost over a long period of time, treatment there is defined as catastrophic illness and the Department of Social Services supplements the family contribution for those who do not have applicable health insurance.

For fiscal year 1971-72 the Convalescent Hospital budget is $1.5 million, which comes from the following sources in approximately the percentages shown here:

County Department of Social Services	21%
Voluntary health insurance	17
State Department of Mental Hygiene	14
Federal government staffing and training grants	12
State Department of Education	11
County mental health board	7
Community Chest	6
Patient fees	5
Medicaid	5
Endowment fund income	2

The funds from the State Department of Education represent a payment of $2,000 per year for each child in residential and day treatment. The County Department of Social Services pays the room, board, and related maintenance expenses (but not the costs of treatment) for children whose families have no other resources to pay; this comes to about $30 per day for residential treatment, $14 per day for day treatment.

Convalescent Hospital receives funds both from the county mental health board and from the Community Chest on a "deficit financing" formula. The county meets 75 percent of the deficit, utilizing two-thirds state and one-third county funds. The Community Chest then provides funds for the remaining 25 percent.

Convalescent Hospital will have federal staffing funds at the 30 percent level until 1973. The assumption would seem to be that the Community Chest and county mental health board will then assume a larger share of financing. While this is an obvious financial danger, as all deficit financing is, in actual practice the center has been able to expand its financial base faster than these funds are withdrawn, primarily through improved insurance arrangements, increased educational funds, and smaller but significant sums from other sources.

The unit costs of service are approximately as follows: outpatient, $34.00 per visit; day treatment, $39.50 per day; and inpatient residential treatment, $58.00 per day.

Kedren Community Mental Health Center
Los Angeles

The area served

Kedren Community Mental Health Center has a catchment area of just over ten square miles, with a population in 1970 of 200,000. It includes much of the Watts area where the major riots of 1966 occurred, and a portion of neighboring Green Meadows. With a median household income of $4653 (compared to $7046 for Los Angeles County as a whole), with an average educational level of 9.46 years (compared to 12.1 years for Los Angeles County as a whole), the catchment area is among the poorest and most troubled in the Los Angeles area. During the 1960's it became increasingly Negro, changing from a 66 percent black population in 1960 to 90 percent black in 1970; practically all of the remaining ten percent are Mexican-Americans. There is scarcely any urban problem that the Kedren catchment area does not exhibit to a high degree: crowded schools, alcoholism and illegal drug use, substandard and deteriorating housing, a high crime rate, and so on. Before the advent of the mental health center, there were no mental health resources of any kind in the catchment area.

Origins

Kedren Community Mental Health Center was established on the initiative of a black child psychiatrist, Dr. James L. Jones, who became the center's first director.[1] After completing his work in child psychiatry at the Reiss-Davis Clinic, Dr. Jones went into the private practice of child psychiatry at a location about twelve miles away from the present mental health center. In this neighborhood, which was losing white residents and gaining black residents, Dr. Jones saw mainly middle-class white patients. But a growing number of black families came to him. He was impressed that many of them seemed to do well after a short time in treatment.

> Many of us had been taught [he told us] that black patients don't benefit from psychotherapy—that they are "acter-outers" and not "talker-

---

[1] Dr. Jones died of a heart attack in January 1971 and was succeeded as director by Dr. Alban Niles, an attorney.

104

outers." But these patients kept coming to see me regularly, and the only thing that kept them from continuing was the fee. After the third or fourth visit, they started to ask, When am I going to get well? So in many cases I reduced the fee, because I was eager to keep them coming, because I thought I had discovered something.

Consequently, Dr. Jones went to the Los Angeles County Department of Mental Health to see if it could provide subvention to cover the treatment of these low-income black patients; the department said it was unable to do so because of a shortage of funds.

Shortly afterward, Dr. Jones received from his congressman a copy of the federal community mental health center legislation. After reviewing it, he consulted Alban I. Niles, an attorney with a doctorate in jurisprudence, who advised him that by forming a nonprofit corporation he could develop a vehicle for providing low-cost community mental health services while at the same time continuing his private practice. The Department of Mental Hygiene of the State of California had divided the County of Los Angeles into catchment areas, which posed problems, since the director of mental health for Los Angeles County had already made his own geographical divisions which were larger than the state-defined catchment areas. The director of the county service was not in sympathy with the application made by Dr. Jones and the new corporation for a mental health center construction grant.

The initial application requested a grant for the catchment area where Dr. Jones' practice was located. However, it was pointed out that the Watts-Green Meadows area was more in need of the kind of services which Dr. Jones was proposing and therefore had a higher priority. The application was revised and submitted, seeking a grant for the Watts-Green Meadows area. After a great deal of effort by Dr. Jones and his wife, Shirley H. Jones, Paul O. Hise, an architect who drew up preliminary plans for the new center, James Woods, chairman of the board of Watts Manufacturing Company, and Dr. Niles, all local questions concerning the need for the center, what it proposed to do, the benefits it would provide to the community, and so on, were dealt with. With the support of every local politician and more than thirty agencies and community organizations, the corporation received a construction grant in November 1967 and a staffing grant in April 1968.

The construction grant provided $700,000 from the federal government, with $700,000 to be furnished by the State of California and $987,000 by the center through fund raising and philanthropy. The matching money was not raised. However, the Watts Model Cities program in time agreed to provide the matching money and it is now anticipated that construction on the new center will begin in January 1972 with completion scheduled for July 1973.

The staffing grant with its declining basis also posed a problem in terms of matching money. Most of the clients coming to the center were indigent. In the second year of the staffing grant a contract for partial hospitalization was negotiated with the County of Los Angeles and this contract has been renewed each year.

In the 1970 amendments to the Community Mental Health Centers Act, Congress revised the legislation to provide more money to poverty-area centers such as Kedren. Now, in its fourth year, the center's federal funding is at 65 percent instead of the 33⅓ percent which would have applied before the legislation was amended. As of mid-1970 the center was still trying to eliminate a $150,000 deficit incurred in its first two years of operation.

Philosophy, purposes, and policy

Dr. Jones said that during his training in child psychiatry at Reiss-Davis "I came to realize in dealing with children that a little bit can go a long way." He later received training at the Center for Training in Community Psychiatry, where he came to feel that the crisis-intervention approach to treatment might have particular applicability in the Kedren catchment area.

> The community is crisis oriented. Our people come to us in acute emergency situations. Everything is near crisis. There's more involvement here than in most communities with social agencies, child protective services, probation officers. And so from the beginning, we determined to have short-term services for children and adolescents. We find that many of these young clients are basically healthy. If one forms a relationship with them, if they can see that a responsible adult is interested in them, if we can make them see themselves as worthwhile, one can accomplish a lot in a short time.

This translates into a program that sees the ideal span of treatment as three to six months. Thus, autistic and severely retarded children are usually excluded, on the grounds that they are almost certain to need a longer period of service.

Consonant with the crisis-intervention approach is the practice of providing day treatment that is scheduled for only two three-hour sessions per week. "This works quite well for many of the children," one of the teachers in the preschool program told us. "It is not adequate for some of the others. But we work with what we have."

The clinical activities appear in general to focus much more on the assets, strengths, and realities of the patient, and more on the social pathology within which the patients live than on intrapsychic processes. The clinical approach is mainly through an educational focus, attempting to remediate deficits, through a supporting system of mental health workers, through advice, through dealing with the realities of the patient's everyday environment.

Administration and staffing

The nonprofit corporation whose formation was mentioned above was Kedren Community *Health* Center, Inc., which in its initial program incorporated two principal activities: the community mental health center and a large Headstart program with units throughout Los Angeles. Certain members of the board of directors of the health center comprise an executive board which oversees activities of the corporation between meetings of the board. The board members include a physician and two dentists, all three of whom practice not far from the catchment area, the architect who designed the new building which the center hopes to build, and two members of the mental health center staff, the director and Mrs. Jones. Before his death Dr. Jones was also a member of the board as well as its president. There is also an advisory board made up of area residents and personnel of agencies which are located in the catchment area. The advisory board meets once a month at the center and serves primarily to identify problems in the community with which the center should be involved and to help educate the community on mental health.

The board of directors meets monthly, the executive board "as needed." A Headstart committee comprised of board members, parents of Headstart children, and some community representatives meets once a month. The committee establishes priorities for the Headstart program and reports them to the full board, which generally follows these recommendations.

When the mental health center began operating in 1968, the staff consisted only of Dr. Jones, as the medical director; Dr. Niles, who, in addition to being an attorney, was a certified public accountant and had spent four years in "the medics" while in the Air Force, as the administrative director; and Shirley H. Jones, trained as an elementary school teacher with postgraduate training in child-care services, as the director of the therapeutic nursery school. These three members were also organizers of the corporation and continued as board members after becoming staff members. Other members of the board felt that these staff members should continue to serve on the board because of the unique circumstances under which the Kedren center was formed. They felt that "since other corporations do it, why not one in community mental health?" As to nepotism, "it was the long lead time which forced us into the role of staff members," said Dr. Niles. "Who else would have donated the kind of time that was involved? We had thousands of dollars invested prior to receiving a nickel in salaries. It definitely wasn't the money involved."

Some five months after the initial three staff members were hired, an accountant was hired, then a social worker, then another psychiatrist. They were augmented by a large battery of mental health workers (described below), and in those early days all of the clinical service was rendered from a unitary arrangement.

The limited number of professionals at the outset was a result of several factors. For one thing, it was important to provide jobs early on to residents of the catchment area, since this had been one of the most important concerns voiced by some of the agencies whose support had been sought. For another, there was a fairly intense and widespread feeling that most of the staff should be black, and here, as everywhere else, it proved difficult to recruit black professionals.

By the time of our visit several professionals, some black and some white, had recently joined the staff, and there were authorized positions for still others. Dr. Jones had felt the need to move slowly in integrating the staff and was continuing to do so. As the mental health workers became established in their responsibilities, they came to feel some prerogatives of seniority: since they were there first, there was some annoyance at the prospect of any professional, but particularly a white one, coming in to perform a supervisory function that had not previously existed. There was also a note of resentment that the professionals, precisely because of their formal credentials, had far greater career mobility than the nonprofessionals.

Dr. Jones reported that the situation had, nonetheless, improved considerably. He believed that to have brought white professionals into the program at the outset might have created a disruption so great as to threaten the existence of the center. By moving gradually, it had been possible to augment the staff with some white professionals, in the absence of enough black professionals to fill all the available slots.

With this expansion of staff, clinical services had been divided into three departments: Outpatient, serving all age ranges; Adult and Adolescent Day Treatment; and the Children's Service. Each was headed by a psychiatrist. The one nonclinical department was the business office. In addition, there were single individuals charged with *a*) public relations and fund raising, *b*) coordinating the mental health education and consultation activities, and *c*) coordinating the planning activities.

Within each of the three clinical divisions there were now some professionals, as indicated below, but the considerable majority of staff continued to be mental health workers.

The mental health workers. When the center first opened, it invited applications for ten mental health worker positions. Eighty people applied, ranging in age from 19 through 37, in education from 11th grade through three years of college. These people were interviewed by Dr. Jones in groups of ten, and the applicants were reduced to 22. The center asked the members of the advisory board if they would interview each of the prospects and decide which were acceptable and which were not. There was agreement between Dr. Jones and the advisory board on all except one of the ten persons to be hired.

This first group was given a twenty-session inservice training program by the professional members of the staff on personality development, normality, neurotic styles, anatomy, and how to work in a therapeutic nursery.

In the ensuing two years the number of mental health workers was increased to fifteen. Those subsequently hired have not had the same orientation training. This training has been done in the clinical department to which they are assigned.

Dr. Jones cited certain problems that had developed with a few of the mental health workers. Some, he said, had tended to get overinvolved with their clients. "Much of their work they do with their guts and not with technique," he said. He also found among some a tendency to become depressed and to project their discouragement either onto fellow staff members or onto particular patients.

But these were viewed as exceptional and not general problems, not only by Dr. Jones but by every member of the professional staff whom we interviewed. The favorable points of the mental health workers appeared greatly to outweigh the disadvantages. (It should be noted that, by the time of our visit, a considerable majority of the mental health workers had completed two or more years of college.)

"We have been successful, we feel," Dr. Jones said, "in selecting people who have a capacity to relate to others—the kind of people who might be good as a maître d' in a restaurant. They are outgoing and sympathetic and have a natural understanding. They are also committed to their work and eager to do a good job. They have a therapeutic zeal that we professionals sometimes lack, and they do not lower their expectations for a given individual on the basis of a diagnosis. Furthermore, since they come from the population they're working with, they identify very highly with their clients."

Said the psychologist from the outpatient department:

> While the mental health workers sometimes lack confidence in themselves and are uncertain about how much precisely they can do, at the same time I have seen very few instances in which a mental health worker has overstepped appropriate bounds and done something presumptuous or foolish. Quite honestly, I think they are less rigid and calcified than most professionals. They're willing to try new things, in contrast with professionals I have worked with in other programs, where the watchword was, Never do anything for the first time.

Dr. Jones did not hesitate to characterize the interactions between mental health workers and patients as "psychotherapy," although a more cautious term might be "relationship therapy." By and large the focus of the mental health workers is on manifest behavior, and their relationships with the children and adolescents seem to be principally those of appropriate adults who see the young patients as being worthwhile persons that they care about.

We were particularly impressed with the mental health workers assigned to adolescent day treatment. A parent described to us how, when she was away from home, her daughter called one of the mental health workers to say that she had taken some pills. The mental health worker immediately arranged for her to be taken to the hospital and arrived there at the same time as the parents. "Anytime you need them you can call," this mother told us. "They go out of their way to come to the house, to go to the school, to do anything that needs to be done."

The clinical services

In general. Children and adolescents are variously seen in the three clinical departments—Outpatient, Adult and Adolescent Day Treatment, and the Children's Service. An applicant for service would be seen by a mental health worker on intake duty. If it appears that the problem is situational and/or represents an acute problem of recent onset, the child or adolescent is ordinarily channeled to the general outpatient department. If it appears that the problem concerning a child is of long duration or is likely to require more than brief contact, he and his family are channeled to the children's department, where he may either be provided outpatient service or be placed in day treatment. All adolescents who seem to require outpatient treatment are served by the general outpatient department, while those who appear to need a more intensive exposure are put into the care of Adult and Adolescent Day Treatment.

While the center accepts all kinds of children and adolescents except those who are autistic or have considerable brain damage, well over half (62 percent) are diagnosed as having behavior disorders and adjustment reactions of childhood or adolescence.

Medication is sparingly used with the children, and scarcely at all with the adolescents. Stimulants are sometimes prescribed for children with hyperactivity, and tranquilizers for those who are overanxious, highly aggressive, or destructive. With the adolescents, the program "attempts to employ more interactional techniques and de-emphasize the use of psychotropic drugs, although tranquilizers might be used in states of acute or chronic agitation."

In all of the service components combined, about two hundred children and two hundred adolescents had been seen in the year prior to our visit.

The clinical services take place in a large building on the edge of the Watts area. This building was converted from a theater and ice-skating rink and an adjacent auto-supply store. The administrative offices are located in the former auto-supply store, whose walls were broken through to allow connection with the former ice-skating rink. The reception area and the offices are attractively decorated and furnished. In converting the rink, partitions were put up and a false ceiling added, thus providing offices, interview rooms, and some larger areas for group activities and day treatment.

The center considers the physical plant grossly unsatisfactory, and it is hard to disagree. These inadequacies were listed: no outdoor play area; inadequate heating capacity for the winter and cooling capacity for the summer; insufficient toilet facilities for children; no kitchen; inadequate storage facilities; not enough room in the offices for the needed number of desks and chairs. The lack of recreation facilities within the center was seen as a particular problem in trying to work with the adolescents.

A site has been acquired and architectural plans drawn for a new facility about forty blocks from the present one.

Outpatient services. At the central point of entry, the intake worker obtains basic statistical data and performs a short screening interview, then decides to which of the three major departments to refer the patient. As we have described, children can become outpatients either under the general outpatient service or through the separate children's service; adolescents generally become outpatients as part of the general outpatient service, but occasionally a younger one may be assigned to the children's service. We have mentioned that a major determinant is whether the problem appears to be critical and likely to be resolved in a very short time or less critical and in need of somewhat extended care. Other determinants are the indication of need for the parents to be involved concurrently in treatment, in which case the referral would be to the general outpatient department, and the indication for remedial educational therapy, which would result in referral to the children's department.

The respective numbers of children being seen in the two departments were in process of change at the time of our visit. By mid-1971, all children were being assigned to the children's service, while the considerable majority of adolescents continued to be assigned to the general outpatient department.

The staff of the children's department is headed by a half-time child psychiatrist, who had obtained a leave of absence from one of his regular assignments in order to help get the children's service started. It was his intention when the program was further along to help in recruiting a full-time child psychiatrist, at which time he would return to his former activities. The other professionals in the children's service were a doctoral-level psychologist and a master's-level social worker, both of whom had only recently joined the staff. There were also two "master teachers," specially trained schoolteachers who exercise leadership in therapeutic, educational, and recreational roles with children and supervisory roles with the mental health workers of the day-treatment division of the children's services department. The master teachers have had special training in child development, child psychology, and child therapy interventions. (Shortly after our visit both master teachers left, and the center replaced them with a clinical psychologist with a doctorate in educational psychology.) There was also an educational therapist who was principally involved with the children in day treatment (see below).

In addition, there were six mental health workers.

After the child has completed the intake process, he is referred to one of the mental health workers, who does an interview to obtain further information. If it seems indicated, psychological tests are requested. This is the exception rather than the rule. The psychologist, who does such tests as are done, said that he had spent much time with the mental health workers educating them to the indications for requesting psychological tests.

Ever since the program began, each child had also been seen by a child psychiatrist—Dr. Jones, as long as he was the only child psychiatrist on the staff, and Dr. Ramon Alcerro, after he became director of the children's service in early 1970.

With the recent addition of a social worker, it was planned to institute formal diagnostic conferences on new patients, and by early 1971 this had been accomplished.

At the time of our visit the procedure was much the same for children and adolescents being seen in the general outpatient service. This department, which serves all ages, has a psychiatrist as its director, a doctoral-level psychologist, two master's-level social workers, and seven mental health workers. Here, too, the psychologist does testing when the mental health worker believes it is indicated, and the psychiatrist sees each child and adolescent as part of the process of formulating a diagnosis and plan for treatment.

Just under a quarter of the children and just over a quarter of the adolescents are seen once only (a low figure in comparison with some other clinics). As at most other outpatient mental health facilities, well over half are seen three or less times. About one fifth are seen for more than eight interviews.

The children and adolescents are seen in a variety of patterns, as follows:

	Children	*Adolescents*
Individual therapy only	15%	22%
Family therapy only	18	17
Group therapy with other children or adolescents only	17	14
Family group therapy only	0	3
Combinations of the above	50	43

The approach to treatment seems to emphasize heavily the belief that there should be minimal involvement regarding such social needs as food and clothing, but that there should be much emphasis on providing through mental health auspices a corrective emotional experience, with a focus on reality goals, an assessment and remediation of educational deficiencies, and, in appropriate circumstances, behavior modification. The center encourages the participation of parents either in family treatment or in collateral appointments, but does not make this a condition of acceptance for a young client whose family consents to his treatment. Even when it is the parents who apply on their own behalf, the problem often concerns one of their children, a social worker from the general outpatient department told us. "Very few parents come in here because of marital problems or other difficulties of their own," she said. "Just about all of them seek us out because of their alarm about what is happening to one of their children." She estimates that about three quarters of all the people coming to the outpatient service are there in actuality because of a child-related problem.

It is interesting to note that Kedren has evening hours. It is open until 9 p.m. on Monday through Thursday.

Day treatment for children. At Kedren, as at many other facilities serving children, the treatment load is related to the school year. That is, a certain number of children are either carried over from the previous year or are identified quite early in the new school year as seeming to need some special help, while additional numbers are identified as the school year progresses. Our visit to the center took place only a few weeks after school had started, and thus it seemed likely that the existing groups would each become larger and that additional groups might be added.

Four groups had been under way for some time, and another was just starting. Specifically, four children ranging in age from three and a half to five were being seen on Monday and Tuesday mornings; another group of ten children, from four and a half to six, were being seen on Wednesday and Thursday mornings; a "transition group" of eight children, from six to eight years old, who, as they grew older, had been transferred from the regular groups, were continuing to come to the center one afternoon a week; and a group of ten latency-age children who were attempting to continue in the regular schools were coming in from 12:30 to 3:00 p.m. on Mondays and Wednesdays. A second latency-age group was in process of being formed. Altogether about thirty children were being seen on day-treatment status, and it was anticipated that the number might grow to about fifty.

At the time of our visit each of these groups was headed by one or the other of the two master teachers. For each group, the teacher had two mental health workers assigned to assist her. In addition, the educational therapist was involved with every group, and she spent time with particular children who seemed to need individual educational intervention.

The treatment rationale seems to be one of specialized education which relates to the specific disability of the children, in a milieu focusing on individual attention both to educational and emotional needs. The children exhibit a variety of behaviors that make them difficult to contain in regular settings—the public school classrooms for the school-age children, and the Headstart programs for the younger ones. They are variously hyperactive, distractible, acting out, and subject to substantial inner tensions.

One of the teachers characterized the transactions with the children as intended to provide them

> a kind of attention, acceptance, warmth, feeling of mattering, and gentle firmness that is missing from their family lives.

Although she was somewhat impatient with "terminology," she felt that the term "relationship therapy" might be aptly used to describe the intended rapport between staff member and child. The teachers talk informally with each child to identify areas of insecurity and to ascertain the nature of the home and school environment.

At the same time, there is a notable emphasis on remedial education. Most of the children have deficiencies in language development, concept formation, perceptual and motor integration, and problem solving. To illustrate how these therapeutic and educational goals are combined, we can consider the schedule of the transitional group.

These children meet at two thirty and spend a half hour in free-choice activities through puzzles and hand-eye coordination toys, while the teachers talk with them informally. Then comes a brief snack period, followed by a discussion. Then comes a period in which the children split into two groups to work with the teacher in reading, printing, arithmetic, learning games based on academic readiness, then an arts-and-crafts session, followed by cleanup and treats.

Behavior modification is used with particular children, but is limited to a system of rewards without punishment. For example, a particular mute child who craves physical attention receives it when she verbalizes, but otherwise she is ignored.

The program attempts to involve the parents in a continuing relationship. All parents are seen by the psychologist as part of the admission procedure, and some continue to come for regular appointments, but others do not, usually on the grounds of work commitments and other schedule problems. None of the families of children in day treatment were involved in either family therapy or parent groups.

Day treatment for adolescents. The day-treatment program for adolescents falls under the aegis of the Adult and Adolescent Day Treatment service, which is headed by a black psychiatrist who had previously worked in one of the other Los Angeles mental health centers serving a predominantly black population. His staff for the adolescent day program consists only of two mental health workers, both of whom have completed some college work; they seemed to us extraordinarily well qualified in terms of personality and viewpoint to work with troubled adolescents.

When the intake worker interviews an adolescent who seems to require more than outpatient visits, she calls the day-treatment service, and one of the mental health workers then joins the intake worker in a meeting with the adolescent and his parent. Following this a mental health worker sees the adolescent alone, usually within a week, to take a detailed history.

Then the application is brought before a weekly staff meeting, at which time the psychiatrist and his staff make a tentative treatment plan. The psychiatrist does not routinely see prospective adolescent day patients, but he spends some time each week observing the program in order to "get a feeling of the affect and to make sure that we're not dealing with something that's more disturbing than we had originally assessed." He usually talks to the group at this weekly visit.

The majority of adolescents are diagnosed as having transient situational disorders or character disorders. They have behaved in ways that have led to their being extruded from school, or to being under threat of extrusion if they do not participate in a special treatment program. Only an occasional adolescent is psychotic, but the staff has found that the fellow patients give a great deal of support, "and they are the ones that do the treatment; they pull them out of that withdrawn world, so that they usually reconstitute pretty well."

A great many of the adolescents have had some experience with illegal drug use. The psychiatrist estimated that about three quarters of them are involved to some degree with drugs when they first enter the program.

The approximate limit on size of the adolescent day program is 25. At the time of our visit there were 18. In the relatively short time the program had been in existence, there had not been a waiting list.

The group comes twice a week, on Mondays and Wednesdays from 4:15 to 9:00 p.m.; these hours were set to allow them to attend the regular schools, as most of them do.

On Mondays, after a brief full-group discussion, the young people split up into smaller groups for tutoring, a current events group, and arts and crafts. Then they regroup into two groups for therapy, each led by a mental health worker. They then go out together to various eating places in and out of the catchment area for dinner and return for separate activity groups such as sewing and grooming for the girls and body building and personal hygiene for the boys. At 9 p.m., after a brief "wrap up" session, a bus owned by the mental health center takes them to their homes.

The Wednesday sessions begin on alternate weeks with psychodrama and an arts-and-crafts class, followed by a recreational hour, then dinner. After returning from dinner, the adolescents and their parents meet in a large group. The extent of participation by the parents at first was disappointing, with fewer than half attending, but later improved.

One or more times each month the mental health workers accompany the adolescent patients for an outing; for example, one of the churches in the area has made its large activity center available. There are occasional additional outings on Saturdays. Some of the adolescents are seen on other days of the week for individual psychotherapy.

It appeared that the day-treatment program had proved a satisfying and meaningful experience for these young people, as evidenced by the very low dropout rate and their remarkable reliability in calling the center to cancel if for any reason they cannot come for a particular session.

Emergency service. Any person who telephones during the hours that Kedren is open would be put through at once to the intake worker. At night and on weekends, an answering service takes over. This answering service is backed up by Kedren staff, assigned on rotation; they receive extra pay for being on emergency call, and to qualify for this pay they must telephone the emergency service at the beginning of their hours of duty to verify that they are available. These staff members are in turn backed up by the psychiatrists, who rotate "second call" for duty periods of one week at a time.

If the emergency situation is one that seems to warrant hospitalization, the staff member will refer the call to the psychiatrist. He, however, can only recommend that the person go to a hospital outside the catchment area—to the county general hospital's psychiatric service if the person cannot pay, or, if he can, to Glendale Adventist Hospital, located in an all-white community some distance from Kedren. In actuality fewer than a dozen persons of all age ranges are hospitalized each year under such circumstances, and scarcely any children or adolescents.

If the situation seems to be one that does not call for immediate intervention, then the person is invited to come into the mental health center on the following day.

Inpatient service. There are no psychiatric inpatient facilities within the catchment area. Kedren has variously had affiliation and contractual arrangements with the Glendale hospital mentioned above and with a private psychiatric hospital, for patients who can afford to pay. These facilities will accept occasional adolescents for placement on the adult service. The Glendale hospital will place an occasional disturbed child on its pediatric service. There are, in fact, very few such admissions. More often the child or adolescent from Kedren who requires inpatient care is served by Camarillo State Hospital and then comes back to the Kedren center for posthospital treatment. During 1970, two children and four adolescents from the Kedren catchment area were admitted to Camarillo.

Consultation and other community services

Kedren does not have a separate consultation service but rather utilizes staff members from clinical services to devote a portion of their time to contacts with various community agencies. Even so, many of the contacts are "case centered," concerned with a particular child or adolescent in treatment, rather than "program centered." One deterrent to broader-scale program consultation is financial; the schools in particular have no funds to pay for consultation, and consultation is not reimbursable through the state-county program, as clinical services are.

A number of staff members are on a roster of speakers available on request to community agencies. About one hundred such presentations were made during 1970.

The schools. Kedren had, by the time of our visit, established some degree of continuing collaboration with five of approximately fifty elementary schools in the catchment area. The program is

> geared toward increased understanding, increased coping abilities of school personnel, increased healthiness in the emotional climate of the school, increased healthiness in communications within the school, better communication between school or agency and parents and/or children.

Such activities are viewed by the center as one form of primary prevention.

Relatively few of the schools have any special education classes of their own, and some do not have guidance counselors.

In general, the overtures of the mental health center to particular schools have been met enthusiastically, although in the actual consultation process there has been some resistance to the mental health worker; the teachers and administrators are inclined to want to deal only with doctors.

There has been particular emphasis on helping individual teachers learn how to manage children in the classroom. It was apparent that many teachers felt themselves poorly prepared in this matter, and as a result some of them have come individually to Kedren to talk about ways of handling classroom problems.

In the spring prior to our visit, a new school had opened, and Dr. Alcerro and three Kedren staff members conducted a six-week summer workshop with twelve of the new teachers, to the considerable satisfaction of the principal. She told us that during the short time her school had been operating she had referred six children to Kedren. These, however, were only those with the most severe problems; asked how many she would think it appropriate to refer if the center had unlimited capacity, she replied that perhaps as many as one hundred out of 1300 students might benefit from some service from Kedren.

The psychologist for the children's service told us that the very knowledge that the Kedren staff is available has proved helpful to those schools with which they have had dealings.

> When we get a kid raising hell in the classroom, we find that a contact with the teacher is very productive. People in all the agencies in this community are really crying out for some help in dealing with the children, and just the fact that they know we're here has had a terrific positive effect.

The welfare department. Several staff members from Kedren had met on three occasions with staff members of the Los Angeles County Department of Public Social Services, to inform them of the services available at Kedren and to become better acquainted themselves with the services available through welfare. A social worker from the welfare department told us that she views Kedren as "an educational facility" and in this respect had herself referred three children. She said that if the program had a greater capacity she would like to refer a number of others from among her caseload of sixty children and their families. The welfare department will pay approximately 25 percent of the fee for treatment at Kedren.

The courts and probation. There are scarcely any dealings with the courts or probation concerning children, but extensive contacts concerning adolescents. Two probation officers described their experiences with Kedren. One said that since the program started she had referred more than twenty adolescents, many of whom had come before the court on drug charges. A number of these, additionally, were young people with severe acting-out behavior or extreme difficulties at home. Some were being seen in the adolescent day-treatment program, others in the outpatient service.

> We have a list of places we can turn to [the probation officer told us], but Kedren is the one place that if I called today, tomorrow someone would call the youngster and say, Your probation officer called, and we have set up an appointment for you. I remember particularly one girl who was grossly overweight and quite violent; Kedren followed her from the beginning of her probation, they're still with her, and when she was sent to the detention home the psychiatrist and mental health worker went to visit her, and they helped me work out a placement plan.

The other probation officer told us that Kedren has called from time to time, asking if she has any young people with problems for whom they might render help. "It's not like those clinics that tell you you have to wait," she said.

Headstart. We have mentioned that the parent body of the mental health center is also responsible for a Headstart program. This essentially separate program serves at a given time approximately three hundred children at eleven different settings, only one of which is within the catchment area. There is close cooperation between Headstart and the mental health center in terms of mutual referrals and inservice training programs for the staff of both agencies. One Headstart locus was used for a summer program for 53 children, from three and a half to fourteen years old, many of whom were in treatment at Kedren. These children spent their time at the camp in recreational and educational activities in a simulated "family environment."

Training

We have mentioned the systematic twenty-session inservice training provided for the original mental health workers. These employees are also permitted up to eight hours per week of released time to continue their formal education in courses related to their work.

There is no training program in any of the three traditional disciplines at Kedren; this relatively new mental health center did not seem to have evolved to the point that it could realistically support a formal training program. The few professionals present were extremely busy with clinical responsibilities and supervising the mental health workers and teachers. If the center can henceforth build a larger permanent professional staff, it would seem to be an ideal place for training in community psychiatry, psychology, and social work, provided it were possible to keep the mental health workers from viewing the students as competitors for their jobs.

Research

No research had been undertaken concerning either children or adolescents, largely because no funds were available, but also because "the time of those staff members who are research competent has been taken up entirely with clinical duties." Some beginning efforts had been made to obtain treatment outcome data, by requesting information from families, friends, school officials, and agency personnel about behavior and emotional changes in the children. For those children whose treatment includes specific emphasis on language and other cognitive development, standardized tests have been used to measure progress.

Financing

During 1971 Kedren was operating on a total budget of $436,000, which came from the following principal sources:

Reimbursement by the state through the county mental health department	38 %
NIMH staffing grant	35
Welfare department	25
Private individuals	.8
Vocational Rehabilitation	.7
Health insurance	.3

Patient fees are set on a sliding scale, from $1 to $30 per week for outpatient or day treatment. In actuality, most patients pay a very small amount, and there did not seem to be any prospect that fees would ever account for a considerable part of the income.

Alger-Delta-Marquette Community Mental Health Center

Marquette and Escanaba, Michigan

The area served

Michigan's Upper Peninsula is a substantial mass of land, more than three hundred miles across, bounded on the north by Lake Superior, on the south by Lake Michigan, on the west by Wisconsin, on the east by Canada. It is almost one third the size of the lower, main portion of Michigan, to which it is connected by a bridge at the Straits of Mackinac. Although the Upper Peninsula is now accessible by superhighways and has regular jet air service, it remains relatively isolated geographically, socially, and culturally.

Almost exactly in the middle of the peninsula are the three counties served by the Alger-Delta-Marquette Community Mental Health Center. The most distant points of this irregularly shaped area lie about one hundred miles apart. But almost half of the 110,000 inhabitants live in only two developed areas: Marquette, the adjoining towns of Ishpeming and Negaunee, and Sawyer Air Force Base, with a combined population of approximately 45,000; and the city of Escanaba and surrounding towns, including Gladstone and Rapid River, with approximately 30,000 population. Since the mental health center operates services in both these communities, a large percentage of the population can be served in their own home towns. The other half of the population is thinly spread through a number of quite small towns; substantially all live within a one-hour drive of Marquette or Escanaba.

The area has known hard times economically. The major industry, iron mining, declined markedly in the 1950's. With new technical processes introduced in the 1960's, there has been something of a comeback. During these years the other traditional industry, lumbering, held its own, and the newer industry of tourism increased. All in all, the area has grown, but at a slow rate. Many young people have left to relocate in cities. Delta and Marquette Counties showed in the 1970 census a small increase over 1960, while Alger County showed a small decline.

The population is particularly homogeneous. Most of the residents are

122

of Scandinavian extraction. The nonwhite population is less than two percent, and these are mainly Indians.

The median household income of about $5500 is somewhat higher than the national average for counties. The percentage of families on relief, the illegitimacy rate, and the infant mortality rate are all below the national average. However, between 16 and 20 percent of families are considered poor, as established by some combined figures from the Michigan Employment Commission and the Alger-Marquette Community Action Board. The unemployment rate is chronically higher than the national average.

The cultural and intellectual climate of Marquette has been enhanced in recent years with the growth of Northern Michigan University, from fewer than a thousand students in 1960 to more than 8000 in 1970.

In the way of mental health resources other than those the center provides itself, the center lists the following:

- The probate courts of the three counties
- The departments of social services of the three counties
- The intermediate school districts of the three counties
- The state hospital at Newberry
- Three Catholic social service agencies
- The counseling center at Northern Michigan University
- Michigan Children's Aid and Family Service, a private social service and adoption agency
- Alger-Marquette Community Action Board, Inc., an agency of the Office of Economic Opportunity
- Two residential treatment programs for alcoholics
- Alcoholics Anonymous
- Vocational Rehabilitation
- Clergymen
- The Veterans Administration Hospital at Iron Mountain

There are no psychiatrists in private practice in the entire Upper Peninsula.

Origins

The first mental health resource in the three-county area came in 1944, with the establishment of the Upper Peninsula Child Guidance Clinic, with its head office located in Marquette and four branch clinics elsewhere in the peninsula.

Many years later Michigan enacted a community mental health act patterned after those of New York and California, under which an adult outpatient clinic was established in Marquette in 1960. The state paid all professional salaries of both the child guidance clinic and the adult clinic, while the community was required to furnish the physical facility and to meet all expenses other than salaries. Dr. David Wall, a psychiatrist who has since become director of the new community mental health center, came to Marquette in 1963 to head the adult outpatient service.

For several years the children's and the adults' services continued their separate existences, sometimes with stresses and rivalries. In 1966, aware that federal matching funds had become available to help meet the payroll costs of new community-based mental health services, Dr. Wall and his associates submitted an application for such funds for a program to serve Marquette and Alger Counties. When application for a staffing grant was made, the state department of mental health changed the state plan to add Delta County, thus meeting the minimum population of 75,000 required for federal funding. A staffing application was submitted in May of 1966 and approved with an effective date of March 1967. There was a considerable amount of covert antagonism between the cities of Marquette and Escanaba, but this has been largely resolved. Additional staff were recruited, services were expanded, and the new mental health center began operating in mid-1967.

The largest component is in Marquette, where inpatient service is provided through an affiliation agreement with St. Mary's, a general hospital, and the other services through the mental health center offices located in a wing of St. Mary's. A four-man staff provides outpatient and consultation services in Escanaba, in Delta County. Certain staff members from Marquette spend two days a week providing services in Munising, which, with a population of only three thousand, is the largest town in Alger County.

From the outset, this mental health center has directed a larger proportion of its services to children and adolescents than have most others. The principal reason appears to be the long history of child guidance services in that area.

Philosophy, purposes, and policy

"In a general sense," Dr. Wall told us, "our philosophy has departed a great deal from the old traditional delivery of services for children, in that we are concerned with the public health preventive approach, hopefully getting away from the illness concept which traditional child services have carried. In delivering direct treatment and preventive services, the role of the professional staff member depends not only on his training but on his personal attributes, interests, and ability to cope with a situation, thus getting away from the traditional model of the psychiatric team and expanding to a generalist approach in which many staff people take responsibility outside of their traditional professional training."

Beyond this, the program of the center is consciously and deliberately based on several premises that have come increasingly to characterize community mental health practice.

• Services should be conveniently available in local communities. As we have described, the center has established services in the three communities having sufficient population to justify them, and the rest of the population live within reasonable driving distance.

• The response should be immediate. Said one of the staff members, "When somebody calls expressing a need, we try to meet that need. This is better than having fifty or sixty people waiting for three months, so that when you do get to one of them he's resolved his problem in a way that is not as good as one that we might have helped him to find."

• There should be a continuum of service, so that individuals with various degrees of difficulty can be helped, and particular individuals can be provided various intensities of care dependent upon their needs at given stages of illness.

• At the same time, all persons should be dealt with at the lowest intensity of care consonant with their needs. Thus, outpatient treatment is preferable to daytime hospitalization; daytime hospitalization to inpatient treatment; brief and intensive inpatient treatment to longer-term inpatient care.

• Almost all people disabled or troubled by emotional difficulties also have some intercurrent strengths, and it is important to identify and capitalize on these strengths in one's efforts to help the individual cope.

• The emphasis is on dealing with people in terms of crises in living; thus, efforts are most frequently directed toward helping the individual to resolve the crisis.

These persuasions seem to underlie the services to children and adolescents quite as much as they do the services to adults. One breakdown in application comes in the availability of a range of services. Because of limited demand, there is no regular short-term inpatient service for children, and inpatient adolescents must be placed in the regular adult service rather than in a separate adolescent unit. Short-term inpatient care for children age twelve and under is available in the pediatric service at one of the local hospitals, with collaboration by local pediatricians and the child psychiatrist[1] as well as other professionals on the staff. The center

---

[1] Who was added to the staff subsequent to our visit.

has thus had to compromise a complete range of services for children and adolescents in light of the realities of limited resources and need.

A PAPER DESCRIBING BROOKRIDGE, the center's relatively new residential facility for moderately disturbed young children, sets forth a philosophy of treating these children that we believe can be said to apply to all of the services for children.

> . . . the child with emotional problems is viewed as an individual with both strengths and problems, and we choose to focus on the child's strengths. . . . [This approach] assists the child in expecting positive behaviors from himself and provides him the opportunity and support to give up old ways of behaving that were ineffective and devaluating.

Elsewhere the report states that

> we do not view any of the . . . staff (nor do we wish them to view themselves) as miniature psychoanalysts; we do not desire a situation where the child feels that everyone is scrutinizing him and probing his mind. The most appropriate ground to be on with a child is the here and now and in the universe of activities and play.

No categories of children or adolescents are excluded from the program. Every applicant is seen at least for an initial screening interview. The program acknowledges, however, that "some children require levels of structured care that we are not able to provide and a length of care beyond which we cannot realistically extend." In these situations, the center must try to arrange to get the child accepted in a specialty institution outside the catchment area, but in practice this is scarcely ever necessary.

Administration and staffing

The ultimate authority for the center is a twelve-member board, selected by a committee appointed by the boards of commissioners of the three counties under the provisions of the Michigan Community Mental Health Act. The board itself has five representatives each from Marquette and Delta Counties and two from Alger County. The board meets monthly. The director of the center and representatives of the staff meet with the board.

Within the center, the 29-man professional staff, plus 20 auxiliary paraprofessionals and secretarial staff, is, on paper, highly organized. For example, there is an executive committee, headed by the center director, which consists of the director of psychology, the director of psychiatry, the director of social work, and the business manager. These designations, based on traditional hospital practice, can have only limited meaning when, in addition to the director of the center, there is only one other psychiatrist, and when there are only six other social workers and four other psychologists. Several other staff personnel have been designated specialty consultants to the director, in the areas of psychiatric nursing, special education, occupational therapy, vocational rehabilitation, and the services for retarded children. In actuality, the staff relationships, while evidently quite harmonious, appear to be extremely informal. Frequently both the director and staff members spoke of their "democratic organization." This appeared to mean that the director has confidence in the capabilities of his staff members and as a result gives them considerable freedom to pursue, expand, and revise their mode of operation, with little formal supervision. "We're all available to one another to talk about a case," said a staff member. "We hope that the person who gets in over his head will recognize it and ask for help. If he doesn't recognize it, it's likely to be spotted at the weekly meeting of the staff. If not there, the patient will probably ask to see some other member of the staff."

The services provided for children and adolescents are administratively divided into five areas.

• Outpatient service for all ages.

• A program for the retarded, particularly focused on day training for severely retarded children from the ages of four to eighteen. (A program was recently developed for adult retarded from eighteen on up.)

• A consultation program to schools, courts, and other community agencies that deal with young people.

• The intermediate-term residential facility for children twelve years of age or younger.

• The adolescent inpatient service (actually, a "capability" rather than a service, since adolescents are admitted to the adult inpatient ward).

A particular staff member is designated to oversee each of these services, and these persons are in turn responsible to the executive committee. The children's residential facility admissions policy is governed by a board comprised of representatives from other children's agencies throughout the community, plus the child psychiatrist and psychologist assigned to Brookridge, with the program director retaining final decision. The considerable majority of children and adolescents are seen, however, in the outpatient service at the clinic facility located at St. Mary's Hospital. Until a few months before our visit there had been no special referral route for these younger patients (and their families). The need was eventually seen to designate a particular staff member to oversee the assignment of children and adolescents, and thus one of the social workers was named Coordinator of Outpatient Services for Children. He does not necessarily supervise the assignment of every child; for example, a school may refer a young person to some other staff member who works particularly with that school. But in the usual course, a new application for service would go to the coordinator, who then would effect assignment to a particular member of the staff. He serves "as a focal point for both the staff and the community for resolving problems concerning children."

This leads us to what is perhaps the most significant aspect of the staffing plan at this mental health center. Quite deliberately, a "generalist" approach is used, by which we mean that all professional staff treat all ages of patients, in contrast to the practice of assigning children and their parents only to particular staff members with special training in treating children. Some of the staff at Marquette are light in traditional academic credentials for working with children, but several professionals have had on-the-job experience with children in other agencies, have a particular penchant for younger patients, and thus make themselves readily available to accept children and adolescents. Other staff members who have no particular interest in seeing younger people are free to decline them. Thus, individual staff members to a large extent are permitted in a quite informal way to emphasize, if not specialize in, those areas of treatment and those categories of clients that they find most satisfying.

Dr. Wall was asked what particular advantages and disadvantages he saw to the "generalist approach." He responded that in a small staff it seemed important to avoid a degree of specialization that removes particular staff members from a broad range of activities needed of them. Furthermore, "if you don't know enough to know that you're going to have trouble, often you don't have that trouble. It's also important to know enough not to get too deeply involved."

The arrangement appeared to be working to the considerable satisfaction of the staff and the director. Crises had been very few. A child psychiatrist from Chicago is available for telephone consultation, but he is almost never called. He also comes to Marquette for two days of consultation each six weeks, and at that time he reviews with the staff both general and specific problems that they have experienced in their dealings with children.

These observations about staff apply to the Marquette program. The four staff members at Escanaba adhere to this same "generalist approach," also evidently to their satisfaction. The director of the overall center and various staff members travel to Escanaba for a half-day meeting every other week.

The size and qualifications of staff. Because of the "generalist" approach in serving the total population, including parents of children as well as children, it is difficult to break down the delivery of services in terms of hours per week with children and hours per week with adolescents. However, it is estimated that at the Marquette installation about 110 hours of professional staff time are spent each week with children and another 110 hours with adolescents.

Since it is often assumed that mental health programs in rural areas will be unable to recruit a full complement of staff, it is interesting to note that the Marquette center had all of its positions filled except for one slot in social work which had been deliberately held open. Only three of the six psychologists held a doctorate (although another had completed all except the dissertation). Six of eight social workers had a master's degree. The bachelor's-level social workers and two master's-level psychologists were being used by design, not by default. The center director considers that appropriate personal attributes and a good deal of on-the-job experience—none of the staff had come to the center without some intervening experience—can be adequate to offset the lack of ultimate professional credentials.

Nine of the staff members were "native sons and daughters" who had decided to return to the relatively uncomplicated life of the Upper Peninsula. Some others who had been recruited at national meetings were deliberately seeking a locus removed from the problems that characterize urban living. Clean air and opportunities for fishing, hunting, winter sports, and summer water sports on still-unpolluted Lake Superior have proved an adequate lure to keep the center's positions filled. (One must remember, too, that Marquette and Escanaba are both linked to Chicago and Detroit by daily jet flights, that Marquette's university provides a variety of cultural and intellectual associations, and that the growth of tourism to this area has resulted in the development of a number of the amenities associated with more "sophisticated" areas.)

The attractive staff appeared to be energetic, responsible, and deeply invested in their work.

Dr. Wall believes, nonetheless, that services for children and adolescents would be improved if it were possible to find one or more specialists, particularly a child psychiatrist (as has since occurred). Such persons would not take over the direct clinical services so much as they would use their knowledge and experience to provide inservice training to the present staff and to provide more continuous backup and interpretation.

The Clinical Services

The services in Marquette

The outpatient service. The customary route of entry into the Marquette treatment program is by way of the outpatient service. The formal service operates from 8 a.m. to 5 p.m., Monday through Friday. However, many staff members can and do arrange to see applicants and patients in the evening on a regular basis. Half of the staff, since about fifty percent of their caseload are children and adolescents, are involved in outpatient services.

Unless an agency being consulted to refers a particular applicant to some other staff member, the coordinator of children's outpatient services will be the person who deals with the applicant, or, more accurately, his parents, since in Michigan persons under the age of eighteen cannot refer themselves for treatment (although children will be seen initially without such permission and are instructed to get the parents' permission before treatment can be begun).[2] Almost all applications come in by telephone, and certain basic information will already have been taken by the secretarial staff member who took the call. The coordinator reviews this information, then decides to whom the case should be assigned.

This staff member then schedules an intake interview for the parents and the child. He or she operates independently in deciding whether psychological tests are indicated, whether the child's behavior suggests that he may need medication or that he should for any other reason be seen by a psychiatrist or other physician, whether the treatment should be individual psychotherapy with the child and/or parents, family therapy, family group therapy, and so on. Following the initial interview, or at any time he thinks necessary, the therapist may bring up his case for discussion at a weekly staff meeting, but there is no routine provision for each new case to be "conferenced." There is, in other words, no formal stipulated diagnostic evaluation, precisely because it is felt unnecessary.

During the first half of 1970, there were 68 children taken into the outpatient service. Fifty-one percent of these were referred by the schools; 26 percent by parents or other immediate family members; 16 percent by the courts; and six percent by four other sources. There were

---

[2] A subsequent change in state law now makes it possible for a person under eighteen years old to refer himself because of drug problems without the consent of parents.

31 new adolescent cases during the same period. Thirty-five percent were referred by family physicians, 23 percent each by the schools and by parents or other relatives, 16 percent by the courts, and three percent by the welfare department.

Among the children discharged during the first half of 1970, only two diagnoses were provided to us. More than half were *adjustment reactions of childhood.* About ten percent were *hyperkinetic reactions of childhood,* and the rest were undiagnosed. "The staff philosophy is such that we avoid labeling, in the best interests of the child," Dr. Wall told us.

Composite diagnostic figures for adolescents were not available. Something over half are seen only as outpatients. A number of this group are categorized as "maturational difficulties," oftentimes "compounded by a difficult home situation." The remaining adolescents—about 43 percent —are admitted to the inpatient service at St. Mary's, in most cases after having failed to respond to outpatient treatment. The diagnoses for inpatient adolescents in 1970 were:

Psychoses	31%
Characterological and situational disorders	26
Brain syndromes, drug abuse	26
Neuroses	17

Because staff members are operating individually and for the most part independently as therapists, it seems probable that there is a great deal of individual variation in the delivery of outpatient services.

As for the particular form of interaction with the patients, we were given the following estimates:

With children and their parents

Individual contacts	34%
Individual psychotherapy	21
Family therapy	18
Counseling with parents groups	18
Group therapy	9

With adolescents and their parents

Individual contacts	25%
Individual psychotherapy	25
Group therapy	20
Family therapy	17
Counseling with parents groups	13

Despite the fact that many of the children are not seen in the course of treatment by a physician, a review of the case records suggested that, if the question of medication arises, a physician is involved.

During the first half of 1970, 99 children were terminated from the outpatient service in Marquette. Sixty-one of these were discharged as requiring no further service; 12 refused further service; 11 were referred to some other agency for nonpsychiatric services; eight were referred to some other treating agency; four refused to enter treatment; and three moved out of the area. In this same period, 74 adolescents were terminated. Twenty-eight of these were discharged as requiring no further service; 12 were referred to some other agency for nonpsychiatric services; another 12 refused further services; 11 were referred to some other treating agency; six moved out of the area; two were placed in the day-treatment program at St. Mary's; two were transferred to the state hospital; and one refused to enter treatment.

Emergency service. A staff employee is available to respond to emergency calls during the hours the clinic is open. At other times a generic emergency service for all age groups is operated through the switchboard and emergency room of St. Mary's Hospital. If the call is psychiatric in nature, it is referred to a member of the mental health center staff, who take turns on a duty roster. This includes all of the professional staff. In addition to this an extension line from the center is answered during nighttime hours or over the weekend on the psychiatric unit. The attendant personnel on the psychiatric unit have been trained in the use of the emergency line and, when indicated, refer calls to the staff person on call. Those who are not physicians are in turn backed up by Dr. Wall and the child psychiatrist. There are relatively few calls concerning children and adolescents—rarely more than one or two a month. The disposition will depend on the evident degree of emergency and may result in advising the parents to present the child for admission to the hospital. This is rarely necessary, and in the more usual case the parents are advised to come to the mental health center the following day.

Inpatient service. At St. Mary's Hospital there is no provision for inpatient treatment of children under the age of twelve.

Another hospital in Marquette, St. Luke's, has a very adequate pediatric service. Infrequently and in emergency situations, admissions to the service are arranged through the local pediatricians with consultation from the psychiatrist or other staff member from the center until the emergency has passed and a referral to the outpatient service can be arranged. In actuality, only five children under thirteen were admitted as inpatients for psychiatric reasons at St. Luke's during 1970.

Adolescents are admitted to the psychiatric unit at St. Mary's, where they are handled along with the adults. There is no formal limit on the number of adolescents who can be accommodated at one time on this

16-bed service; the range has been from none to five, and usually there are two or three. The most common reasons for their admission are psychoses, characterological or situational disorders, acute brain syndromes, usually secondary to drug abuse, and neuroses. The service is seen as short term, and an adolescent who does not respond within a month or so would then have to be considered for transfer to the state hospital. However, only two such transfers took place during 1970. The major treatment device in the inpatient service for adolescents is an ongoing adolescent group which includes outpatients as well as inpatients. Dr. Wall and his staff feel that this arrangement for adolescent hospitalization is an expedient; there are neither the physical facilities nor the particular staff that would be required to provide the separate, more active program that they think would be best for the adolescents. At the same time, the number of adolescents judged to need inpatient treatment is too small to justify the expense of a separate program.

Partial hospitalization. There is no provision at St. Mary's for partial hospitalization for children under twelve. A limited number of adolescents come in to the inpatient service two days a week, from 9 a.m. to 3 p.m., where they join the inpatient adolescents in a program of group activity and group therapy. For the most part, these are adolescents who have been on inpatient status and are being "phased down" in intensity of treatment. The number of adolescents coming in on day status ranged from one to seven during 1970; typically there are about two.

Brookridge

On the outskirts of Marquette, on a 27-acre tract, is Brookridge, a residential and day-treatment facility operated by the mental health center for moderately disturbed children through the age of twelve. Formerly the county "poor farm," the property is rented from the county for one dollar per year. The large, red-brick Victorian building was built about 1900. In the basement is a very large, well-equipped kitchen, a large, well-equipped activities room, and a rumpus room. The first floor has a large living room, a very large classroom, and adjacent to it a smaller room for any child who needs to engage in a separate activity. The second floor has two large dormitories, one for the boys and one for the girls, and separate bathroom facilities for each. There are also some offices for the staff. The building was well renovated, at a cost of $79,000 which came from the three counties and individual contributions. It is pleasant and cheerful throughout. The spacious grounds are wooded and make an excellent place for the children to play.

The inpatient capacity of Brookridge is fifteen children. However, since it opened in 1969, the highest census has been fourteen, and at the time of our visit there were four children in residence (with two others to be admitted the following week). With the present staff, a maximum of twelve children can be served, including day care and residential treatment. The largest census on day care has been four, as it was at the time of our visit.

There was some question, at this early stage of Brookridge's development, as to whether its full capacity will prove in time to be needed for the three-county area that it serves. When the mental health center was being planned, it was widely believed that fifteen inpatient beds for children would certainly be suitable, but this was in the days when services for children were limited to a rather small guidance clinic that had almost always had a waiting list. With the advent of the mental health center, a larger outpatient program became available in Marquette, a smaller outpatient program in Escanaba and Munising, and a school consultation program. These additional resources have served to take care of some of the children earlier considered to be candidates for residential treatment. On the other hand, the facility was still quite new, had not been widely publicized because of the desire to develop services in a gradual and orderly manner, and had not yet attempted to return to Marquette any of the children from the catchment area who had been sent to distant residential treatment programs. It remains to be seen whether this 110,000-population catchment area will produce enough children who appropriately need intermediate-term residential treatment. A further factor is the reluctance of some parents to accept the service even in cases where a careful evaluation indicates the need. In the first year of operation, five sets of parents refused to have their children admitted. [Dr. Wall comments: "Present indications are that this facility could be filled when the staff is increased, and as of mid-1971 a waiting list (of one) had been established for the first time. When space has been available, children from out of the catchment area have been admitted."]

A particularly careful screening process has been set up for two reasons: a) to make certain that the proposed child does in fact appear to be unable to respond to a lesser intensity of treatment than residential care; b) to determine that the child, even if severely disturbed, seems likely to be able to benefit from the particular kind of program offered at Brookridge. Those who deal with children and believe that they may have a candidate are asked to consider the following questions, among others:

- Does the child seem to have emotional difficulties in any of these three areas: at home, in school, or with his friends?
- Does he consistently behave in troublesome ways, in contrast to "just every once in a while"?
- Has he been of concern to various people who are responsible for him over a long period of time?
- Are the child's parents concerned and/or willing to do anything about his problems?
- Has the child been evaluated and worked with to no avail?
- Does he require a total-environment live-in program over a period of months?

The child proposed for admission to Brookridge, and his parents, are then referred to the mental health center component at Marquette, Escanaba, or Munising, which in turn, if he seems to meet the initial criteria, submits the case to an admissions committee that consists of the program director of Brookridge, the mental health center's coordinator of special education, Brookridge's special education teacher, Dr. Wall or the child psychiatrist, the Brookridge houseparents, the psychological consultant to Brookridge from the community mental health center, one Brookridge counselor on a rotating basis, an intermediate school representative from the tri-county area, and representatives of various child service agencies making the referral. This committee decides whether the child should be admitted and, if so, formulates an initial educational and therapeutic plan.

The diagnostic work-up is as formal for Brookridge as it is informal for the outpatient service. Each child receives a comprehensive physical examination. An extensive battery of psychological tests is given, if necessary. There is a psychiatric evaluation. A social evaluation of the family is done. All of these focus on "the perceptual, intellectual, and emotional capacities and deficiencies." During a period of months prior to our visit, only four of eighteen applicants were approved for admission. (In the first half of 1971, however, seven of nine children were accepted for admission, "which represents a more realistic expectation from referral sources.")

The philosophy underlying service to the children at Brookridge relies particularly on the need of disturbed children for consistency.

> Children should know on what and on whom they can depend [we were told]. We provide a basic, dependably structured environment in which

the children can learn to trust where there has been mistrust and begin to relax where there has been anxiety about what is going to happen next. This helps the child to organize a life that has seemed to him disorganized and chaotic. It provides him valuable anchors from which he can feel more secure and free to explore less structured and newly creative ways of behaving.

All the staff and volunteers are expected

to appreciate that all children work out much of the learning of life and its accompanying problems through play—individual and group games, projects, exploring, and imaginative exploits. They are challenging to a child, and it is important to him whether or not he can understand the rules of the game, participate, accomplish, have fun, and be free of anxieties. Children not only test out their performance abilities through activities and play, but these are most vital avenues for them to build interpersonal relationships; they learn language and carry on conversation through activities and play. Many of our children need assistance in being able to play with one another, to join in activities, to imagine, and to create. These moments with the child are just as important, sometimes more so, than the individual sessions with professionals who have been trained in specialized techniques.

The treatment philosophy is translated into a program that provides a daily half hour of group therapy, an hour and a half of occupational and recreational therapy, a two-hour afternoon and another two-hour early-evening period of structured activity, often involving trips away from the residence. There are also free periods, during which particular children have individual therapy, prescribed work programs, and occasionally family therapy. The children are required to make their own beds and keep their own "territories" in good order; they are encouraged but not required to help with cleaning the common rooms, setting the tables, and so on.

As progress indicates, attendance at public school, either half or full day, is part of the treatment program. Transportation is provided for these children.

The day-treatment program is essentially the same, with those children who live at home coming in to join the resident patients. Some of the day patients are children who have "graduated" from inpatient status, while others are moderately disturbed children who have supportive home environments that they can tolerate and which can tolerate them.

The diagnoses of children admitted to Brookridge have been predominantly acting out and behavioral disorders. To date, three autistic children have also been admitted. In addition, at least three children with minimal brain damage and/or undifferentiated retardation with emotional complications have been admitted. From opening up to mid-1971, twenty children have been patients. Of the nine who have been discharged, two completed a full year in public school and adjusted well socially as well as academically. Four others completed at least a half year in public school and were continuing to do well within the community. One child was removed by his parent against the advice of staff. The intermediate school district consultant affiliated with Brookridge spent considerable time in liaison with the schools to which the children were sent in this follow-up work. Foster homes have been used in three instances as an intermediate step before return to the natural home. Due to finances and the type of child, obtaining a foster home has proved to be very difficult.

The parents of all the Brookridge children are expected to attend biweekly therapy sessions at the clinic facility at St. Mary's. One set of parents that we interviewed told us that they had found these sessions helpful in many ways—in better understanding their child's behavior and how to cope with it, their relationship with him, and the significance of their own behavior as parents. They said that the groups had been well attended and they believed had proved helpful to the other parents. In addition to this, family therapy is provided in all possible cases.

For the number of patients at the time of our visit, Brookridge was heavily staffed. A total staff of 12 included 7½ counselor positions, plus kitchen, maintenance, and housekeeping personnel. The director of Brookridge has a basic nursing education and approximately 15 years pediatric nursing experience. In addition to this, she has a bachelor's degree in psychology and is completing a master's degree in child care from the University of Pittsburgh. The counselors include a practical nurse, a girl with considerable experience as a nurses' aide, two graduates and several undergraduates from Northern Michigan and other universities. The primary qualifications sought in a counselor are their personal attributes and ability to work with children.

The counselors are assigned on shifts. One is on duty at night, for self-evident reasons and purposes. Two are on the day shift, to wake the children and to help them get dressed, fed, and to their classrooms. These day-shift counselors then help with the school program and also spend time individually with the children when they are not in class. They eat with the children. (Dr. Wall adds: "With the admission of younger children, a more intensive staff-patient ratio has become necessary.")

Three counselors are on duty for the afternoon-evening shift, because "emotionally disturbed children are typically more hyperactive at this time after a full day of intensive programs." There are various individual and group activities and a great deal of individual interaction with the children.

Volunteers have been used extensively. At the time of our visit seventeen volunteers were contributing about two hours per week each. They are assigned to spend time with children individually on special projects and tutoring, to conduct group activities, to help with the maintenance of buildings and grounds, and in fund raising. The director and assistant director of Brookridge interview prospective volunteers, acquaint them with the nature and purposes of the program, give them reading materials about the program, and recommend other reading. After the first two sessions of service, each volunteer has a formal follow-up conference, and thereafter meets with the director or assistant director as needed. Ongoing monthly meetings are held with all the volunteers.

The average stay at Brookridge during its brief period of operation had been about nine months, which, by prevailing norms, makes it an "intermediate-term" facility for children. Only two of the original eight children admitted were still in residence by mid-1971, one awaiting foster care and the other long-term placement elsewhere. The goal is to refine the program so that the average stay will be shortened to no more than six months.

One must admire the energy and dedication that went into the creation of an attractive residential program for children in an area where none had existed. (Even the state hospital that serves this three-county area had closed down its children's service.) It is too early in its operating experience to judge whether a facility of this size and cost (discussed below) is generally viable for an area with a population just over 100,000. Because a substantial part of this country does not have locally available residential resources for seriously disturbed children, the operation of Brookridge during the next several years should furnish important information to communities and regions that have yet to create this kind of service.

Treatment services in Escanaba

Prior to the establishment of the mental health center, mental health service for children in Escanaba and the rest of Delta County was limited to a one-man guidance clinic, whose activities consisted mainly of making diagnoses and of intelligence testing of children referred by the schools. Rarely were any children seen for what would be called therapy, and for the testing and diagnostic work there was a wait of several months.

Under the mental health center, the four-man staff at Escanaba—three social workers, including the director, and a psychologist—provide treatment services to clients of all ages and carry out certain consultation activities described below. Figures were not furnished us on the numbers of children and adolescents seen there, their referral sources, diagnoses, dispositions, and so on. The director estimated that in 1970 approximately 150 children and 50 adolescents were seen, for the most part in individual sessions. There has been no waiting list since services were established under the mental health center's aegis. Ordinarily, when a school social worker, physician, or court official initiates a referral, the parents are invited to come in for an interview. The staff member takes a social history, then attempts to collaborate with the parents in determining a plan for further appointments. If a child or adolescent seen in Escanaba should appear to require more intensive or specialized services than are available there, he would be referred to the Marquette clinic at St. Mary's.

The local general hospital has no psychiatric unit but will admit such psychiatric emergencies as suicide gestures or serious assaultive behavior, who, if it proved necessary and they were more than twelve years old, might subsequently be transferred to the inpatient service at Marquette. The director of the mental health clinic estimated that such emergencies number less than one per month.

Treatment services in Munising

Two members of the Marquette staff travel two days a week to Munising. Much of the activity is consultative, although some individuals and several groups are seen in therapeutic relationships. The only one of these involving young people is an adolescent group, made up usually of seven or eight boys who have delinquency charges against them and are referred by the courts. A court worker, who has extensive on-the-job training but little formal background, acts as cotherapist with a member of the mental health center staff.

Consultation and Other Community Services

Marquette

Consultation to schools. Dr. Wall describes the three basic goals of the mental health center's school consultation program as:

- The development with individual teachers of a specific program to alleviate specific behavioral problems in individual children

- The development of increased ability of schoolteachers to handle various types of troublesome behavior
- Facilitation of communication among schoolteachers and between teachers and the administration

The center's director of consultation programs believes that consultation

> provides an avenue whereby school personnel can discuss with the mental health worker the needs of individual children, the group, and the total school system.

Personal contact between the mental health worker and the school personnel results in "a more consistent and workable plan for the child." The consultation also is intended to upgrade the skills of teachers in ways that they can apply autonomously in future dealings with children.

The kinds of needs described here are perceived as resulting from deficiencies that are believed to be characteristic of present personnel and programs of schools.

> We find that much of the existing emphasis and values within the educational system tend to block flexibility, openness of communication, motivation, and involvement, thereby often removing the challenge and thrill of discovery and learning. Both the teacher and the school system all too frequently value a well-controlled, well-behaved classroom in which all children are expected to proceed at a uniform pace towards a uniform predetermined goal. . . . The values placed on uniformity and conformity tend to stifle and hobble the individuality, flexibility, openness of communication, motivation, and involvement of both students and teachers.

This conception of the value of consultation is translated into a program that, as of the time of our visit, reached a number but by no means all of the individual schools within the mental health center's catchment area. During 1970 there were ten staff members who provided regularly scheduled consultation to a total of twelve schools. As with the clinical services, a "generalist" approach is used; each school consultant is a staff member who also participates in various other facets of the center's program. Some of the staff have had formal training in human-relationship groups which were found useful in the school consultation program; several staff members had been previously involved in various kinds of service agencies that deal with children; and some had been schoolteachers. The director of the school consultation program has a master's degree in special education of emotionally disturbed children.

Typically, each school is visited by one or two staff members every two weeks, for a three-hour period. The principal notifies the teachers that the mental health personnel will be on hand, and those teachers who choose to call on them to discuss particular "problem children" do so. The majority of contacts are individual, although there are occasional meetings with groups of teachers. An occasional teacher who has decided problems of disruptive behavior in her classroom is urged by the principal to see the mental health center personnel.

The consultation transactions do, of course, sometimes lead to "case-finding." Particular children whose behavior suggests a degree of emotional disturbance that might call for treatment are referred to the mental health center. The consultation personnel find, more typically, that the teachers are overly inclined to label behavior as deviant, in large part because their education in child development is sketchy and their training in classroom management nonexistent. The mental health center staff attempt to help them to understand that a good deal of behavior that may be irksome to the teacher is appropriate to school-age children.

We interviewed the curriculum coordinator from a large elementary school in Marquette County, who told us that 16 of the 22 teachers in her school had voluntarily participated to one extent or another in the consultation program.

The mental health center has entered into an arrangement with the city school system of Marquette, under which the center provides regular consultation to all of the system's five elementary schools, for which the school system pays 35 cents per school year for each pupil enrolled. The contract interestingly stipulates that

> to facilitate appropriate use of mental health center personnel by school personnel, members of the professional staff of the community mental health center will be regarded as employees of the school system whenever school personnel engage them in professional activities concerning specific students.

This contract has proved valuable in resolving the sometimes sticky question of confidentiality. The center also serves school systems in adjoining cities and towns, and the same arrangements exist throughout the tri-county area.

In addition to the schools regularly visited, a number of others have asked for services sporadically, which the center has rendered without charge. Still other schools have not been contacted by the center, simply because of the lack of staff time. And a few others which have been contacted declined the offer of service. Said the director of the school consultation program:

> Some are not really in the market, at least not at this time. In the junior and senior high schools it's hard to get the teachers together. They have

about 150 students each, and consequently aren't as involved with particular students as the elementary school teachers are. In our own priorities, we've stressed the elementary schools, because we believe we can have a greater impact on these younger students.

The welfare department. The mental health center receives frequent requests for consultation from welfare caseworkers, generally about particular clients. Welfare workers sometimes attend mental health center staff meetings when they have clients who are in therapy there. The center provides evaluations of individuals who are applying for disability benefits on the basis of a psychiatric disorder. There were plans under way at the time of our visit for the center and the welfare department to collaborate in creating a group counseling program of high school students whose parents are welfare clients.

The courts. Substantially all of the court contacts that relate to children are those with the juvenile section of the Marquette County Probate Court. The relationship was described to us, both by court personnel and the mental health center staff, as one that had improved. Certainly in its earlier years it was troubled. Because the nature of the trouble is a fairly classic example of the stresses and dissatisfactions that are apt to characterize the efforts to build relationships between a community mental health service and other community agencies, it may be useful to describe the specifics.

The community mental health center had set for itself the primary goal of making the knowledge of its staff members available to community agencies in the form of program consultation that would enhance the capacity of these other agencies to make their own appropriate decisions about children in their jurisdiction. The court, on the other hand, wanted direct service in the form of evaluations of the cases before it. As a result, children were referred for evaluation in numbers that put a considerable strain on the resources of the mental health center. The kinds of information needed by the court were not always spelled out, background information that would have facilitated the evaluation was not always furnished, and, perhaps most difficult for the mental health center staff to accept, its recommendations were frequently not followed. During the first two years of the center's operation, well over a hundred evaluations were requested. Many were carried out; some were not because of the center's persuasion that there was nothing in the particular case to suggest either the need for or the usefulness of a psychiatric evaluation. Thus, the relationship continued in a manner that was generally unsatisfactory to both sides.

Perhaps a successful resolution would have taken place in time. In actuality, the problem was solved circumstantially. A social worker from the mental health center staff was hired by the court, thus providing it with professional capability that had previously been unavailable. In the following year the number of requests for referral from the court dropped to less than a dozen. The mental health center altered the nature of its contact with the court to reserving a weekly time slot for which the court could indicate its need as late as the prior afternoon. During the several months before our visit, the court personnel had rarely asked for this time. When meetings are held, they continue to focus in most cases on the specific cases before the court.

The center's relationship with some other courts in the catchment area, as described elsewhere, has been more satisfying. One member of the center staff, a psychologist, is designated coordinator of court services. He has prepared a statement of principles that he feels should apply to community mental health center relationships with courts which can be summarized as follows:

1. It is important to help the court ascertain which cases before it call for referral to the mental health center; these should be limited to situations where the court needs specific information that can be most appropriately provided by a mental health agency, or the court suspects that the child may be a prospect for direct clinical service. In such cases the court should furnish such information as social and family history, past offenses, school records, etc.
2. If the court feels it is germane to have an appraisal of the dynamics that may underlie particular behavior, this need not result in a formal referral but may be discussed by telephone or by a visit of the mental health center staff member to the court.
3. To understand the needs and problems of each other, the mental health center consultant should spend time observing in the courtroom, and the court should acquaint itself with the considerable amount of time involved in full-scale evaluation.

Consultation services in Escanaba

The four-man staff at Escanaba spends approximately ten percent of its combined time in consultation services, principally to schools but also to the courts and to the district health department.

The services to the school are divided informally between the mental health center and the "intermediate school district" in what appears to be a manner satisfying to both agencies. The intermediate school district is a state-operated service that provides a variety of special services to local schools that lack the funds to furnish them. A recent expansion of the intermediate school district services resulted in some fall-off in requests to the mental health center. However, particular teachers and schools that have been satisfied with the response from the mental health center continue to call on it. "The intermediate school district actually welcomes this," we were told, "because *in toto* the services are not all that extensive, so they need all the help they can get."

The Escanaba staff regularly consults to five schools. A good deal of the service is diagnostic testing, but the staff do become involved from time to time in discussing particular problem children with teachers. "I've seen some gratifying carry-over from a specific problem case to the way the teacher handles the other children," said one of the staff members.

One social worker has a twice-monthly appointment with the court worker of the juvenile division of the probate court. Otherwise, service to that court and to the district court, which handles some adolescents, is done on request. Similarly, service focused on particular cases is provided to the district health department on request.

Consultation services in Munising

At the instigation of the mental health center, an interagency group of "caretakers" was organized to meet weekly. These include representatives from the school system, the welfare department, a local poverty program, the courts, Alcoholics Anonymous, and certain clergymen. These people meet for an hour and a half to "discuss our jobs, our clients, ourselves, and how to serve the community more effectively." The goal is to help these agency personnel "to better understand themselves and the people they serve, and improve the communication between these agencies."

Mental retardation services

The Michigan Community Mental Health Act covers the mentally retarded and requires that service be provided to them in the programs it funds. Three day-training centers are operated in the catchment area, in Marquette, Escanaba, and Manistique. Children proposed for enrollment are given psychological evaluations by the community mental health center. Only severely retarded children are accepted. The enrollment averages six children per center. For six hours a day they are provided a "developmental training program" aimed at teaching self-care, social skills, simple work skills, and language development. The staff consists of teachers' aides, one for each six children.

A part-time coordinator for the mental retardation services was employed by the tri-county mental health board subsequent to our visit, with the expectation that his services would become increasingly available to the other areas of the Upper Peninsula, which would then assist in financing this program. His main purpose as of mid-1971 was to coordinate services through existing community agencies, to enhance the mental retardation program, and to attempt to eliminate duplication.

Financing

This community mental health center has been supported in part by a federal staffing grant which at the time of our visit had phased down to the 30 percent level. In developing a budget, the total anticipated revenue is first calculated; the federal funds come "off the top" for those particular services which they cover. Then anticipated patient fees are deducted. Thereafter the State of Michigan pays 75 percent of the balance, and the local community must contribute the remaining 25 percent.

During 1969-70, the mental health center operated on a budget of $548,000. This does not include any expenses of the inpatient service other than the salaries of three staff members assigned there, since the inpatient service is, as an affiliation arrangement, separately budgeted. The principal sources of funds were: State of Michigan, 62 percent; the three county governments of the catchment area, 15 percent; the federal grant, 12 percent; and patient fees, nine percent. During this same year, more than four fifths of the budget (81 percent) went for salaries and fringe benefits. Another 12 percent covered rent and maintenance. No other item accounted for as much as two percent of the budget.

We were furnished a tentative breakdown of the distribution of expenses by services. The largest expenditure was for outpatient services ($166,000). Although philosophically the program feels that its greatest thrust is in consultation, in terms of money the expenditures assigned to consultation came only to $67,000.

The operating costs of Brookridge were $135,000. Should this program eventually build up to a capacity of 15 inpatients and 15 day patients, and if the costs do not increase greatly, it could provide service for approximately $3500 per day patient per year and $7000 per inpatient per year. This would be a reasonable figure in comparison to what other such specialized facilities cost. At the present time, with its small capacity, the cost per child is of course much higher.

The center did not have fiscal data that could be translated into units of service, such as the cost per outpatient interview; however, the per capita cost of population served has been calculated by the State of Michigan at approximately $5.

The budget for fiscal 1971-72 is anticipated to be $828,000, which includes the operation of Brookridge and the cost of hospitalizing indigent patients on the inpatient service.

Aspirations for the future

Dr. Wall indicated two activities that he hopes the center will be able either to establish or to help others to establish: a foster home placement program of high quality both for children and for adolescents, and a halfway house for adolescents. He also expressed the hope that in the future long-term inpatient facilities of the kind needed for an occasionally seriously disturbed child could become more readily available; he thinks this unlikely in the Upper Peninsula, given its particular circumstances, but would welcome the availability of such resources somewhere in the state.

[Dr. Wall adds: "Late in 1970, a new child inpatient treatment service at Traverse City State Hospital, approximately three hundred miles away, became operational and we have been able to utilize this treatment resource for our area on several occasions.

"Because of the lack of adequate community services to retarded children, this has high priority for future development in the community, including return of retarded patients from state hospitals and development of adequate foster home facilities for such individuals, along with community activity programs and halfway houses."]

Arapahoe Mental Health Center
Englewood and Aurora, Colorado

The area served

The Arapahoe Mental Health Center serves a three-county area contiguous to Denver, with a total population in 1970 of 180,000. Two of these counties, Douglas and Elbert, are predominantly rural, although in recent years some portions of Douglas County have experienced a spread of suburbia from Denver. These two counties have a combined population of only 20,000; they were placed with Arapahoe County to form a regional community mental health center catchment area as part of the Colorado state plan for local mental health services. While there have been some referrals of children and adolescents from these counties to the mental health center, and some consultation on request to the schools, the extent of service is not only numerically, but also proportionately, small.

Arapahoe County, where the two installations of the community mental health center are located, has about 160,000 people, or 89 percent of all those in the catchment area. All of the county can be considered a part of metropolitan Denver. It has grown substantially, with the 1970 population 41 percent larger than the 1960 population. While it is the second wealthiest county in Colorado in terms of per capita income, about 40 percent of the Arapahoe patients seen at the mental health center come from families that would qualify as economically deprived (that is, a family of four with an income below $4000 per year). Communities in the county range from extremely wealthy Cherry Creek downward through Englewood, which, while predominantly middle class, has some clearly identifiable poverty pockets, and finally to Sheridan, which has many deprived families. The population of the entire catchment area is overwhelmingly white. About seven percent of the people are of Mexican extraction, and there are scarcely any Negroes.

Within Arapahoe County is the well-known Fort Logan Mental Health Center, a small and progressive state hospital that serves Denver and several surrounding counties. It has provided inpatient treatment for an

147

occasional child referred by the Arapahoe center and for a time it provided some day-care services for children and adolescents. The University of Colorado Medical Center provides some day care for children and has an inpatient ward for adolescents. There are also two nearby private general hospitals that have inpatient psychiatric facilities for those who can pay. An unknown but perhaps large number of children and adolescents who live in Arapahoe County are treated by the large number of psychiatrists, psychologists, and social workers who are in private practice in metropolitan Denver.

Origins

In 1955, largely as the result of the concern of some public health nurses and teachers, a small psychiatric outpatient clinic was established in Englewood, a principal community of Arapahoe County, with the support of nurses from the Tri-County District Health Department and Englewood educators. While it served all ages, the chief focus was on children. During the early years there was little expansion, and by 1961 the staff consisted only of a psychologist, a social worker, and a half-time child psychiatrist.

At that time Colorado had no provision for special education services for emotionally disturbed children. The clinic staff worked with the superintendent of the Cherry Creek School District to help establish a special education class for such children. A demonstration grant was sought, but when the funds were unattainable the school district, working in close conjunction with the clinic, established a special education class in the fall of 1961. Later, in 1965, when Colorado created a provision for two categories of children with educational handicaps—those with minimal brain injury and those with emotional problems inhibiting normal educational growth—the class was able to receive special funding.

During that same period, while the special classroom was being planned, the Western Interstate Commission for Higher Education offered the clinic two summer work-study college students; they were put to work as group therapy assistants in some groups for children between the ages of six and twelve. After "a small and shaky beginning," the program was expanded for the following summer into a day camp that operated three days per week, five hours per day, with first priority going to children being considered for the special education class and second priority to those who were on the clinic's waiting list for treatment. Parents, seen in groups or as individual couples, were required to participate. The camp flourished and soon inspired an after-school group therapy program during the school year, with college and high school students serving as assistant therapists along with the clinic staff.

In 1966, when community mental health center staffing funds became available from the federal government, the Arapahoe clinic applied for and received a grant to become a community mental health center. Since at that time the center provided only outpatient and consultation and education services, contracts were established with the Colorado Psychiatric Hospital and Fort Logan Mental Health Center to provide partial hospitalization, inpatient services, and some emergency services in order to provide the five basic elements of service necessary for a community mental health center. With the assurance of this grant, even though formal written approval was not received until the day before the grant was to become effective, it was possible to expand into other services. A second grant request was written (which later became part of the initial grant), largely to support mental health services which the new center proposed to provide to two school districts that were "having serious difficulties with personnel in their psychological services division." The school districts agreed to furnish the required matching funds. Specifically, the grant was to provide clinical psychologists, psychiatric social workers, and child psychiatrists to work in teams, mainly within the schools, providing diagnostic and consultative services, backed up by some direct therapy with children and their parents within the clinic. Some rather considerable initial problems, described below, were brought under control in a reasonably short time, and in 1969, at the request of the three additional school districts in the county, the mental health center submitted a second grant request to help meet the cost of establishing new services in the previously unserved districts and to augment services in the two original districts.

Philosophy, purposes, and policy

Dr. Thomas Glasscock, a child psychiatrist who for some years was director of this mental health center (and is still on the staff part time as a child psychiatrist), and Dr. Morton Flax, an educational psychologist who is director of the school program, have forthrightly asserted the unifying persuasion that underlies the services of this mental health center.

> [We must break] away from the old traditions and enter into a situation in which the needs of children can be met most effectively—which is in the classroom, not back in the clinic in play therapy or the individual treatment room which typifies most mental health programs. School

consultants can no longer just sit back and simply run an evaluation and make recommendations for the schools.[1]

This is by way of saying that the school is the normal socializing institution for the child, while the mental health service is by definition a deviance-intervening agency, and consequently, to the greatest extent possible, the child should be retained, maintained, and served in the former rather than the latter. As translated into a program at this mental health center, it involves actually carrying into the school itself many activities which can only be called psychotherapy.

A hope and an ultimate goal of the mental health center is that schools will assume increasing responsibility for the "total child," so that school personnel will include people with the capability and experience to provide some of the clinical interventions which must, for the time being, be furnished by the mental health center.

Consonant with this viewpoint is the center's practice of providing various intensities of care. Thus, as spelled out below, some children are seen in "low-intensity groups" that meet during the school day, others in groups with a more discernible therapeutic intent that meet at the school but after the regular school day, while others are referred, with and through their parents, for service at the clinic. There are several determinants of where the service will take place. A significant one is the mental health center's conviction that each child should be dealt with at the lowest intensity of care consistent with his problems, and that the status of patienthood should be conferred with caution and reluctance. Another is the willingness of the parent to be personally involved. Wherever the child is to be seen, parental permission is required, and in every case some degree of parental involvement is sought. But if the parent refuses to come for appointments, the child himself may be seen in a school program, if the parent agrees. In those cases where close family involvement seems indicated, the mental health center staff will propose that treatment take place within the center itself. In a very few cases, when the parents decline to pay the sliding-scale fee that is levied there, the child may be seen in the school, where no fees are charged.

Because of the hope that school personnel will eventually be able to provide their own services to troubled and troubling children, classroom teachers, guidance counselors, and school social workers and psycholo-

[1] T. T. Glasscock and M. Flax: "How a Community Mental Health Center Can Provide a Comprehensive Mental Health Program in the Public Schools," in A. Beigel and A. I. Levenson (eds.), *The Community Mental Health Center, Strategies and Programs.* National Institute of Mental Health, in press.

gists are used as cotherapists for the groups meeting in the schools. Said Dr. Flax:

> We believe that we can help to develop proficiency and skill in a guidance counselor that will give him the confidence to do what he's now afraid to do. In fantasy, I can see not only secondary but also elementary schools all having some form of guidance service. We'd like to capitalize on all the talents within the school. Thereafter we could reserve the after-school and clinic groups for children who are having such severe problems that they need a higher order of intervention.

Their treatment philosophy within the clinic they describe as primarily crisis oriented, working within an ideal time span of no more than two or three months. This has come about in part because of pressure for service but also as the result of interest in new treatment techniques and in streamlining. The new director, Dr. Thomas Nelson, aptly describes the treatment, evaluation, and consultation philosophy as eclectic.

> I feel we should fit together whatever contribution we can make, to whomever our client may be, in the interest of meeting his needs. During the past twenty years I have seen many forms of treatment and many methods of evaluation which come and go, while we continue to depend basically on "what makes good sense."

At the same time, there is tolerance for experimentation. Several of the treatment groups were using behavior modification techniques, others were applying the concepts of transactional analysis, and so on. For those children who are brought into the clinic there continues to be a high value on diagnostic evaluation. While the mechanics of evaluation have been streamlined, as described below, the thoroughness of the procedure in this center surpasses that of a number of other mental health centers we have seen.

Administration and staffing

From the outset, the center's eighteen-member board of directors has had several members representing the schools. This reflects the initial interest in starting the outpatient clinic in the mid-1950's, and it also accounts for the particular emphasis on providing services for children. In addition to representation from each of the five major school districts, lawyers, businessmen, pediatricians, and clergymen have been members of the board. More recently, a law enforcement officer, a college student, and representatives from poverty and minority groups have been selected. There have always been housewives, mothers, and professional women on the board.

Still another reflection of the interest in children is seen in the fact that the director for many years, Dr. Glasscock, is a child psychiatrist. Late in 1970 he resigned as director but stayed on half time in the children's service. He was succeeded by Dr. Thomas Nelson, a psychologist with many years' experience with children and adolescents, who had been assistant director of the center for a number of years.

One of the principal administrative problems of this center has been rapid growth. For example, its professional staff increased between 1967 and 1970, from nine to 44. Thus, a great deal of effort has been invested in the mere process of keeping abreast of expansion. The satellite program at Aurora, described later, while reporting to the overall direction at Englewood, has been somewhat autonomous ever since it was created. At Englewood, where the majority of staff are located, a unitization had taken place shortly before our visit. All of the professional staff had been divided into two teams, each assigned to two community areas and school districts; thus, with the Aurora staff, there are now three teams.

Some team members spend their time entirely in the schools, others entirely in the clinic, and others divide their time between school and clinic. More time is allocated to school activities than to clinic activities, primarily because the school grants are the largest part of the program. The assignment of the seventeen members of "Team B" will serve to illustrate.

Exclusively in the clinic	Hours per week	
Social worker (team leader)	10	
Psychiatrist	10	
Psychologist	20	
Social worker	30	
Mental health nurse	40	
	110	

Exclusively in the schools		
Six psychologists	40 each	
Psychologist	20	
Social worker	40	
	300	

Divided between schools and clinic	Hours per week in schools	Hours per week in clinic
Social worker	20	12
Social worker	20	20
Social worker	32	8
Social worker	11	29
	83	69

The assignment amounts to a "geographical unitization"; for example, Team B staff working exclusively in the clinic usually treat only children from Team B's two school districts. This new arrangement was clearly still in the "shakedown" phase and undoubtedly will go through various refinements. It is appealing as an arrangement whereby services can be better focused and monitored in a center where both the size of staff and the amount of service have grown rapidly.

Each team member reports clinically to the chief of his team. In addition, there were discipline chiefs, so that all social workers, for example, related to the chief of social service. (This was subsequently modified, with social workers and psychologists maintaining discipline lines only for the supervision necessary for certification as an ACSW or as a psychologist. Previously named chiefs no longer provide all the supervision; although the chief social worker and chief psychologist are now team leaders, the supervision is parceled out to other staff members who are qualified to provide such supervision.) Beyond this, there is a psychologist designated as director of school services. And we have mentioned that Dr. Glasscock has the role of providing many kinds of children's services. Ostensibly, then, particular staff members could have a number of masters to serve. One of the team leaders expressed it in this way:

> I can be considered the "primary employer" of the people on my team. But some of them have a particular assignment to work in the schools, almost in the sense of a subcontract. Thus they have to keep the director of school services satisfied; he will do a periodic evaluation of each person, and I will consider his evaluation in determining whether an individual remains in his present job or is shifted, whether he gets a raise, and so on. Those team members assigned exclusively to the clinic must similarly satisfy the clinic director. And of course those who divide their time between the school and the clinic must satisfy not only me but also the directors of the clinic and the school programs.

The age ranges reported to us are unusual (0 through 14 for children, 15 through 19 for adolescents), because many years ago, in conjunction with other agencies, this age breakdown had been used. Dr. Nelson feels this is entirely erroneous—that essentially adolescence starts with puberty and if any artificial age ranges are used they should be perhaps 0 through 12 for children and 13 through 18 for adolescents. Certainly, in his view, "a six-foot 13-year-old cannot be considered in the same classification as a three-foot eight-year-old." The total professional staff time available for these categories was 15½ full-time equivalencies for children, five full-time equivalencies for adolescents. All of these staff members have at least a master's degree. As we have described, schoolteachers, other

school personnel, and students frequently participate as assistant therapists in the treatment program. But in this mental health center, the
term "therapist" is reserved for the person with formal training in mental
health.

The Service Activities

Programs in the schools

Because the children and adolescents seen in the schools are not considered patients or clients, and a mental health center record is not opened
for them, we do not have figures as exact as for those children seen in the
clinic. Nonetheless, it is clear that considerably more of the center's
service takes place in the schools than in the clinic. Typically, during
1970, about 300 different children were being seen each month in the
schools, in contrast with about 140 in the clinic.

The Englewood School District team, in a report of its activities during
1969-70, set forth its goals in a manner that seems representative of all
the school efforts within the center.

> Our goals include early identification of children's problems, consultation
> with teachers around management of problem children, consultation with
> parents, treatment of the special child in the school setting, referral when
> necessary for longer-term treatment to other persons or agencies, and
> planning primary prevention and mental health education programs.

This team, like all the others, concentrates its efforts on the lower grades,
partly because the secondary schools have guidance counselors while
most elementary schools do not, but also partly because it is felt that the
interventions with younger children will have a greater payoff.

Because the program centers on the school year, it is subject to a
certain degree of redefinition each fall. At the time of our visit in
October, the school year was just getting under way. The typical adjustments of prior and new mental health center personnel and prior and new
school personnel to each other were still being worked out, and the treatment groups were just getting established. There are 72 schools in the
Arapahoe County catchment area, with a total enrollment of about
50,000. Each school has its own personality, and consequently the
mental health center staff must be sensitive to the directions to take with
each. Obviously the nature of the individual school will largely determine
the extent to which it is willing to collaborate with the center. Despite the
considerable accomplishments of the center in mounting programs, there
have been predictable resistances on the part of individual teachers and

principals. One staff psychiatrist sees the principals as presenting more difficulty than the classroom teachers.

> I think this is because many teachers feel the need for relief from the troubling student behavior that confronts them every day. Furthermore, the principal feels he's captain of the ship, and if he construes that you're trying to change his procedures, he becomes quite angry. He can interfere with our efforts either by approving few or no referrals or by insisting that he be present at every session with an individual teacher.

Another staff member told us that

> some teachers don't buy the program. They resent our being in the school in the first place, and some even seem to try to sabotage our efforts.

A psychiatrist team leader told us that his staff's principal complaint about trying to work in the schools was "the unpsychological-mindedness of some teachers," including particularly those who feel that the proffers of service from the mental health center staff imply that they do not know how to handle their classrooms. One of the school administrators told us:

> While many of the school personnel think the psychological services program is great, others feel there's not much to it. They have their own preconceptions of what the services should be, and if the mental health center people suggest an alternative approach, then they feel they're not being appropriately served. In other cases teachers have said, He's not telling me anything I didn't already know; what I want to know is what to do about it.

These resistances seem not to be particular to the Arapahoe Mental Health Center, but altogether typical of the efforts of mental health programs to bring mental health professionals into the schools. What seems to be called for is patience, persistence, a helpful, nonauthoritarian attitude, and an intense effort to understand the reasons for the resistance. The Arapahoe center appears to have dealt with these problems with both fortitude and understanding. Said one of the psychiatrists:

> In almost every case, after six months to a year, there's been a subtle and rather smooth change, whereby the teacher has come to realize that the mental health center personnel are people who really want to help, who are trying to say, We're available to you if you feel the need to use us in some way.

The typical process for initiating an evaluation of a child begins with the teacher, usually because of a problem either in the child's behavior in the classroom or in his academic progress. She will take the problem to the principal, who then, if he thinks it appropriate, will ask the personnel from the mental health center to review the case with him. If they believe there are indications for evaluating the need for treatment, they determine what kind of diagnostic study should be done. Before any action is taken, however, the parents will be invited to discuss the situation; in many cases they will already have been alerted through contacts with the teacher that something is amiss with their child. One representative from the schools told us that the substantial majority of parents cooperate. If they are felt to be needed, and if the parents agree, psychological tests may be carried out. In particular cases where the school and mental health center personnel think it will yield useful information, they jointly visit the child's home. If the mental health center staff suspect that there may be neurological or other somatic aspects, they request an evaluation by a psychiatrist from the mental health center.

Thereafter the information which has been developed will be presented at a weekly to twice-monthly staff meeting, which may include the teacher, the principal, the school nurse, and the psychologist, social worker, or mental health nurse from the mental health center. A decision is made as to whether a) the child does not seem to need treatment, b) he should be placed in one of the school-hour groups, c) he should be placed in an after-school-hours group, d) he and his parents should be referred to the mental health center for further study.

Formal diagnoses are not made on those children whose evaluations do not involve service at the mental health center. This is largely because those seen in the schools are not counted as patients and partly because there is a reluctance to give the child a label that might create problems for him. The criteria for those contained in the treatment program in the schools are behavioral—those who have difficulty in settling down in the classroom, in focusing on their work, in achieving constructive relationships with their fellow students, and in responding to authority figures. The intention, as one staff member expressed it, is

> to remove them part of the time from the difficult situation, to provide a deliberate, programmed, positive experience, then to return them to the situation where the problems existed in the hope that they can then relate in ways that will be more satisfying and helpful both to themselves and to their teachers.

Most of the children served in the schools are seen in groups. The number of groups at a time, or within a school year, will depend on several factors. To start a group requires the permission of the superintendent in that school district and approval of the principal and the teachers, and a sufficient number of children to justify the expenditure of staff time. For the 1970-71 school year, it was anticipated that there would be about twenty groups involving about one hundred children at a time. While in general the timing is oriented to the semester and the school year, nonetheless the groups are open-ended and there is some turnover. In the previous year, one group that combined children from two different school districts had an average enrollment of 12, but the length of stay ranged from two weeks to the entire year, and thus there were 21 different youngsters involved.

It is common practice, when there are not enough children from a single school, to combine several schools into a single group. At the time of our visit a small group was just beginning—six children from five different schools. Necessarily, this group met after school hours, and there had been complicated logistical problems about transportation, but with persistence these had been worked out. In another case, an after-school group of children from several different schools was taking place in a church near the mental health center.

The nature of the groups ranges from those that concentrate largely on activities to those with a strong emphasis on discussing problems. Most fall somewhere in between. In general, the groups are aimed at providing corrective emotional experiences, catharsis, opportunities to interrelate with peers, and role playing. A staff member described a group that consisted of eight- and nine-year-old girls who were withdrawn, had low frustration tolerance, poor body image, mood swings, poverty of peer relationships, lack of self-confidence, and a generally unhappy time in school.

> The cotherapist and I strive for a fine balance between action and talking. Some of the time our group engages in projects that involve skilled planning on their part, so that they can get a sense of mastering something. Some of the time we split into two smaller groups and talk. The girls are more verbal if they have some goodies, so we come in, we eat cookies, we talk. There's a lot of talk about things that went badly in school. Then we re-create the situation and talk about suitable ways to respond. And sometimes we simply play, because the passive little girls don't know how to play the games that are appropriate for their age.

Concurrently, for those parents who are willing to participate, there are group meetings of parents, so that they "can be kept abreast of the purposes of our work with their children."

The adequacy of physical facilities available for these programs varies greatly from one school to another. In general, they were characterized as "fairly adequate."

Services at the clinic

The Englewood clinic is housed in a wing of the county health department, the building and utilities being provided by funds dispensed by the County Commissioners. The modern building is attractive. The facilities for the center consist of various offices and treatment rooms that seem of good quality but were not particularly designed with a children's program in mind. With the growth in staff, the facilities have been greatly overtaxed, and at the time of our visit plans were being completed for some of the staff to move to more open space that had been rented in an adjacent building. (We are informed that since the visit, new furniture has been added, framed posters hung on the walls, and most clinic offices converted to group rooms which are individually scheduled, hour by hour, as needed by staff members. When not seeing clients in these offices, many of the staff will be in the adjacent building.)

The clinic opens at eight o'clock on Monday through Friday. It is open until five o'clock except on Mondays and Wednesdays, when it stays open until nine. By using the adjacent building, groups are now seen also on Tuesday and Thursday evenings. There are no weekend hours. However, the clinic began providing crisis service 24 hours a day in April 1971, staffed by personnel from the schools and clinic.

Because of the relatively high income in the catchment area, a number of families have incomes that require them to pay substantial fees. If the fee scale calls for a payment that approaches the cost of private treatment, the family is encouraged to see one of the numerous private practitioners in the Denver area, in order that it may reserve its services to those of limited income and at the same time avoid building up a waiting list.

Over the years the procedure for taking a child or adolescent into treatment has been revised and simplified. Several years ago a "traditional" child guidance intake procedure was followed. When a family applied, the parents were first seen by a social worker for two or three interviews. Then the child was scheduled to be tested, and in most cases to be evaluated by the child psychiatrist. After all three disciplines had seen the child, there was a case conference at which plans for therapy were formulated.

Subsequently a lengthy "child and family information" form was developed, to be filled out by the parents prior to their first interview, to obtain a great deal of information about the child's development, school history, health, and so on. This was seen as saving an hour or more of time previously spent in taking the social history. Following this, a procedure was developed whereby the parents, after having submitted the form just described, came in with the child; while the social worker interviewed the parents for about one hour, the chief psychologist or the child psychiatrist interviewed the child. The two staff members then met briefly to discuss their findings, then met with the parents, and, whenever it was felt appropriate, the child as well, for an "interpretation hour." Thus, they accomplished in a two-hour period an evaluation that might previously have lasted over a period of several weeks. If additional psychological, neurological, or other tests seemed indicated, they were done subsequently. With this revised procedure, therapy could be instituted almost immediately.

At the time of our visit, this streamlined procedure was still being used in some cases, but it was clearly giving way to an even less formal process. Since the majority of referrals come from the schools, and most of these are children who have already undergone some degree of evaluation by mental health center personnel assigned to the school, a formalized intake is now done upon indication rather than routinely. There appears to be at least a temporary effort to ascertain whether the diagnostic evaluations did in fact yield information sufficiently useful in developing a treatment plan to justify the time and expense involved. The center director, the child psychiatrist, and other team leaders seemed to have confidence that the professional staff would be alert to indications for further evaluation. One of the staff psychiatrists described the new procedure in this way:

> Cases are not always presented at staff conferences any longer. Rather, each therapist is expected to make a realistic formulation of the dynamics within the family and to set some realistic goals. And at the end of about two sessions it's expected that he will have a pretty clear idea of what's going on in this family. He might say to them, Let's try working together for six sessions. Then we'll review what we've accomplished. If by then he feels that the family hasn't moved along as much as it should, there's nothing to prevent his going on for six more sessions, or for several more months.

The form of treatment has, as this suggests, moved greatly toward a short-term focus, with the goal the amelioration of stress-inducing situations in the present life of the family. Treatment has also moved decidedly toward family therapy, so that, by estimate, the majority of "individual" treatment now involves the child and his parents together, occasionally some of the siblings, and even grandparents and other family members when the circumstances suggest that this might be helpful. Perhaps even more important, treatment in the clinic has moved toward groups. In the recent past, about 30 percent of all the contacts regarding children have been in groups—a fivefold increase over 1966.

During the first half of 1970, 145 children and 62 adolescents were accepted as new patients. Almost two thirds of the children—63 percent —were referred through the schools. Twelve percent were referred by their parents, eight percent by hospital psychiatric services, both public and private, seven percent by family physicians, and a few each from the courts, the welfare department, and private psychologists and psychiatrists. The largest source of referrals for adolescents was families (34 percent), followed by the courts (18 percent), the schools (16 percent), and hospital psychiatric services (15 percent), plus a few each from the welfare department, family physicians, and psychiatrists and psychologists in private practice. The considerable difference in rate from the schools reflects the center's substantial emphasis on services to the elementary schools.

Among these new patients, the diagnoses were as follows:

Children

Adjustment reaction of childhood	39%
Overanxious reaction of childhood	5
Other reaction of childhood	5
Withdrawing reaction of childhood	4
Unsocialized aggressive reaction of childhood	4
Specific learning disturbance	2
Encopresis	2
No psychiatric disorder	4
Not diagnosed	35

Adolescents

Adjustment reaction of adolescence	54%
Anxiety neurosis	7
Passive-aggressive personality	5
Transient situational disturbance	5
Schizophrenia, chronic undifferentiated type	2
Other reaction of adolescence	2
Hyperkinetic reaction	2
Other	7
No psychiatric disorder	9
Not diagnosed	7

There were 86 children and 45 adolescents discharged from the program during that same period. Their status on discharge was judged to be as follows:

	Children	Adolescents
Improved	59%	51%
Unimproved	0	7
Against advice	5	20
Evaluated only	23	11
Unknown	13	11

We asked, for this same period, to know the dispositions of children and adolescents. About 74 percent of children and 27 percent of adolescents were "discharged as requiring no further service." A few of the children (eight percent) were referred to nonpsychiatric agencies for other services. Only one child and two adolescents were transferred to other kinds of psychiatric agencies. A very substantial proportion—49 percent of the children, 64 percent of the adolescents—either were withdrawn from clinic service by their parents or declined to accept treatment following the evaluation procedure.

Included in the above figures are the children and adolescents seen at the Aurora facility. This clinic, set up to be closer to its area of service, describes itself as providing services in the schools and within its offices along lines generally similar to those of the Englewood clinic. The Aurora offices are located in one part of a new building which was built by the local school district in order to provide quarters for a day program operated by the Aurora facility (and described below).

Only about three percent of the children and one percent of the adolescents seen in both the Englewood and the Aurora facilities are on psychoactive medications. These include amphetamines for children with minimal brain damage. Tranquilizers are rarely used, and then only for extremely anxious children. Antidepressants are also rarely used. Each child who is on medication is examined by one of the staff psychiatrists. An individual program is planned for each child on medication. This may vary from weekly visits during initial phases to once every two or three months if long-term medication is warranted.

Among the special services of this center is a therapy group for unmarried pregnant girls. Most of them are welfare recipients who are referred by the welfare department. Few enter before the fourth month of pregnancy, and some, because they do not apply for welfare assistance until they are far along, not until the seventh or eighth month. The group averages about ten, although in the course of a year there may be as many as 60. The staff member who directs it, a psychiatric nurse, described herself as "extremely directive," helping the girls with advice about whether to keep the child or put it up for adoption, the need to avoid further out-of-wedlock pregnancies, and so on.

Emergency services. Emergency calls during clinic hours are accepted by both the Englewood and the Aurora facilities. At Englewood a daily appointment is reserved for any emergency that may arise. At an earlier time, when evening and weekend emergency coverage was provided by Fort Logan Mental Health Center, there were 86 after-hours contacts in one year from the Arapahoe catchment area; these were not separately categorized by age, nor by whether they were considered to be emergencies. It would appear that emergencies concerning children and adolescents average fewer than one per week.

Partial hospitalization. The Englewood facility does not provide any partial hospitalization services for children. The Aurora facility operates a class in conjunction with the Aurora school system, a special education program for children who are educationally handicapped as a result of emotional disturbance. It takes place in a large, well-equipped classroom situated in one end of the building that houses the Aurora clinic. With a staff of three—a social worker who heads the program, a teacher with a master's degree in special education, and a licensed psychiatric technician —the class generally consists of about twelve boys who are eight and nine years old. These children are referred by teachers from Aurora elementary schools. Following evaluation of a proposed child by the mental health center staff, the application is referred to a committee consisting of center staff, the principal of the particular elementary school to which the class is attached, and the staff of the class. The requirements are that the child have average intelligence and that his parents participate in his treatment program. Most of these youngsters remain in the class for the school year. As they improve in behavior, they are assigned part time to regular classes in the school, and are then progressively integrated into the regular program. If their improvement is sustained throughout the year, they are re-entered into their regular class and school. The program consists of academic courses and programmed play and crafts. None of these children are seen in formal therapeutic sessions. Their parents are seen weekly near the beginning of the school year, and later on a monthly basis. Since the start of the program in 1968, seventeen children have been discharged—fifteen to regular classrooms, one to a mental retardation program, one "disposition unknown."

The mental health center does not itself provide partial hospitalization for adolescents. The occasional adolescent who appears to need a full day of treatment is referred to the nearby Fort Logan Mental Health Center, which is usually able to accept the referral, although a waiting period is sometimes involved.

Inpatient service. The mental health center does not provide inpatient service either for children or for adolescents. The children's inpatient service at Fort Logan accepts some referrals but is generally full and therefore a waiting period is often necessary. Colorado Psychiatric Hospital operates an inpatient ward for adolescents, and when that program is needed Arapahoe adolescents can be admitted there.

Dealings with community agencies other than the schools

The welfare department. Both the Englewood and the Aurora clinics receive occasional child and adolescent referrals from the welfare department. In most such cases, because most of the welfare caseworkers are untrained and inexperienced, they encourage their participation in the work-up. The child psychiatrist has provided consultation over the years to the welfare department on particular request.

The courts. One of the staff psychiatrists regularly spends two hours each week consulting to the juvenile evaluation unit of the local juvenile court. Beyond this, case consultation is available to the court at any time on request. Eighteen percent of adolescent referrals are from the court, although, since in this center the "adolescent period" is only from fifteen to nineteen years of age, this does not represent a large number. There were plans at the time of our visit for the center to negotiate a contract with the court to provide evaluations of children being considered for admission to a court-sponsored group home and to provide consultation to the houseparents.

Other agencies. A mental health nurse goes twice a month to the Tri-County District Health Department. At one session she conducts a group meeting "to deal with whatever the staff need to discuss—sometimes internal organizational stress, sometimes a particular patient, sometimes a category of patients." At the other session she is available to any individual nurses who want to discuss a patient or request interpretation of the work they are doing.

Although not in the usual sense a community agency, one public housing project is served by the mental health center staff. Two staff members, a social worker and a psychologist, go twice a week to this project, which had been identified as having a large proportion of multi-problem families. There one staff member meets with the children while the other meets with the mothers.

Mental retardation services

The school teams evaluate children in the mental retardation programs in Arapahoe's five school districts, and provide consultation if requested by the personnel from these programs. A special community program for the severely retarded operates a school for trainable children and a work-shop for those with multiple handicaps, and various members of the mental health center staff have been called on to help screen children being considered for admission to this program.

Training

Of students. One first-year psychiatric resident from Fort Logan is assigned to the Aurora clinic. Two graduate students in psychology from Colorado State University are assigned to the Englewood clinic for their practicum. Six graduate students from the University of Denver School of Social Work are assigned to Englewood for their field placement. Four undergraduate nurses from the University of Northern Colorado and two graduate nurses from the University of Colorado are at Englewood for a three- to six-month placement.

Inservice. The following regularly scheduled inservice training activities take place for staff in the children's and adolescents' services:

• A child seminar conducted by the child psychiatrist.

• Supervisory and consultative hours for those staff members assigned both to the schools and to the clinic.

• Use of less experienced staff members and counselors and teachers as cotherapists.

• Consultation to teachers, counselors, special services personnel.

The experience of the child seminar suggests the need for high-level inservice training to be conducted in small, intensive groups. Said one staff member:

> The child seminar was extremely useful. But the welfare department began to send people over, and there were various students, and in time it grew to 25 or 30 people. The discussions became inhibited; people were hesitant to disclose their problems to so many people. And so the seminars were redesigned for small groups and are once again quite useful. This means that our director of children's services has to spend his time conducting several seminars.

Research

This community mental health center is distinguished by the fact that it requested and got a position of research psychologist in its federal staffing grant. An extremely ambitious program of research was drawn up, with the principal intention of providing information that would enable the center to make its program more appropriate and effective, and also, hopefully, furnish information that would validate the worth of the program to the funding agencies.

For a variety of reasons the research effort got off to a slow start. While at the time of our visit there were many projects in process, few were near completion. The projects for the most part consist of evaluating treatment approaches through pretreatment and posttreatment ratings and testings of various groups of children. Apart from the major consideration that there will be no control groups, the designs seem to be sophisticated and the results should be interesting. Among the projects are the following:

- Evaluation of the effect of treatment on twelve children who were admitted to a day-care school program for six- to ten-year-olds
- Evaluation of a therapeutic summer camp experience using the David's rating scale
- Study of two groups of nine children divided between a behavior modification attack on problem behavior and a Schieffer-type activity group approach
- Determination of the value of a diagnostic remedial battery given to kindergarten and second-grade children, by means of a questionnaire survey of their teachers
- Study of a program designed to reduce truancy at a junior high school
- Analysis of pretreatment and posttreatment reports by teachers concerning a group of children being given medication for hyperactivity
- Evaluation of improvement in children, changes in parents, and professional development of teachers as the result of a three-hour-per-week therapy group conducted at the Englewood clinic
- Posttreatment interviews of children and adolescents seen at the mental health center, involving forced-choice responses concerning the principal presenting complaint, relationships with others, self-concept, and impact on work, family life, leisure time, and social life

Financing

The center is partially financed by federal funds; a 1967 grant provided funds for the center and the original school program, and a second grant, in 1969, provided funds to augment the Cherry Creek and Littleton school programs and to add services for the Aurora, Sheridan, and Englewood school districts.

The budget for the year ending June 30, 1971·was $691,000, from the following sources: federal funds, 38 percent (14 percent for the center and original school program and 24 percent for the expanded school program); school district contributions, 24 percent; State of Colorado, 21 percent; clinic fees, nine percent; Arapahoe County Commissioners, six percent; miscellaneous, one percent.

The center does not have separate breakdowns for children's and adolescents' services, but believes that approximately 75 to 80 percent of the total income, allowing for administrative expenses, goes into these programs.

The prospect for future financial participation by the schools was uncertain. It had been assumed, at the time of submitting the grant applications for school services, that the schools would be able to assume increasing financial responsibility as the percentage of federal funds phased down. However, unanticipated financial pressures had developed within various of the school districts. In general, expenses, particularly salaries, had risen at a higher rate than the total budgets of the school districts. One district suffered a costly strike. In another district, financial problems resulted in an absolute cut of one million dollars in the school budget. The mental health center staff expressed the belief that if federal funding could be extended at the thirty percent level, as provided in the 1970 amendments to the federal mental health centers act, there would be adequate funds to continue services within the schools at approximately the same level. Otherwise, services might have to be cut back. It was anticipated, however, that in any case the schools would continue to contract with the mental health center for certain basic services such as psychological testing and evaluation, in preference to attempting to establish these services for themselves.

The fees levied for services at the two clinics ranged from $2 to $25 per week, depending on the size and income of the household. The schedule was developed some years ago on the basis of fees charged at the University of Colorado. In the recent past an increasing number of clients have had voluntary health insurance that pays part of the fee for outpatient service, and for this reason the center was considering establishing a "standard fee" to be used in billing patients with insurance coverage, with a discount for lower-income families that have no insurance. A family of four with an income of $8,000 pays a weekly fee of $8. Only when income reaches $19,000 does the fee for a family of four reach the maximum of $25, the approximate charge for an appointment with a psychiatrist in private practice in that area. An important difference between private charges and the mental health center's charges is that the fee levied by the center covers all treatment for the family; that is to say, even if the child is seen twice a week and the parents once a week, there is still only a single $25 fee.

Aspirations for the future

The accomplishment of this mental health center in accommodating to rapid growth in staff and service in a short period of time and in establishing harmonious relationships with community agencies was impressive. (The demand for service had increased to the point that the center had temporarily found it necessary to refrain from advertising its availability.)

Among the staff there appears to be a realization that the program still meets only a fraction of the need for services for children and adults. The center would like both to increase the extent of its present activities and to add some new ones. Various people that we interviewed felt that there was a need for many more groups within the schools. We were told that, by observation, each school probably had five or six seriously disturbed children who still had not been brought into the service of the center. The need is felt to considerably expand the consultation services to the courts and the welfare department.

The center would like to help in the creation of nonhospital placements for adolescents who must be temporarily removed from their homes. It would like to collaborate with other agencies in developing preschool programs "both as a social-educational venture and as a primary prevention technique through early screenings and effective group work with these young children and their parents." It would like to join with the local health department to develop primary prevention projects with pregnant women and new mothers, in groups and individually, including providing indigenous substitute mothers for very deprived mothers-to-be and new mothers, under the supervision of experienced clinic staff members.

Dr. Nelson expressed an interest in creating seminar groups to work with parents of normal children who would like to learn how to improve communications within the family.

Dr. Glasscock expressed the hope that in time the center might

> become an all-purpose center in which families could obtain a variety of services pertaining to their own needs, with broad-scale preventive services readily and immediately available.

Said Dr. Nelson, "We would also like to help relatively well-adjusted people become even more self-actualizing, rather than exclusively focusing upon those who are already in some sort of trouble. Hence, to help a well-rounded, successful, achieving person who might at times be subject to some anxieties to realize as much of his potential as possible would be one of our long-range goals." Dr. Nelson says that he has based his goals for many years upon Maslow's hierarchy of needs, each of which must be satisfied before one can go further toward self-actualization. He also sees some of this self-actualization applying to his own staff, hoping that each individual will grow emotionally and professionally.

Western Missouri Mental Health Center

Kansas City

The area served

Western Missouri Mental Health Center is one of Missouri's three state facilities that have responsibility for providing a range of services to the people of their respective designated areas of responsibility. The Western Missouri center is responsible for a 31-county area covering the western third of the state, with a population of 1.3 million. Like all other such facilities with a large service area, the clientele "fan out" in terms of distance, so that the substantial majority of people seen at the facility are in fact from the Kansas City area.

In addition, the center has particular responsibility for the catchment area in which it is located, for which it has a staffing grant under the federal community mental health centers program. This 20-square-mile area consists of the central urban core of Kansas City. Its 52 census tracts were estimated, in 1965, when the application for federal support was submitted, to contain about 197,000 people. The 1970 census disclosed that the area had lost, largely because of urban renewal, far more population than had been supposed—a drop of 60,000, to about 137,000. As a result, the boundary lines of the catchment area may be redrawn.

The area has more than its share of urban problems. It contains over half of all the Kansas City census tracts with a) the lowest median incomes, b) the lowest educational attainment, c) the highest rates of unemployment. It contains a large proportion of the tracts having the highest crime and delinquency rates. It contains nine census tracts whose racial makeup is more than ninety percent Negro, and eighteen of the city's nineteen tracts that have a Negro majority. All of the areas designated by the local program funded through the Office of Economic Opportunity are in the catchment area, and virtually all of the Model Cities neighborhoods.

With an obligation under the terms of the federal grant to give priority to applicants from the catchment area, the mental health center estimates that approximately 25 percent of child and adolescent outpatients

169

and 35 percent of child and adolescent inpatients come from the catchment area.

Other treatment resources for emotionally disturbed children and adolescents include:

- Limited outpatient service, for those who can pay, at Children's Mercy Hospital
- Menorah Medical Center, where children are admitted to the adult psychiatric unit
- Several small, voluntary residential facilities—the Gillis Home, Spofford Home, Niles Home, Ozanam Home, and Marillac School
- The HEED School for autistic children, started within the mental health center but now autonomous
- The Crippled Children's Nursery School
- A number of facilities operated by city and county correctional agencies for children who are neglected or have a charge against them
- A variety of voluntary agencies providing various kinds of family services

Origins

The oldest predecessor of the current services for children and adolescents was the Kansas City Child Guidance Clinic, established in the late 1930's and then, in 1953, merged into the newly created Greater Kansas City Mental Health Foundation. This private foundation was established to help develop public mental health services in Kansas City at a time when state funds were not available to support local services. The Guidance Clinic's Community Chest support was transferred to the foundation, while the formerly administratively independent clinic continued to operate clinically in a largely independent way.

Just prior to the merger the clinic, by means of establishing a Child Research Council at the request of the school system, contracted to provide the first consultation services, specifically in the form of diagnostic and evaluative services for a maximum of one hundred children to be referred from the schools each year. A further form of consultation started the following year—through the Department of Child Psychiatry, the fellows offered consultation at Children's Mercy Hospital on a rotation basis.

In 1954, the Mental Health Foundation and the city government of Kansas City joined forces to create a new facility known as the Psychiatric Receiving Center, in the interest of providing local treatment services. "PRC," as the pioneering facility came to be called, soon began a limited public education program for personnel of community agencies and institutions, much of which was concerned with the mental health needs of children. Concurrently it established an emergency service that served some children, but it was not publicized because of limited resources.

For the most part, PRC during its early years focused its efforts on adults, while the child guidance clinic continued its semiautonomous activities, providing a limited amount of service to selected children.

In 1966, after state support for community-based services had become available, the general hospital operating PRC and the state entered into an arrangement to operate PRC jointly. The name was changed to Western Missouri Mental Health Center. At that time comprehensive programs for children and adolescents were contemplated.

Concurrently, an application was made for a federal community mental health center staffing grant specifically to develop services for children and adolescents. When this grant came into effect, late in 1966, a combined child-adolescent short-term inpatient service was established. A year later, when additional space became available, this service was divided into separate children's and adolescents' services.

Two years later, major emphasis on treating children as outpatients was introduced by Dr. Nicola Katf, who became the superintendent in 1968.

Philosophy, purposes, and policy

The philosophical cast of the services for children and adolescents stems from the particular conception of community psychiatry that developed at this facility during the late 1950's and the 1960's. Dr. Katf did his psychiatric training there, and he believes that the manner in which psychiatric service evolved at PRC during those years was correct, appropriate, and progressive. It incorporates these philosophical facets: *a*) service should be immediately available; *b*) it should be available to all who request it; *c*) it should be as brief in length of contact as is compatible with the condition of the applicant; *d*) it should take place at the lowest intensity compatible with the patient's need; *e*) its primary goal is the relief of psychic pain; *f*) it minimizes individual psychotherapy except in cases where there are clear indications that it is the treatment of choice; *g*) it favors the use of groups as the most appropriate treatment mode for the vast majority of patients. The groups provide the patients with an opportunity to share feelings, to reach new understandings, to be influenced by group structure, and avoid placing the patient in a traditional therapeutic relationship in which verbal modes and expectations may be beyond his understanding.

Dr. Katf feels that these advances, as he clearly views them, in the treatment of adults are quite appropriately incorporated into the design of a service for children and adolescents. He considers them, in a quite outspoken way, to be antithetical to his conception of "traditional child guidance practice."

> The child guidance model [he told us] does not feel itself responsible to serve everybody who requests help, but rather permits one to choose among applicants. It operates during a stipulated workweek and accepts no responsibility for 24-hour coverage. It disdains brief hospitalization, and in general conceives of treatment as long term, sometimes extending over two or three years.

Determined that his philosophy of treatment would be incorporated into the children's and adolescents' services then being developed, Dr. Katf, in the absence of a staff child psychiatrist who shared his persuasions, and unable to recruit one from the outside, assumed the role of acting director of children's services along with his job as superintendent of the total facility. At the time of our visit, after two years of this interim arrangement, he had identified a new staff psychiatrist, Dr. Huseni Poonawala, who shared his convictions, and the job of heading the children's services was to be turned over to him.

Dr. Katf freely acknowledges that the model for children and adolescent services is based on his own experience in adult psychiatry. "I know how often those engaged in services to children assert that children are different. I'm aware of the differences and try not only to modify programs so that they will be suitable for younger patients but also to encourage the staff to modify them for each individual younger patient. But it is easy to assert differences—Negroes are different, Chicanos are different, alcoholics are different—and equally easy to forget that among human beings there are also many similarities." There is, however, one differential socioeconomic determinant of treatment. Whether a given child and his parents are assigned to longer-term dynamically oriented individual psychotherapy or to brief here-and-now-oriented group therapy often depends on social class. Said Dr. Katf:

> We believe that people of lower socioeconomic status often do not conceptualize things in a psychological manner and do not want all the interpretation, but rather want to know exactly how to get out of the rut they're in. Thus one has to be more directive, telling them what to do and how to do it. If you start talking about psychological concepts, it won't work. If someone is poor, black, can barely arrange to get here, and is hurting very much, then in three or four weeks if he's not better

he'll tell you that he doesn't want to come any more, that his problems are solved.

Administration and staffing

Western Missouri Mental Health Center does not have its own board of directors. Rather, the superintendent reports to the director of the state's Division of Mental Health, which is part of the Department of Public Health and Welfare. The director in turn is accountable to a seven-man Mental Health Commission.

The center is organized into seven services: a screening clinic; adult psychiatry; child (and adolescent) psychiatry; an alcohol and drug abuse service; community services, involved principally with service to agencies and fellow institutions; training; and a mental retardation service. All of these have separate directors, separate staff, and separate budgets. All except adult psychiatry and the alcohol and drug abuse section are concerned to one extent or another with children and adolescents.

The staffing arrangements for the various components will be described later, but at this point it is necessary in order to understand the organization of service to consider the general delineation of responsibility. The sole point of entry into service for all age groups is the screening clinic. Among its personnel is a special subunit of four persons concerned exclusively with children, adolescents, and their parents. These personnel are, however, full-time members of the screening clinic and not of the children's service.

The children's (and adolescents') service itself operates outpatient services beyond those provided in the screening clinic, the inpatient services, and the partial hospitalization programs. This service consists of three "mobile" teams made up of mental health professionals and trainees, and of the "fixed" staff that operate the inpatient services and the day hospital.

Both the unusual terminology and the different statuses of the "fixed" and "mobile" teams make the arrangement difficult to understand. A partially apt analogy would be that of one of the better psychiatric services in a general hospital. The screening clinic is much like an emergency service. Staff with intermediate training are assigned there to provide immediate service to all who apply. They are backed up by a cadre of professionals who are much like the house staff backing up the typical general hospital emergency service, available both on call when a particular situation goes beyond either the capabilities or the authority of the emergency service staff (for example, the decision to hospitalize), and for referral for further service.

The "fixed" staff of the day hospital and inpatient services are like the ward staff of a particularly well-endowed therapeutic community. Various nursing, educational, and supporting staff are assigned to provide a 24-hour milieu that includes behavior modification techniques and a programmed educational and activities service. Certainly much that is provided by the fixed staff can be considered *therapy* and *therapeutic*.

The "mobile" team members serve the day hospital and inpatient services much like the attending staff serve the general hospital psychiatric unit. They provide formal psychotherapy, both group and individual, and they act as case managers for the patients while collaborating with the fixed staff in overseeing and evaluating the progress of particular individuals.

Altogether, on the screening, mobile, and fixed staffs, there are about 88 professional personnel who spend the majority or all of their time providing service to children. With the exception of one dissatisfied staff member who was about to leave, those that we interviewed impressed us as enthusiastic, deeply invested in their work, and well informed.

The clinical services

In general. During 1969 there were just under twelve hundred children and adolescents seen for one appointment or more, and in 1970 the number rose to fifteen hundred. The pattern of referral was as follows:

Children
Schools 41%
Family 20
Welfare 13
Courts 10
Family physicians 4
Self-referred 2
Other sources 10

Adolescents
Courts 28%
Family 23
Schools 15
Welfare 8
Self-referred 7
Family physicians 7
Other sources 13

About 25 percent of the applicants found their way into the inpatient services, about two percent to day status, and the rest—almost three quarters—were served either by being retained for the brief service provided by the screening clinic or were processed on for outpatient treatment by the mobile teams. Rather complete data were provided for the children admitted to the inpatient service, but data were not separately available for those seen as outpatients. We thus do not have a picture of what percentage were seen only once, how many were seen in the crisis-intervention groups limited to six visits, and how many were seen for longer periods of time. The maximum capacity for the inpatient and day services are indicated below. We were told that there is no maximum for outpatient treatment, but obviously the time could come when requests for service will exceed the staff time available. That had not happened up to the time of our visit, and every applicant was seen promptly.

The screening clinic. If an application for service for a child or adolescent is made between the hours of 8 a.m. and 5 p.m. on weekdays, it will be handled by one of the four members of the screening clinic staff that have particular responsibility for children and adolescents. These are three master's-level social workers and a "clinical casework assistant." If the application comes by telephone, an appointment is made for the applicant to see a member of the screening clinic staff within the week. If the applicant comes in person, he will be seen with no wait beyond taking his turn in the waiting room. If the call comes after hours, it is taken by the evening and weekend emergency service staff, who are less trained. If the situation is an emergency, the psychiatric resident on call is summoned and can arrange immediate hospitalization. Otherwise, if it involves a child or adolescent, the social worker in charge of the children's unit of the screening clinic is called for advice. This process was instituted because the relatively untrained residents had been admitting children to hospital so freely that many were discharged after only a day or two. In actuality, few calls concerning children and adolescents come in during the evening and night; the head of the children's unit of the screening clinic said that, among these few, rarely is inpatient admission indicated.

The initial interview usually lasts the better part of an hour. The particular individual from the screening clinic staff may then decide that the situation warrants assignment to a short-term crisis-intervention group without further evaluation or work-up.

These groups, open-ended and with each family scheduled to attend from four to six times, are run jointly by one of the screening clinic staff and some member of the mobile teams. They were created in the belief that many of the kinds of problems and situations that lead people to apply for help from a mental health service are temporary and situational, and that a moderate amount of support and the passage of time will prove to be all that is necessary for the person to experience relief and to continue coping with his day-to-day responsibilities. If a child or his parents complete the stipulated maximum number of crisis-intervention sessions and still seem to need further help, referral can then be made to a "non-crisis group." (In actuality this rarely happens.)

Crisis groups are focused on family changes or family problems, teaching family coping mechanisms through role playing, interpretation, and confrontation. Families are always seen together in their crisis groups; usually the parent and the identified patient are seen, and other siblings are sometimes included. The approach is concrete and directive; often weekly assignments are given to parents around a particular behavior of the child, and successes or failures are reported the following week. The cases best helped with such an approach are those of families having discipline and control problems with children, and those dealing with feelings around a crisis resulting from a loss, such as death.

Crisis groups are also used in ongoing evaluation of the family; these families could rejoin the group if a new crisis developed as much as a year later.

Typically there are about four crisis-intervention groups in process at any given time.

The mobile teams. Although exact figures were not available, it seems that most applicants are referred to the mobile team rather than being held in the screening clinic's crisis-intervention groups. By one estimate, 85 percent of all children and adolescents, and their parents, are seen by the psychiatric residents or child psychiatry trainees.

There are three mobile teams, one for children and two for adolescents. Each is headed by a child psychiatrist and contains as well a psychologist, a social worker, a nurse, a guidance counselor, a psychiatric resident who is doing his child psychiatry rotation, and a fellow in child psychiatry.

Once the application has been referred from screening clinic to mobile team, the individual to whom the case is assigned may review it and decide that sufficient information is in hand to warrant assigning the family to therapy; or he may ask for psychological tests, physical and neurological examinations, or additional background material. After all of the requested information is in hand, the case is discussed by the entire mobile team at its weekly meeting and a decision reached as to the nature of treatment indicated.

This may consist of individual psychotherapy, most of which is done by the trainees in child psychiatry. At a given time in 1970 about eighty children and adolescents were being seen individually. When necessary, the parents are also seen, by either the therapist or a social worker. Or it may consist of referral to any of a number of groups. Typically about fifteen different groups are in process, ranging in duration from a few weeks to about six months. There are groups for children alone, for adolescents alone, for their parents alone. There are "groups" consisting of a single large family. There are family groups in which the parents and children from two or more families meet together. Most groups meet once a week.

The established hours for the mobile teams are from 8 a.m. to 5 p.m., Monday through Friday. But several of the groups, typically crisis groups, are scheduled to meet in the evening, to facilitate attendance by working parents. One special evening group is made up of parents of children who are in treatment in the children's service at St. Joseph State Hospital, about 45 miles away, which serves Kansas City.

Altogether there are usually about one hundred children and adolescents being seen in groups at a given time. Some of the groups see the parents together with the children for part of the time, following which the children are taken out by one therapist while the other discusses with the parents what is happening in the group. Other groups see the parents and the children concurrently and the two therapists coordinate their efforts later on. All members of the mobile teams participate as group leaders, and every group has two therapists.

Data were not available about attrition from the groups, but this was estimated at about 40 percent. (These are the cases in which termination occurs not at the advice of the therapist, but simply because the patient stops coming.) Compared to public adult psychiatry, this figure appears to be low. Dr. Poonawala said that a limited amount of contact with these dropouts indicated that they stop coming mainly because the parent perceives that the child's condition has improved, but also in some instances because the parents could not see that anything useful or helpful was happening.

Included among these groups are crisis groups for adolescents and children and specific selected groups, such as groups for adolescents in correctional facilities, run by the county juvenile court; re-entry groups for patients discharged from the state hospital; groups for parents of children in the state hospital; child-management groups for parents who may need help in providing consistency and controls; groups for black adolescents; and racially mixed groups in recently integrated schools. The approach is eclectic when all groups are considered; however, each therapist and each group is consistent in its approach, which is selected by the therapist and the supervisor. Some groups use a combination of approaches, determined by the needs of different clients.

Factors considered in making assignments to groups include the age of the patient, the type of pathology, the focus of the group, and the interests of the family. These groups vary in length from three to six weeks up to six to twelve months depending on the goals.

The groups are also used to train the residents and fellows. A few of them use an analytical approach; others are supportive and directive. Some use the transactional approach while others have better results with reality therapy. In general, patients are asked to learn to put feelings into words and to solve problems rather than act them out.

Partial hospitalization. The mental health center sets a capacity of ten each for children and adolescents on day status. This is not a separate program, but rather one in which the patients on day status come into the center from 9 a.m. to 3 p.m. to join the inpatients while spending the rest of the time in their own or a foster home. The day patients are a mixed group; some are those who are undergoing extensive evaluation and have home environments that seem satisfactory, while others are children and adolescents who have "graduated" from inpatient status and are thus being phased down in intensity of treatment. No limit is set on the length of time one may remain on day status, but in actuality the average stay is only six to eight weeks. At no time has either the children's or the adolescents' service reached the stipulated capacity for day patients. The range on the children's service has been from four to seven, and the typical day census is about five. At the time of our visit, there were no adolescents at all on day status; this was principally because the school year had just started and the four adolescents who had been on day status during the summer months had been discharged in order to have a try in school. The range of day patients on the adolescent service has been from two to eight, and the typical day census is about four.

The children's inpatient program. The children's ward is located on one floor of a large wing of the recently renovated mental health center. There is a capacity of 23, provided in rooms for two and three; adequate lavatory facilities; a large dayroom-dining room; and several professional offices. The large and well-equipped classrooms and activity rooms are on the floor above. There is a large outdoor recreation area.

The stated purpose of the inpatient service is to provide diagnosis and short-term treatment. The limit on stay is generally viewed as two months. Many of the children stay a shorter time, since the principal purpose of admitting them—particularly the 25 percent that are referred by the court—is to make an intensive diagnosis, usually requiring a stay of two weeks or less. In some cases children who are grossly psychotic or severe management problems are quickly evaluated as requiring longer-term treatment than the center can provide, and are soon transferred to the state hospital. The average stay is, in actuality, less than a month. At the same time, exceptions to the two-month limit are sometimes made, and at the time of our visit there were two children in special circumstances who had been inpatients for more than a year.

The inpatient service has not at any time reached maximum capacity, and the usual range of census is from eight to twelve. In part, this is accounted for by the fact that the staff are reluctant to admit children to the inpatient service, and even when they recommend doing so, the parents are often unwilling to have their children hospitalized. The readily available outpatient treatment also undoubtedly provides for many families the relief and support without which inpatient treatment might be necessary. There were, in 1970, only fifteen children from the catchment area in the state hospital. Consequently, when one considers the large population that the center serves, and the long-perceived shortage of inpatient facilities for mentally ill children, the low utilization poses something of a mystery. One can wonder if there are unidentified severely disturbed children who should be brought to treatment; yet this mental health center has considerable dealings with the various agencies that ordinarily identify disturbed children, and it provides service to all who are referred. We are confronted once again with the fact that there are no definitive epidemiological data that enable one to formulate the needed inpatient capacity for mentally ill children.

There are seven nursing staff each on the day and the evening shifts. Each shift is headed up by a registered nurse, and the day shift has an additional nurse. All of the rest of the nursing staff are aides and attendants. Three attendants are on duty for the night shift. During the day there are three teachers, all with bachelor's degrees, and two with some training in special education. There is also a full-time guidance counselor with a master's degree and a half-time speech pathologist. The activities program is supervised by a half-time occupational therapist, who has a team of activity instructor and activity aide for the day and the evening shifts.

A highlight of the center is the work of the "nonprofessional" staff on this inpatient unit. These people, some with no formal education beyond high school, seemed to deal in warm, appropriate ways with the children, to have good relationships with them, to be deeply involved in the behavior modification, educational, and activity program.

Usually a few volunteers are involved in the inpatient program, typically about six devoting four hours per week each, helping out particularly in the educational and activity aspects.

Forty-eight children were admitted as inpatients during the first half of 1970. Almost half of these were diagnosed as having a behavior disorder, and the modal group (21 percent) was a subcategory of this diagnosis, those with unsocialized aggressive reactions of childhood. The other diagnoses were as follows:

Transient situational disturbances	10%
Mental retardation	10
Neurotic disturbances	8
Personality disorders	8
Hyperkinetic reactions of childhood	8
Withdrawing reactions of childhood	8
Overanxious reactions of childhood	6
Psychotic disorders	6
Other behavior disorders	4
Special symptoms	2
Other miscellaneous diagnoses	6

One index of the remarkable social disorganization of the families of these children is that fewer than half come from intact homes; the head nurse estimated no more than a third.

Some of our children behave in a pretty normal way [she told us], but they come from the most severely disturbed families, with the most chaotic backgrounds. The histories of the children are like nightmares. When there is a family to work with, we involve them as much as they're willing, and many of them do cooperate because, even if there's some hostility mixed in with it, they're desperate and really do want help for their children. But sometimes we can't send the children back home, because the situation is such that it would simply undo what we have been able to accomplish with them.

She described the majority of children, about two thirds, as coming from white, lower-middle-class backgrounds.

Dr. Poonawala described three categories of children for whom inpatient admission is appropriate: those who are dangerous to themselves, those who are dangerous to other people, and those who are severely disorganized. There are some of each among these children. A larger category is those admitted for evaluation at the direction of the juvenile court. Because the center feels that such children can often be suitably evaluated as outpatients, it has increased its activities at the court, some-

times providing on-the-spot evaluations. Nonetheless, the judge sometimes decides that a particular child should have an inpatient evaluation,
and the center has no course but to admit him; by one estimate, in no
more than half of these cases is inpatient admission really indicated.

Every child admitted to the inpatient service is given a physical examination and a battery of psychological tests. The WRAT and Peabody
tests are given as a quick measure of achievement and intelligence, to help
the teacher to plan the child's curriculum. The WISC, Bender-Gestalt,
and Frostig are often administered for determining or detecting level of
intelligence, perceptual-motor development, organicity, and so on. Tests
such as the Rorschach and the TAT are used less frequently, to evaluate
and diagnose psychoses, when the interview has failed to completely con-
firm one. Most children are given a psychiatric, neurological, and educational assessment. When indicated, many are seen by one or more
members of either the fixed or the mobile staff for individual or group
psychotherapy, family therapy, or combinations of these.

The day begins for the children at seven thirty. They make their beds,
dress themselves, have breakfast, help to clean up afterward, take their
medication, and at nine o'clock report to the classroom. Two and a half
hours are then divided between an academic class and an activity group.
After lunch the children return to the classroom for another activity
group, followed by recreation. At this point the day-treatment children
go home, the inpatients return to the ward and have dinner. The evening
is spent in indoor games.

Throughout the day a behavior modification program is in operation,
whereby the children may earn points by conforming to the requirements
and expectations of the staff. Originally, the behavior modification program required the children to earn their dessert and crackers but not the
rest of their food. This was changed four years ago to allow only positive
reinforcement to be used; that is, food, treatment, and normal activity
could not be withheld. To reward the patients, points that have been
earned can be exchanged for outings, special treats, and merchandise in
the "country store." Occasionally, with an autistic child, the behavior
modification has been extended to the point of requiring points for any
food at all. Said the nurse:

> Some of our staff shook their heads at the prospect of letting any child go
> without food. But we tried this with one four-year-old girl who was
> extremely withdrawn and bizarrely destructive. She came here not talk-
> ing and always hitting her head on the floor. But with the point system
> we finally made a breakthrough with this child, and brought her to where
> she could feed herself and then dress herself.

Because the average stay is a matter of less than a month, the school program does not really attempt to keep each child abreast of the academic work he would be doing in his regular classroom. Rather, it is an effort to keep him habituated to schoolwork. An important concurrent purpose of the educational program is to assess academic capabilities, in the interest of identifying deficiencies that may stem from or contribute to the emotional disorder. The teacher's main purpose, then, we were told, is

> to diagnose the educational problems, the behavioral problems that affect classroom accomplishment, and to correlate these with the findings of other staff members so that we can make an informed recommendation to the public school, if the child is to go back there, or to the state hospital, if he is to be transferred there, or wherever he might go.

Of 51 children who were discharged from the inpatient service during the first half of 1970, eight were returned to the jurisdiction of the juvenile court. Of the rest, almost half (49 percent) were returned to their parents or foster home, with follow-up outpatient treatment at the mental health center; 42 percent were transferred to the state hospital; five percent were transferred to another psychiatric facility; and one child each was placed in a foster home and in a hospital for retarded children.

The adolescent inpatient service. Located on another floor of the same wing as the children's inpatient service, the adolescent inpatient service has a capacity of thirty. The physical facilities are similar to those for children. Classrooms and activity rooms for the adolescents are located on the same floor but on a separate wing of the building. The numbers and kinds of staff positions are approximately twice that of the children's ward.

The adolescent service also has never reached its maximum capacity, although the percentage of occupancy is consistently higher than in the children's service. The census varies from 20 to 25. A principal reason for the higher utilization rate is the larger number of court referrals.

During the first half of 1970, there were 201 admissions. By far the most common diagnosis was behavior disorder of adolescence (27 percent). Other diagnoses were as follows:

Transient situational disturbances	17%
Psychotic disturbances	12
Personality disturbances	10
Neurotic disturbances	9
Mental retardation	9
Organic brain syndromes	4
Others	10

Regarding the behavior patterns of the adolescents admitted to the floor or asking for outpatient services, a large number (almost half) have problems with school, ranging from minor disruptive behavior to truancy, theft, drug use, and assaultive and destructive behavior, necessitating either suspension or referral to the facility. Many of these adolescents have an overlay of learning disabilities, borderline intelligence, or organic impairments.

Nearly a fourth to a third of the referrals are from the juvenile courts; here the behavior again may run the gamut from minor thefts or infringements of the law to larceny, assault with a dangerous weapon, or even homicide. Almost one in four referrals carries a history of either drug experimentation or abuse.

The behavior most difficult to contain on the ward is not so much the assaultive or disruptive, but rather running away, not conforming to acceptable norms, and at times verbal acting out. Most patients settle down to ward routines after an initial restless period of about 24 to 48 hours.

Believed both to contribute to and to stem from the emotional disturbance are the academic deficits that characterize many of the adolescent patients. Said one staff member:

> I was amazed when I learned that many of these young people who had reached the tenth and eleventh grades in school were reading at a second-grade level. We don't have most of them with us long enough to do much remediation; the most we can do is to point out the need, and quite often the schools say, We're sorry, but we don't have the resources either.

Newly admitted patients are given a printed set of regulations and policies concerning such matters as visiting hours, telephone privileges, smoking restrictions, passes, canteen privileges, and so on. They are also told about the work required of each patient, about restrictions for infractions of rules, about the weekly ward "patient government" meeting, and so on.

The patients get up at six thirty, clean their rooms, and breakfast. Their day is much like that of the children, except that somewhat more time is devoted to academic subjects. Classes include English, mathematics, science, social living, and home economics. During a free period in the afternoon a number of the patients are involved with staff members in psychological tests, physical examinations, individual and group therapy, psychodrama, role playing, and family therapy with members of the two mobile teams assigned to adolescents.

The behavior modification program was introduced in 1967. Originally set up to give tokens for desired behavior, it was changed to a point system when a problem arose about tokens being stolen. According to the number of points earned, the patient may be on any of five levels: first level, ward restriction; second level, which allows him to leave the ward only for scheduled activities; third level, which allows him to go to the cafeteria whenever he is free of other responsibilities; fourth level, which gives all privileges except using the telephone and visiting the canteen; and "bonus level," which gives all privileges, including trips outside the hospital and weekend passes.

Each patient receives a card each day, which is punched for each approved behavior. These punches may be used to buy whatever the patient wants at the ward store. The following guidelines were established to aid the staff in implementing approved behavior:

1. Punches must be accompanied wherever possible with verbal praise.
2. Verbal praise should consist of telling the individual exactly what he is doing correctly in as precise language as possible.
3. Students stating that they are owed punches are to be ignored.
4. The patient is responsible for his own card; if it is lost, the point sheet will be used as a backup to substantiate the number of punches gained.
5. The patient must earn the punches. They are not simply to be given out; he must know exactly why he earned each punch.
6. At no time is a punch or punch card to be taken away from a child as a punitive gesture. Once he has earned punches they are his, and he is entitled to cash in the number he has earned.

Examples of observable positive behavior to be rewarded are: being helpful to others; good group behavior in activities, school, and ward games; constructive use of time when not engaged in a structured or planned activity, for example, reading, knitting; appropriate mealtime behavior; care of materials, room, and one's property; and one special "target behavior" for each child, which is decided upon by the staff and noted on his card.

The ward is left unlocked, and occasional patients will leave without permission. Substantially all of them are returned in a very short time. Those who have left are then placed on ward restriction for three days, must wear hospital clothing, and so on.

There were 181 adolescents discharged from the inpatient service during the first half of 1970. Twenty-one of these were returned to the jurisdiction of the juvenile court. Of the rest, almost three quarters (73 percent) were returned to their homes, with recommendation for follow-up treatment at the mental health center. Twenty-two percent were transferred to the state hospital. Three percent were referred to other treating agencies, and foster home placement was arranged for another three percent.

Consultation and other community services

While many staff members whose primary assignment is elsewhere participate to some extent in working in the community, the center has a separate community service which works in three major areas.

• Patient-oriented activities, such as casefinding of clients in contact with community agencies, screening of prospective patients, home visits to people who have been in treatment at the center, and so on.

• Consultation and education programs for a broad variety of community agencies, typically in the form of specific programmed seminars.

• A "development" responsibility, through which the staff attempt to identify gaps in services of all kinds and to collaborate with other agencies to develop the missing services.

As an example of the last, John Hassinger, a social worker who is chief of the Community Liaison Service, as it is called, provided this example. When one of his staff members working with particular schools discovered that many of the children were coming to school without breakfast, he went to the Human Resources Corporation (the local OEO program) and acquainted them with this situation, which led to their setting up satellite food distribution centers.

The staff of fourteen people consist by discipline and training of the following: the director, who is an M.S.W., eight M.S.W. community workers, and five registered nurses. Three of these, the director, a community worker, and one registered nurse, are Negroes.

This staff is deployed geographically, with five persons assigned to the federally funded catchment area, the rest to three satellite facilities which the center operates outside the federal catchment area. In addition to the geographic assignment, there is some degree of specialization by agency, with particular people devoting most of their efforts, for example, to schools. These staff members are involved with clients and prospective clients of all ages, but Mr. Hassinger estimates that about half of the total effort is directed toward the needs of children and adolescents.

When asked what competence and expertise he thinks the mental health professional brings to the problems of social disorganization, he cited two: a sensitivity that he believes characterizes most people with training and/or experience in the mental health field, and an understanding of interpersonal and interagency process, particularly cause-and-effect relationships. When we asked him if the center's concept of its appropriate role with community agencies is consonant with the expectations of these agencies, he said there had been some problems.

> The agencies often want to use us as investigators, as people who can lower the boom on particular people they don't like—for example, to come into the agency and take away a troublesome youngster. They tend to equate us with welfare workers. Beyond this, there's a real "trust gap" in the black community. They're reluctant to buy anything from us.

Altogether his staff, along with personnel from other services that spend some time in community activities, is dealing with 33 agencies. He believes that, while the result has not been measured and would perhaps defy measurement, these activities do influence the lives of a great many people. He cites a particular training program that involved ten staff members of the welfare department, each of whom had a caseload of about one hundred clients. As a result of what they learned, he believes, some favorable effect touched the lives of a thousand people. He estimates that the number of people who are thus indirectly affected by the community activities of the center staff would be at least twenty thousand.

In considering the center's activities with various agencies, as described below, it is important to realize that the relationships develop in one of two ways: either at the request of the agency (including, for example, a particular school) or because the center offers its services to some agency where from observations there seem to be problems that the center could help to solve (for example, a particular school that refers a disproportionate number of young people for treatment). Dr. Katf does not seek to expand these community activities to the point that every individual schoolteacher (or even school) would be involved in a continuing consultation relationship; the goal, in other words, is to provide service when there is a specific indication and not as a routine matter.

The schools. The schools comprise a major source of referral, and the center has accordingly focused much of its effort on attempting to help improve the competence of teachers in mental health matters and to effect a practical referral system. In the year prior to our visit, center staff had conducted nine training and consultation programs for teachers, each typically involving about 150 teachers and lasting for about two weeks. The content focused on such matters as management of students and improving communications between teachers and administration, between teachers and parents, and between teachers and students. The center also offered to the schools a set of tapes developed by Dr. William Glasser; these had been used with evident satisfaction in the Los Angeles County schools to acquaint teachers and administrators with "a new approach to handling problem children." About ten Kansas City schools had taken up the offer. This new approach is conceived along the line that it is not necessary to have special education classes in the schools. Problem children, retarded children, and those with learning disabilities are maintained in the regular classroom, and then are assisted by a resource teacher who helps the regular teacher in setting up the programs for these children. These additional teachers serve as helpers as well as consultants.

To facilitate the referral process, a member of the center's screening clinic who has a master's degree in special education developed a "behavior index packet," which asks for judgments about many aspects of the behavior of children and adolescents. When any schoolteacher or principal suggests that a particular child may need treatment, the center sends out the behavior index packet as a means of obtaining a great deal of background information. Part of the packet is filled out by the parents and in this way the parents' perception of the child's problem is obtained. In a recent 12-month period, 220 packets were sent out and 219 of these were returned.

Each returned packet is discussed at a weekly meeting of the screening counselor, the screening social worker, the child psychology consultant, and the assistant director of community services. In some cases it seems evident that no more is required than suggesting that the child be transferred to another classroom, or that there be some modification of approach to him. Such cases are usually handled within the school, by having a member of the mental health center staff go there to discuss the child with the teacher and/or principal. The content of other responses suggests the need for evaluation, and accordingly a referral is made to the mobile child or adolescent team. Among the 219 cases just mentioned, about half did in fact become treatment cases at the mental health center. The development of the packet was done by a single individual, and it has been neither standardized nor validated. In our discussions about it with several staff members and one representative of the schools, it was clear that it was well regarded and that there was considerable confidence in it.

The school personnel that the center deals with include particularly the social workers, since these are the people to whom teachers and principals usually turn when they think a child may be emotionally disturbed. One of the social workers told us that from two elementary schools he received 150 referrals in a recent year. The great majority of these involved situations which he felt he could clearly identify as not calling for evaluation for emotional disturbance. He did, however, make ten referrals to the center. These were children who

> were fighting with their classmates and their teachers, were absent from school frequently, were quite hyperactive and unable to concentrate very long, did not seem to be interested in anything.

He felt he could identify only two children in the total of five schools he serves who were grossly disturbed.

The welfare department. Collaboration of mental health center staff with the welfare department started in 1966, in the particular form of consultation to the Jackson County welfare office. This service was initially for ex-patients who lived in a housing project and were receiving public assistance, but it later involved regular tenants and welfare recipients. Simultaneously, the center staff met with the caseworkers for case presentations, role playing, and reading assignments intended to enhance their skills and techniques in casework relationships. In the interim, such consultations have become available across the board to any welfare worker requesting it. At a later time, six mental health center staff members conducted a six-month sensitivity training course for welfare staff "to help them gain greater self-awareness in their day-to-day performance as 'helping persons.' " It also conducted a nine-week series on crisis intervention.

The welfare department does not refer prospective clients to the center for evaluation to determine whether they are eligible to receive welfare payments on the basis of psychiatric disability. Rather, such cases are referred to private physicians (not necessarily psychiatrists), evidently because the welfare department views the center as a treating rather than an evaluative facility. Individual welfare workers are authorized to recommend to particular clients that they apply to the center for treatment, and occasionally they do so. However, they may not take any action if the client declines the suggestion.

The courts. In 1968 the juvenile court for the county in which Kansas City is located established its own "treatment, diagnostic, and research unit" to assist in the total work-up of children being brought before the court for delinquent and criminal acts, and, when indicated, for a more specific psychiatric evaluation. The considerable majority of cases are handled within this unit, with some support from the mental health center; on most days when the court is in session, one or more professionals from the center's child psychiatry service are actually present at the court helping out with the evaluation and screening.

This unit does, however, frequently refer children who appear to need a more intensive evaluation than it can provide. During the six months prior to our visit 115 adolescents and 26 children had been referred to the center. About a third of these were referred by the judge, in which case, as we have indicated, the center has no choice but to admit the child, even if the staff should think that an outpatient evaluation would be appropriate. A large percentage of the cases he refers involve drug use, including marijuana. All homicide cases are automatically referred. ("Homicides by juveniles used to be rare," a court worker told us, "but they've become quite common.")

The remaining two thirds of court-referred child and adolescent cases are referred by juvenile officers, oftentimes "because they're stuck." During one recent six-month period two staff members from the mental health center conducted weekly training sessions, consisting of case discussions and case planning, attended by 25 to 30 juvenile officers.

Children from three juvenile shelters and detention centers operated by the court are brought into the mental health center for weekly group therapy sessions.

The police. The mental health center has been involved for many years in training police recruits. This began in the early days of the old Psychiatric Receiving Center, which collaborated with the local mental health association in the training course.

At present each police recruit spends 28 hours in classes dealing with theoretical and clinical aspects of mental illness, and about six hours participating with the ward staff in the children's and adolescents' inpatient unit. In small group sessions, the staff discusses with the recruits ways of approaching and handling problem behavior, and how to communicate with children and adults. A psychiatrist discusses legal aspects and implications of mental illness. Said a staff member:

> Thus, the policemen are made better aware of the facilities available to them, the services offered, and methods of communicating with and responding to child and adolescent behavior.

The center was in process of preparing a section for the police manual on child and adolescent behavior and how to deal with families in crises concerning their children.

Policemen occasionally bring children and adolescents who appear to be disturbed directly to the mental health center.

OEO program. A social worker was assigned to the Human Resources Corporation to help in case planning and to be the liaison with the mental health center. The staff of the community services program conducted a

16-week program for the "outreach staff" to improve "their interview, assessment, and implementation skills," and it ran a two-day seminar for child-care workers. Beyond this, there have been numerous consultations, on request, concerning particular problem children.

Well-baby clinics. The center was planning to conduct a study of the effectiveness of prenatal and postnatal group counseling of first-pregnancy mothers by public health nurses in well-baby clinics. The study will continue over a seven-year period.

Other agencies with which the center is involved include the clergy, the recreation department, and the Model Cities program.

BEYOND THE ACTIVITIES DESCRIBED ABOVE, this mental health center has provided a variety of other kinds of supporting and training services to many other agencies and practitioners, including fellow hospitals, general practitioners, and pediatricians. The scope of its community services is perhaps as broad as that of any mental health facility in this country.

Mental retardation services

Western Missouri Mental Health Center is not a retardation facility by official designation, and while it has handled a number of retarded children, these have all been children who have manifested psychotic or other behavior problems in addition to retardation.

Training

The center is the principal training facility for the Department of Psychiatry of the Kansas City Division of the University of Missouri School of Medicine. The director of training in child psychiatry, Dr. Richard Harte, is himself a child psychiatrist. There is another child psychiatrist on the faculty half time, and each of the three child psychiatrists heading up the mobile teams participates in the training program.

At the time of our visit there were four fellows in child psychiatry, plus six residents assigned to the children's service for their six-month rotation in child psychiatry. Each is attached to one of the mobile teams. A considerable amount of the activities of these men is directed to individual psychotherapy, since considerable experience in this area is the major focus of the training program. While a sizable amount of service is thus provided, the fit of program emphases (see the earlier statement of Dr. Katf) is less than perfect. Dr. Katf is, in any case, persuaded that the administrative and group experiences which the program provides are beneficial to these trainees.

As with a great many other psychiatric residency programs, there is no course content on "the American family," nor on the values and life style of the lower-class Negro family in particular. Since a large percentage of the trainees have come here to study from other countries, such courses might facilitate their approach to all American patients and to ghetto patients in particular.

Group therapy and family therapy are electives, not required courses.

Because of cutbacks in funds, there were no psychology or social work trainees at the time of our visit.

Financing

The children's and adolescents' services operated during fiscal 1970-71 on a budget of approximately $662,000, which came mainly from three sources: the State of Missouri, 58 percent; the NIMH staffing grant, 21 percent; and United Fund money channeled through the Greater Kansas City Mental Health Foundation, eight percent. The cost of operating the inpatient service is calculated at approximately $58 per patient-day; otherwise the financial data are not in such form as to allow one to ascertain the cost of particular units of service, such as an outpatient appointment. Furthermore, the budget figure cited above does not include a good deal of child- and adolescent-directed service provided by such other divisions as the screening clinic and the community service, nor does it include the separately funded services of the trainees in psychiatry and child psychiatry.

Patient fees are set on a sliding scale which starts at zero and takes into account the family income and size of family. For the inpatient service, the fee would approximate $1.05 per day for a family with income of $2,400 per year, and would go up to approximately $58 per day for a family earning just under $15,000.

Collections from patients and from all third-party sources go into the general revenues of the State of Missouri.

Aspirations for the future

Western Missouri Mental Health Center identifies the following goals:

1. Closer cooperation and coordination with the juvenile court, the welfare department, the clergy, and others, so that it might achieve a comprehensive program for children, avoiding duplication as well as

providing services tailored to the needs of the children rather than the needs of the agency.

2. Development of earlier casefinding and intervention, so that inpatients may be limited to severe and socially crippling cases.

3. Homes for group living within the community instead of long-term state hospital stays, using local schools and facilities as resources.

4. Training medical students in child development and family care.

5. Research, including well-baby clinics and program evaluation.

The Children's Re-Education Center
Greenville, South Carolina

THE COMPREHENSIVE COMMUNITY MENTAL HEALTH CENTER in Greenville, South Carolina, consisting of the Marshall I. Pickens Hospital (a division of the Greenville Hospital System) and the Greenville Area Mental Health Center, provides through its combined resources a broad range of mental health services which are available to children and adolescents living in Greenville County. The Children's Re-Education Center (Re-ED) is only one of several components, but it was the particular reason for our decision to visit Greenville. As developed by Dr. Nicholas Hobbs at George Peabody College for Teachers in Nashville, and later extended to other cities in Tennessee, the Re-Education model has had considerable attention as one means of serving particular disturbed children. Rather than visit any of the facilities in Tennessee, we selected Greenville precisely because the Re-ED program there is a component of a federally supported community mental health center.

Our field work therefore focused largely on the fairly small Re-ED component, with relatively little time spent with the staff who are furnishing other mental health services to children and adolescents. But because the program in its entirety is an attractive one, we will briefly describe those other components before concentrating on the Re-ED program.

The responsibilities of and interrelationships between the various components are complicated and difficult to understand. First of all, the Greenville Area Mental Health Center is not a federally supported community mental health center but rather is an autonomous program, operated and supported by the county and the state primarily for indigent patients, which provides outpatient treatment to all age ranges, a portion of emergency services, and a program of consultation and education activities. As an already operating service, it was not eligible to receive federal community mental health center funds. It is, however, in one quite real sense a *portion* of the community mental health center, since through an affiliation agreement it provides those services just enumerated.

Thus, in a sense the mental health center is a consortium of the Greenville Area Mental Health Center and the Marshall I. Pickens Hospital. The Pickens Hospital, as a component facility of the Greenville Hospital System, is the entity that applied for and received federal funds both to help build its present facility and to meet the expenses of staffing. As such it provides inpatient and day treatment for adolescents and adults, walk-in emergency services through the general emergency room of the Greenville General Hospital, and includes the Children's Re-Education Center for treatment of children from the ages of six to twelve.

The area served

This community mental health center has Greenville County as its area of responsibility. With a present population of 250,000, the county has experienced substantial growth during the past decade. Some years ago the considerable majority of its economic production was in the textile industry; in recent years a number of new industries, such as chemicals, fabricated metals, and transportation equipment and machinery have moved in, and with them an influx of population from other parts of the country. The growth is attributed to a favorable location, midway between Atlanta and Charlotte, and a good water and electricity supply. The median household income in 1970 was about $9600. Because the catchment area comprises a metropolitan area, it contains a complete range of socioeconomic characteristics. About twenty percent of the population is Negro. There are 56,200 children enrolled in the public schools, and 30,700 of these are in grades one through six.

There is a single school district for the entire county. It developed psychological services beginning in the early 1950's. They were described to us as having dealt successfully in the schools with a number of problems that might otherwise have required referral to a mental health agency.

Greenville Area Mental Health Center

The Greenville Area Mental Health Center was created in 1950 as a project of the local Junior Chamber of Commerce. Since 1961 it has been jointly funded on a fifty-fifty basis by the county and the state Department of Mental Health under provisions of South Carolina's community mental health services act. It describes itself as

> a diagnostic, evaluation, treatment, and prevention center for mental and emotional illness of children, adolescents, and adults. Treatment for individuals and families is offered on both a long- and short-term basis . . . according to the individual or family needs.

The original staff of three had, by the time of our visit, expanded to fifteen full-time staff members, plus three part-time psychiatrists and four social work students. These staff members include five master's-level social workers, two master's-level psychologists, one "mental health associate," two clinical chaplains, and five clerical and other office staff. The director, Dr. Ingeborg Kruer, is a child psychiatrist.

In 1969, when the new Marshall I. Pickens Hospital was completed, the Greenville Area Mental Health Center, previously located in office space provided in the county office building, moved there, into a commodious and outstandingly attractive wing which was specifically designed for it, and which it rents from the hospital.

During 1970, 1074 new cases were opened. Fifteen of these were children ages 0 through 4. Two hundred fifty were ages 5 through 14 and 173 were ages 15 through 19.

The physical plant has a separate waiting room for children and two playrooms. Treatment includes, in various circumstances, play therapy, family therapy, individual psychotherapy, adolescent groups, and psychoactive medications.

The relationship between this center and Pickens Hospital, including the Re-ED program, is not limited to physical proximity. Of the first twenty children admitted to the Re-ED center, eight were referred by the Area Center. Beyond this, some of the children who are in the residential and day Re-ED units are concurrently seen either alone or with their families for counseling or psychotherapy at the center; of Re-ED's maximum capacity of twenty, the number of children and/or parents being seen at the Greenville Area Mental Health Center at a given time has ranged from two to five.

The Area Center is open from 8:30 a.m. to 5:00 p.m., Monday through Friday. Through a telephone-answering arrangement, it provides emergency telephone service on evenings and weekends. It is manned by professionals and volunteers who have been trained by the center. The volunteers provide counseling and information by telephone to those in crisis. Many cases are referred to the Area Center or other appropriate community services. The volunteer frequently initiates direct intervention in crisis situations, by calling on public health nurses, law enforcement agencies, rescue squads, and others. The volunteers are assisted by center personnel and other professionals in the community who serve in "professional backup" capacities.

Because the demand for service from the Area Center exceeds available staff time, there is often a wait for an initial appointment, usually in the range of three to four weeks. Thereafter, however, those evaluated as suitable for the center's services can be taken immediately into treatment.

Before considering the particular history of the Children's Re-Education Center, we should briefly trace the background of the services which were eventually to become the Marshall I. Pickens Hospital.

Greenville General Hospital, a nonprofit voluntary general hospital in the downtown part of the city, in 1953 initiated a small psychiatric service, one of the first in a general hospital in that part of the country. With time it was expanded to 25 beds which had a consistently high rate of occupancy. As the demand for all medical services increased, the trustees sought a development plan that would permit considerable expansion. An attractive 128-acre tract that had once been a private estate became available on the outskirts of town. There, in time, will be a medical complex that promises to be one of the most attractive in the United States. It will include separate buildings for mental health, medicine/surgery, rehabilitation, pediatrics, geriatrics, and chronic illnesses.

In part because earmarked funds were immediately available, the psychiatric section became the first building to be completed. Known as the Marshall I. Pickens Hospital, and built with a combination of Hill-Burton, Duke Endowment, Appalachian, and local funds, it was designed only after a team of professionals, together with the architect, visited a number of psychiatric services throughout the United States. Their efforts bore rich fruit indeed, for the fifty-bed Pickens Hospital is one of the most attractive, inviting, and functional mental health facilities that the authors and consultants have seen.

After planning for this facility was under way, Dr. Robert E. Toomey, Director of the Greenville Hospital System, who was well acquainted with the Re-ED program in Tennessee, began to express his concern about the lack of provision for inpatient care for younger children. He urged the planning team to arrange for a group of local professionals to visit Cumberland House, the Re-ED facility in Nashville. They did so and were impressed with the evident good outcome with children whose behavior had caused much difficulty to themselves, their families, and their schools. After prolonged consideration, the trustees decided to include a Re-ED center at Greenville.

Late in 1967, Thomas F. Kirby, a psychologist, was hired to be director. He departed at once for a year's training at George Peabody College and at the Re-ED centers in Tennessee. At the end of 1968 he returned to Greenville and began to hire a staff. The residential building, with a capacity of ten, received its first residents in April 1969, and the day program, also with a capacity of ten, was opened the following August.

Philosophy, purposes, and policy

The Re-Education model, as originally conceived by Dr. Hobbs, has been described by him in some detail in the report of the Joint Commission on Mental Health of Children.[1] The following brief synopsis is based on that report.

The purpose of the project is "the re-education of emotionally disturbed children," in residential centers which when developed to full capacity will serve forty to fifty children each. It is felt important that the physical plant be "simple, open, homelike, uninstitutional." In addition to the child's full-time exposure to the re-education effort, there is intensive work with parents, regular school, and community, in the interest of helping the child to return as quickly as possible to his usual environment. The target population is children of normal or higher intelligence who have either had serious trouble in school or have been unable to attend school.

Dr. Hobbs describes the Re-Education model as reality oriented from the start, since it was developed out of the belief that it will never be possible to provide an adequate number of psychiatric treatment centers to serve all the disturbed children; and in any case, such centers are felt to be prohibitively expensive and often not as successful as one would hope.

"The central thrust," he says, "is to help children here and now acquire competence in coping with realistic problems: how to read, how to play first base, how to approach school without fear, how to counter a dominating mother without recourse to asthma, how to take a stand against a bully, how to receive and how to give of one's possessions, how to know joy; in sum, how to be oneself fully, without guilt."

The disturbed child is seen as the victim of a breakdown in "an ecological system" composed of child, family, neighborhood, school, and community. The goal is "not to cure a child or to prepare him to cope with all possible life roles but to restore to effective operation the small social system of which the child is an integral part." Thus, the goal is to bring the child and his environment to a point of adequacy "just above threshold," with Re-ED staff moving out of the system as soon as possible.

---

[1] N. Hobbs: "Project Re-ED: New Ways of Helping Emotionally Disturbed Children," in *Crisis in Child Mental Health: Challenge for the 1970's.* Harper & Row, New York, 1970.

So that the child may be near his family, Re-ED facilities should be located to serve local communities, with the children going home on weekends and vacations, thus affording an opportunity for each child and his parents and brothers and sisters to "practice new learnings and test new resolves, so that the alienation so often a consequence of institutionalization can be avoided." Generally the children make visits to their regular schools from time to time. It is desirable to keep the length of residence in the Re-ED program brief, and Dr. Hobbs reports an average stay of seven months in the Tennessee programs.

As for the meaning of the Re-ED experience to the child, Dr. Hobbs states that

> Re-ED schools are designed with a high expectation of normal behavior, of zestful, purposeful, joyous living. . . . The daily program is planned to be so interesting, so engaging, so tuned to success, so instructive in group living, so self-fulfilling that the child is immediately caught up in behavior befitting a normal child.

The staff members are young in age, trained as teachers or in "other work demonstrating a meaningful commitment to children." They are referred to as "natural workers" to suggest that they have been carefully selected "to capitalize on individual differences in ability to work with children, a product of an entire life history not likely to be modified much by professional training." They do, however, undergo nine months of graduate study leading to a master's degree. And in their work, they have available consultation from pediatrics, psychiatry, psychology, education, and other fields.

D R. HOBBS' DESCRIPTION of the intent and the process of Re-ED applies quite largely to the Greenville program, which describes its philosophy as that of providing a stable and stimulating environment in which expectations are realistic and adults are trustworthy. Every effort is made to provide a setting where the child experiences consistency in management. Limits are maintained. Structure and acceptance help the children to maintain inner controls. Within this general approach there are five facets to the program:

1. Academic and behavioral goals are clearly defined and articulated. These objectives, which are reformulated weekly with the child's participation, are set in such a way that they are possible of attainment, insuring success experiences.

2. Principles of operant conditioning using social reinforcement, token reinforcement, and at times primary reinforcement are utilized to

strengthen appropriate and effective behavior, as well as to weaken or extinguish unacceptable or disruptive behavior.

3. Insight and awareness on the part of the child are the goals of group and individual techniques of counseling, with a view to increasing his motivation to change his behavior.

4. Parents are involved in the program through training, counseling, and family therapy. Parental cooperation and participation are made conditions of admission. The goals are to improve their understanding of their own problems and to improve their skills in the management of behavior.

5. A working relationship is maintained with the school system and community agencies for the purpose of bringing about a smooth transition for the child from the re-education unit back into the public school and the community.

Different facets of this treatment plan become pre-eminent at different times during the treatment of each patient. All are maintained actively throughout the child's participation in the program with the purpose of bringing about his return to his home and a regular school placement as soon as possible.

This is by no means the full substance of Re-ED, either in Tennessee or in Greenville. There are these provisions in the program:

• Each child is given an exhaustive educational evaluation in order to determine precisely the level of educational material to prescribe for him and the nature of the educational transaction that will be required of the counselor.

• The ratio of staff to patient is small enough to allow considerable individual interaction between counselor and each student—far more than would be possible in most public classrooms.

• Children are given an opportunity to explore and ventilate feelings about themselves and each other in brief group sessions, known in the Greenville program as "powwows."

• Children who do well in their studies and earn the necessary credits may be rewarded with free time for recreation, which would be difficult if not impossible in a school.

Mr. Kirby sees as perhaps the most important element for the children the opportunity to have consistent relationships with adults, through which they can learn to trust. "Most of these children, when they come into the program, have trouble trusting adults; here they learn that if an adult says something is going to happen, in fact it does. They are also able to learn that adults can be reasonable people who can be talked to and who will listen. They learn constructively that there is more than one way to handle a problem, more than one solution to a question that comes up, whether it be behavioral or academic."

At the same time, the Greenville program differs in several important respects from the original Re-ED programs. As the psychologist consultant who is a member of the admissions committee put it, "We began to find that the Re-ED model could not be transplanted into our setting without modification." Indeed, the admissions committee itself is one of those modifications. The decision of whether to accept a child in the original program was made by the staff; at Greenville it is made by an admissions committee of which the Director of Re-ED is the chairman. Other members are the medical director of Pickens Hospital, a pediatrician, the consulting psychologist, and the two liaison counselors.

Perhaps the principal distinguishing characteristic, however, is the placement of the Greenville program in a medical facility. The original Re-ED programs quite deliberately were not established in medical settings, and medical participation is limited to a psychiatric consultant available on call. The medical auspice has led to important departures. Among these is the scheduling of 25 percent of the children for individual psychotherapy, at the Greenville Area Mental Health Center. While the Greenville program places the same emphasis as the original Re-ED on assessing the child's functional level and working with him at that level, the medical setting requires more of an interest in etiology of the pathology; for example, a complete social history is obtained on each child and his family, and the school he has been attending is asked to complete an extensive form; the teacher-counselors make periodic written reports about each child which are consistent with the kind of process notes used in medical services.

The Greenville program works more closely with families than the original Re-ED, which took the position that intervening in family pathology was the responsibility, in the usual circumstances, of the agency that referred the child. At Greenville parents are expected to attend a weekly parents group, and those who are considerably remiss about doing so run the risk of having their child terminated from the program. In addition, about three sets of parents at a time are concurrently seen for psychotherapy at the Greenville Area Mental Health Center.

What may prove to be the most significant departure from the original Re-ED is the introduction at Greenville of a day program, under which the children return to their homes each afternoon. In Tennessee, Re-ED has been seen as a venture that requires 24-hour contact with each child.

Eligibility and capacity

By its own definition, the program is available to "mildly and moderately disturbed" children who are at least six but less than twelve years old. Those with less-than-average intelligence or with moderate or severe brain damage are ineligible. (The state hospital also will not accept such children, and thus no resources are available in the Greenville area.)

The residential program's ten children are accommodated in an extraordinarily attractive building on the grounds of the hospital complex. (Only boys are accepted in the residential program, because the referral ratio of boys to girls has been nine to one.)

The second building, adjacent to the residential facility and equally attractive, contains two large classrooms, one for the residential children, the other for the ten children on day status. For both groups there is a swimming pool and a particularly well-equipped playground.

The program operates year round; since the optimum typical stay is designed for about six months, this means that a total of about forty children per year can be served in the total program.

The staff

The medical director of Marshall I. Pickens Hospital estimates that he spends about ten percent of full time with the Re-ED program, mostly as a member of the admissions committee and in regular meetings with the staff. A registered recreational therapist and a registered nurse who serve the whole hospital also spend about ten percent of their time with Re-ED. All other staff members are full time.

This small staff consists of the director; a liaison teacher-counselor each for the day and the residential children, one with a master's degree in psychology, the other with a master's degree in counseling; a day teacher-counselor each for the two groups of children, both with bachelor's degrees; a teacher aide for each group, both with some college work; a residence counselor with three years of college; and a night teacher-counselor with a bachelor's degree in psychology. These staff members are all young, but the majority have had some previous experience in working with special children. One had worked for two years as an aide in one of the Tennessee Re-ED programs; several others had spent periods ranging from two days to several weeks at the original Re-ED programs; but only the director had completed the one-year graduate training program that Re-ED offers in Nashville.

We interviewed all of these staff members about their work. Uniformly they impressed us as well-informed and enthusiastic people who seemed particularly apt for their work.

Referring agencies

Of the 21 children who were accepted into the program during the first half of 1970, ten were referred by the Greenville Area Mental Health Center; seven by the schools; one by a family service agency; two by family physicians; and one family applied directly.

The intake process

When a child is referred to the center, the admission process begins with his parents completing an application, then being interviewed by a staff member regarding the nature of the problem and the sort of help that has been sought in the past, as well as the changes they would like to accomplish. At the same time the child is interviewed by another staff member regarding his reactions to the problems he is experiencing and the prospects of being enrolled at the center. Following these interviews, the parents and child tour the building and grounds, meet the teacher-counselors, and ask any questions they may have.

Subsequently, information is obtained from both the teacher and the principal at the school the child has been attending, and in most cases a liaison teacher-counselor visits the school to talk with the teacher and observe the child in class. She also obtains any such data as psychological evaluations, psychiatric and neurological examinations, and developmental and medical history from agencies and professionals who have been previously involved.

If the child is accepted, he comes to the center prior to starting the program for a complete educational evaluation which may include some or all of the following: Peabody Picture Vocabulary Test, Wepman Auditory Discrimination Test, Spache Diagnostic Reading Scales, Stanford Diagnostic Reading Test, Stanford Diagnostic Arithmetic Test, Metropolitan Achievement Test, and the Illinois Test of Psycholinguistic Ability. Screening visual and hearing tests are performed by the consulting pediatrician as a part of a complete physical. Specific academic goals are set for the child on his first day in class.

One criterion for acceptance is a favorable prognosis for the family as a system. This is considered important because of the relatively brief period of time the child will be in treatment. Quite specific basic objectives are articulated to the parents. For example, a hyperactive child who had been admitted just prior to our visit had these objectives set: *a*) to stay in his seat; *b*) to pay attention to his work; *c*) to be evaluated for indications for medication to help reduce the hyperactivity; *d*) to involve the parents in a parent-education program for all families who have children at the Re-Education Center; *e*) to get the parents involved in marriage counseling, since the child's behavior seemed to have become a point of contention between the two parents.

The program day by day

The residential children spend their weekends at home and are returned to the hospital by their parents on Sunday evening. Each morning they get up, dress, and go to the hospital cafeteria for breakfast, then return to clean their rooms. At about this time the day children arrive, and at eight o'clock classes start for both groups. They spend their mornings on academic subjects, then return to the hospital cafeteria for lunch. The residential boys have a "powwow" (see below) immediately after lunch, then a science class followed by an arts and crafts period, then, until dinner time, supervised recreation, including swimming, basketball, croquet, volleyball, and table games. The day children, following lunch, have supervised recreation, and then a powwow just before leaving for home at four o'clock.

The powwows are actually group therapy sessions, and their stated purpose is to "increase self-awareness and insight and improve motivation for change." The discussions focus on the behavior and performance of the children during that day, and on ways in which they can improve.

Throughout the day points are given for satisfactory behavior. A child can earn 25 points per academic day; for example, two points for arts and crafts, two points for each academic subject, and four points for a subject that gives the child particular difficulty. Bonus points are given for particularly good performance. The points are recorded on individual cards, which each child keeps with him.

The child can then "buy" various activities at a "price" of ten points each. Residential children can use points towards a weekly evening trip away from the hospital, while those not having enough points stay at the residence but buy activities there. Any points left over at the end of the week can be used to buy items in a small canteen.

For a time, points were subtracted when behavior was unsatisfactory, but this procedure had been abandoned shortly before our visit, on the grounds that it was too punitive.

Because of the desired typical stay of six months, the program does not correspond with the academic year of the regular schools; that is to say, a particular child might be seen as ready to return to his school in the middle of the semester.

Approximately four weeks prior to a child's discharge and after a team conference with the parents, the liaison counselor arranges his school placement through Special Services of the Greenville County school system. After the school has been determined, the liaison counselor visits the principal and talks with him about placement plans, the problems the child has had, and his present strengths and weaknesses. With this information, the principal selects the teacher whom he thinks will work most effectively with the child.

The liaison counselor then discusses the same information with the teacher and covers in depth the child's academic strengths and weaknesses and techniques found effective in managing his behavior. The books and assignments the child will be working on for the next several weeks are obtained. His transition back to the regular school may be handled in one of two ways:

1. For most of the children, during the last two weeks at the Re-ED Center, their daily lessons are identical to those of their regular classroom so that they are coordinated with their fellow students when they resume at the regular school.

2. Some children in the residential group attend regular classes during their last two weeks and return to the hospital for the afternoon and night. After a child's return to regular school, he may return to the center on a regular basis as a reward for doing well.

Liaison counselors formally follow up each discharged child for one year from date of discharge. This follow-up consists of calls and visits to the school and visits to the child's home. After this year the case is considered closed, but follow-up services may continue if needed.

Outcome of treatment

Through May 1971, in 26 months of operation, 58 children had been admitted to the program and 41 had been discharged. Of those discharged, 31 returned to regular classes, two returned to public school special education classes for the emotionally disturbed, two to special education classes for learning disabilities, two to special education classes for the retarded, three are not in school, and one is in the state hospital. Average length of stay was 6.2 months and average academic gain was one year, or 1.5 months of academic progress for every month in the program.

Of the 37 who returned to public school, two were suspended for a short length of time but returned, and all finished the school year making satisfactory progress.

Financing

The cost of treatment in Re-ED was calculated, at the time of our visit, at $26 per day for the residential children, $20 for day treatment. These seemingly low figures must be viewed in the local context, however, since the charges at Marshall I. Pickens Hospital ($38 per day in adult psychiatry) are well below those of many other parts of the country (particularly so considering the exceptionally fine quality of the physical plant).

A more meaningful treatment figure is that of $3663 per child, for the average stay of just over six months.

One principal source of funds has been the NIMH staffing grant, which covers all Re-ED staff except for two counselors and two aides who are supplied by the local school district. Most private health insurance policies will cover inpatient status but scarcely any will cover day status. The welfare department and Medicaid have sponsored children in the residential treatment program. Beyond this, the program must rely on collections from families. During a recent year, however, only 43 percent of the fees billed were collected.

There are presently many more children needing services than there are services available. Plans for future development of the Re-Education Center include an additional day-treatment program; perhaps more significant is the proposed use of the Re-Education Center program as a laboratory for teaching and training purposes. This concept would ultimately have its effect on many other children in the community.

Peninsula Hospital Community Mental Health Center

Burlingame, California

The area served

Peninsula Hospital Community Mental Health Center serves one of four mental health regions in San Mateo County, California. This prosperous and rapidly growing county, just south of San Francisco, with a population in 1970 of approximately 570,000, has known most of its development since World War II. Its many towns and small cities have a number of light manufacturing and service industries, particularly in electronics, air transportation, publishing, insurance, and warehousing. San Francisco International Airport, the county's largest employer, lies within Peninsula Hospital Community Mental Health Center's catchment area. The county is well-to-do, with many residents commuting to work in San Francisco. However, there are significant areas of poverty in San Mateo County, inhabited mainly by blacks and Chicanos.

The Peninsula center serves 16 census tracts with a population of 99,000, about 18 percent of the county's population. The catchment area consists of four cities—San Bruno, Millbrae, Burlingame, and Hillsborough. The substantial majority of the people range from middle to upper class, and over 90 percent of them are native-born whites. There are few blacks, but two enclaves of Spanish-speaking families—one in Millbrae, with some 40 families in the main from the Caribbean and Central and South America, another in San Bruno with 50 to 100 families, mostly Chicanos.

San Mateo County has long been considered an attractive place to live and, for several reasons, to practice psychiatry. Particularly, its county mental health service was a pioneer in community psychiatry.[1] The prosperity of the community together with a generally favorable state-county funding pattern for public service have served to make possible

---

[1] See R. M. Glasscote, D. Sanders, H. M. Forstenzer, and A. R. Foley: *The Community Mental Health Center: An Analysis of Existing Models,* Joint Information Service, Washington, D.C., 1964, for a detailed description of how these services developed.

an attractive combination of salaried work within the public programs and private practice. In December 1970 there were 43 psychiatrists on Peninsula Hospital's attending staff. The area is rich, too, in other mental health professionals, many of them combining public and private practice. In 1969 a bylaw change was passed by the professional staff of Peninsula Hospital admitting licensed privately practicing psychologists and clinical social workers to the staff in an affiliate status. They can, in collaboration with a physician, admit and treat private patients in the mental health center. By December 1970, 17 psychologists and 21 clinical social workers had become affiliates of the professional staff.

Origins

Peninsula Hospital was built in the mid-1950's as a district hospital under the provisions of a California law that permits communities to form hospital districts which may levy taxes and float public bonds for capital outlays as approved by the electorate. Expenses for patient care are *not* covered by these tax revenues. They must be billed to patients or third-party payers directly *at cost*. The hospital has steadily grown since its opening. By 1960 it had 374 beds. In 1965 a bond issue was approved to add a new eight-story wing, three floors of which were to house a community mental health center. One third of the cost of the center was paid through the 1963 Community Mental Health Centers Act. This followed, first, a vote in 1965 of the private psychiatrists then on the attending staff to take responsibility for developing and running a community mental health center, and, second, a 1965 resolution of the San Mateo County Board of Supervisors to contract with the Peninsula Hospital District to provide comprehensive mental health services to a catchment area surrounding the hospital.

The first psychiatric service in this attractive, modern hospital was in the form of a twelve-bed "pilot mental health unit" begun in 1964. Its initial staff included a half-time psychiatrist-director, nursing personnel, an occupational therapist, and a part-time social worker. The director, responsible for staff training and for "maintaining a therapeutic milieu," conducted daily group therapy. Medical responsibility for each patient was in the hands of the private attending physicians. Satisfaction with this private psychiatric service led in 1965 to the commitment to develop a comprehensive community mental health center. The center was opened in March 1969 with the full service under the county contract beginning the following October. As the center was being built, many conferences were held among the attending staff, which had grown to more than forty psychiatrists, hospital administration, the county mental health service, community agencies, and various others to plan the form the new center's services would take. Professional services to patients would be provided by private attending psychiatrists and affiliate psychologists and social workers, seeing patients and families both at the center and in their private offices. Their bills would be paid from personal funds by those who had the means or from insurance or public third parties. Individuals and families who qualified for part or full payment under the California Short-Doyle state-county mental health service program (based on income and number of dependents) would have their professional bills paid in part or in full by the Peninsula Hospital District acting through the contract as the fiscal intermediary between the private attending professional and the patient.

The center itself developed new services, including day and night care, an emergency service with crisis intervention teams made up of specially trained nursing personnel, summer day treatment for children, and an evaluation and referral service manned by social workers with consultant psychiatrists. This latter service is charged with placing the patient (or "the crisis") with the most appropriate private professional, be he psychiatrist, psychologist, or social worker. Charges were established for all these center-based services, to be billed to the patient or third parties directly by the hospital.

A number of these programs were still being developed at the time of our visit in January 1971. For example, the adolescent day-treatment program had begun only nine months before our visit, and activity group therapy for children was just beginning. Among the most important changes already planned was the relocation late in 1971 of all social milieu and group therapy services for children, adolescents, and their families other than inpatient treatment, to a separate building adjacent to the hospital. This attractive small two-story building, formerly used by a research firm, was purchased with hospital district funds in fall 1970. It will provide space of a suitable type which will make possible more group activities; the center also believes that the young patients will respond better to a nonhospital setting. Furthermore the new facilities, called the Family and Youth Center, will give the community mental health center greater visibility to the community and an identity separate from the hospital.

Philosophy, purposes, and policy

In briefest terms, the goal of this community mental health center is to develop a program that "will capitalize on the interest of private practitioners who are oriented to community psychiatry and a public health approach, and who want to develop direct services which have a single standard of care, are available close to home, and are comprehensive and provide continuity of care," according to Dr. Warren Vaughan, Chief of Community Services.[2] In its staffing grant application the center stated these aspirations for the services to children and adolescents:

- Promoting mental health by improving family functioning and child-rearing practices through sound medical practice, parent education, and the application of mental health principles in anticipatory guidance and work with nursery school and elementary and secondary school personnel.
- Early casefinding through use of mental health screens and identification of children at risk.
- Development of diagnostic services designed to provide the attending physician, parents, school personnel, and other case collaborators with information and direction needed for successful intervention of a preventive and/or corrective nature.
- Treatment programs using in the main family-centered psychotherapy and group therapy techniques, with the pediatrician or general practitioner continuing to be the medically responsible physician.

It seems accurate to say that these ambitions were being worked toward rather than having been realized, which is hardly surprising in view of the short time the center had been in existence. Within nine months of the center's opening, a number of privately practicing professionals had developed group therapy programs, with the help of the center's referral service. Center staff in the fall of 1969 began to provide regular consultation services to the elementary school districts, the high school district, and parochial schools with the goal of promoting early identification and prompt referral. The center also took over from the county program the consultation services to a cooperative nursery school a few blocks from the hospital.

By fall 1970, the attending and affiliate professionals who treat children and adolescents had been meeting monthly for almost a year. They had identified areas needing special attention, such as the development of parent groups, and the involvement of the private practitioner in the "indirect services" of mental health consultation and education. By the end of 1970 more than one hundred children and adolescents were receiving care and treatment, with costs covered under the Short-Doyle contract. At this point, under the pressure of an impending budget crisis, it became clear that a philosophy and set of guidelines for treatment was

---

[2] And, at the time of our visit, acting director of services for children and adolescents.

needed—for adults, children, and adolescents alike who were referred to the center. Up to then a rather laissez-faire system of administrative approval of treatment plans had been used as the center gained experience with size of caseload, type of problems referred, and style of treatment approach used by various practitioners. Over the winter of 1970-71 a system of peer case review and treatment authorization was established for adult cases. All cases requiring treatment beyond an initial six hours of crisis intervention were brought to a psychotherapy review committee. If psychotherapy were to be continued on a once-a-week basis, the case must be referred to a new therapist. A committee of the professional staff established to develop guidelines for services to families, children, and youth met during the same period, and identified basic principles which should determine guidelines and policies for clinical programs for children and youth. Some of these—still being developed by the committee—are as follows:

1. Children's services need to reflect the nature of childhood. The child is a developing organism, quite fluid and changing with a defensive structure not as firmly established as in adults, is very dependent upon the family and environment for external control, limits, and guidance. Children's services cannot operate in the adult model. The child is not a miniature adult and to understand and work with children special training and experience are necessary.

2. Early detection, early referral for evaluation and treatment, and programs for prevention are important.

3. Child psychiatric services need to be provided within the framework of an interdisciplinary approach.

4. Rational treatment is based on a diagnostic study of the child within the context of the family.

5. A broad spectrum of treatment modalities is necessary.

6. Criteria used for evaluation of emergencies in adult psychiatric work are not applicable to children.

7. The principle of continuity of care is essential.

8. Children's services need a separate budget and a separate director to oversee their operations and to insure that they respond to the needs of the community and to the needs of the individual patients which they serve.

Those who have developed this center believe that intrinsically the private practitioners, or at least most of them, are the kind of people who are themselves receptive to modifications in respects that will move the center toward these goals.

Dr. Vaughan identifies these psychiatrists as people who have come mostly from training in the East and Middle West, many from Boston,

Cincinnati, and Topeka, "where they have been trained to believe that one starts with good, dynamic, psychoanalytically oriented psychotherapy, which one takes for granted, but who are interested in the broader community goals we have articulated. We don't get into an 'either-or bag,' such as psychoanalysis versus social science, or psychoanalysis versus behavior modification, or organic versus functional."

Dr. Vaughan notes, however, that at the same time it becomes important for the center itself to influence the private practitioners.

> In the first year of our contract for reimbursement by the county, we found ourselves discussing with the private practitioners their styles of practice, of trying to encourage innovations, of utilizing group and consultative methods in addition to the traditional psychotherapy hour with the individual patient. Resistance was evident, and it seems that only now, in the face of a financial crisis, can some practitioners take a more objective look at the program. Our talk about innovating created some anxiety and discomfort. Indeed, several of the private therapists withdrew from the program. With those who have continued, we have made some progress in bringing them to see that one-to-one therapy is just impossible financially for every patient. In addition it may not even be desirable for some patients. We have encouraged the idea that group therapy might for some patients be a precursor to individual therapy, that a period of group therapy may facilitate the utilization of individual therapy; also, the reverse—that some patients who have made gains in individual therapy might be helped still further by being transferred to group therapy.

Family therapy approaches, especially with adolescents, have been encouraged.

At the time of our visit, almost three out of four children and adolescents were in fact still being seen in individual psychotherapy. Among the relatively few being seen in groups by private practitioners, most were being seen by psychologists and social workers rather than by psychiatrists.

The center, feeling that it should itself develop milieu therapy programs which require full-time staff and the collaboration of community organizations, started a summer day-treatment program for children in 1969 and a predominantly after-school day-treatment program for adolescents in 1970, with referrals coming from the private attending and affiliate professionals, other professionals, and community agencies. Private practitioners themselves seldom have the necessary physical facilities, supporting staff, or inclination to develop such programs in their private office settings. Only two private practitioners, both psychiatric social workers, conduct activity group therapy programs in their private offices. The center's day-treatment programs will be described later in terms of philosophy and content.

Administration and staffing

The Peninsula Hospital department of psychiatry consists of all the privately practicing psychiatrists, psychologists, and social workers on the professional staff. Psychiatry gained departmental status when the center was opened in 1969. At monthly departmental meetings, issues are debated and voted on by participating members. For instance, it was thus that an obligatory rotating on-call system was created to man the emergency service, and a peer review and prior authorization system was established for adult, adolescent, and children's cases. The department has a number of committees, including record review, proctorship, professional education, the already-mentioned psychotherapy review committees for the center's Short-Doyle cases, and the new committee on Family, Children, and Youth Services. The director of the mental health center, the chief of community services, and other employed professionals attend these committee meetings in an ex-officio capacity. All of the directors of services in the center have been interviewed by members of the department during the hiring process, and also by members of the mental health advisory committee of the professional staff. This committee, appointed every two years by the chief of staff, meets six to ten times each year, and has on it a member from each of a number of departments, such as medicine, general practice, surgery, obstetrics and gynecology, and pediatrics.

Thus, the center is embedded in the hospital organizational structure in such a way that it and its programs remain the concern of key professionals who in their day-to-day professional activity may have limited or no direct contact with the center. However, the center, by virtue of the careful development of these relationships, has continuing support from professionals who have knowledge of what the center's goals are and how, in the development of its programs, it is moving to meet these goals. Such support becomes crucial, of course, at budget time, and when expansion of services is desired.

Citizens advisory committee. A citizens advisory committee makes recommendations regarding the goals of the center and the means of achieving them. Members have included a school principal, a special educator who works with Spanish-speaking children and families, a social worker, a college president, a police officer, two clergymen, a lawyer, a businessman, and a housewife.

The advisory committee was "very active and extremely effective" in mobilizing citizen interest and support at the time of a serious county budget crisis in 1971 which for a time seemed to threaten the continuance of the center as the Short-Doyle mental health service for its catchment area. In a sense, the budget crisis served to weld the committee together into an effective goal-directed group. Such terms as "citizen participation," "orientation and information," and "program review" became specific and concrete as members of the committee contacted influential citizens, wrote letters, and planned meetings with the county board of supervisors. It plans subcommittees on family, children, and youth services and on long-range financing and program development.

The staff. Subsequent to our visit Dr. Marvin Shapiro became director of children's services, and both he and Dr. Murray Bilmes, director of adolescent services, are responsible to the center director, Dr. Donald Newman. As director of community services, Dr. Vaughan is responsible for administering all outpatient services provided by the center and for facilitating the community organization aspects of the center-based direct and indirect service programs for children and adolescents. In a sense, the privately practicing professionals correspond in their roles and functions to the clinical staff of a public clinic or mental health center organized in a traditional way, with salaried professional personnel and with a hierarchical organization along the lines of the professional disciplines.

The professional staff on the center's payroll is relatively small, with the clinical work taking place, in the main, in the offices of the private practitioners. It includes two social workers, two half-time psychologists, two registered nurses, and two indigenous mental health assistants, in addition to Drs. Bilmes, Shapiro, and Vaughan.

A key staff member has been a social worker, Kathryn Williams, who is assistant director of children's service and runs the evaluation and referral service for children and adolescents. As the initial contact point for all families seeking service, she interviews parent and child, develops a working hypothesis regarding the nature of the problem, and arranges the referral of the family to the private practitioner she thinks most appropriate among those available. She also provides a tentative diagnosis, needed for administrative purposes.

The second social worker, who is also trained in art therapy, has developed a center-based activity group therapy program which uses art media and techniques in group work with children and their families, and has participated in educational and remedial programs in schools and other community settings.

The psychologists, one of whom is Spanish-speaking, have worked in both direct and indirect services.

The nursing personnel, including the mental health assistants, form the permanent staff for the adolescent service. They work with inpatients and day patients, provide crisis intervention, and furnish some indirect services to schools and other organizations concerned with adolescents. Like other departments of the hospital, psychiatry requires that all new staff members undergo a probationary period during which their work is examined under a proctorship. Senior members of the attending staff donate their time as proctors. The duration of proctoring may be as brief as a month in the case of highly experienced practitioners or as long as a year or more, for instance in the case of younger staff members just out of training. Psychologists and social workers are proctored in the same manner.

The clinical services

For those families who apply to the center for services relating to a child or adolescent, the route of entry has been almost invariably through an interview with Mrs. Williams. The only exceptions have been direct admission to inpatient service or adolescent day treatment by private therapists, or through the emergency room. No applicants are refused on the basis of particular forms of behavior, symptoms, or diagnosis. Mrs. Williams formulates a statement regarding the nature of the problem and a tentative diagnosis for the center's records. She takes a history of the present difficulty and may see the family several times if necessary to arrive at an initial formulation of the dynamics of the problem, leading to the most appropriate referral. She does not take a formal social history. She may arrange for psychological testing if this seems indicated but rarely does so. Then, from her personal knowledge of the private practitioners who have time available, she selects the therapist that she believes will be most appropriate for the particular case.

Of 43 psychiatrists on the attending staff and 39 psychologists and social workers on the affiliate staff, fewer than 25 have particular training, experience, and/or interest in working with children and adolescents. Something over half of these are psychologists and social workers. There has been little or no wait either for the initial interview or for referral to a private practitioner. Urgent situations are always seen within a day or two; others may have to wait a few days, just as they might if applying directly to a private practitioner.

With the development of a psychotherapy review committee, and the arrival of Dr. Shapiro in 1971, these evaluation and referral functions are undergoing study and reorganization. For instance, the initial interview in selected cases may be conducted by the private professional as part of a diagnostic study, with the case then presented to the psychotherapy review committee for peer review and prior authorization of a treatment program. The committee, comprised of two senior staff members on a rotating basis and one center staff member, is concerned with how much money is available, clinical needs, treatment resources available, setting priorities, and developing guidelines. It is a direct response to the budget crisis and represents the desire of the privately practicing professionals to protect the program in the face of fiscal problems.

Approximately one third of referrals to Mrs. Williams are full-pay families, not eligible for Short-Doyle financial help. These cases have not been subject to treatment authorization procedures, but the therapists are responsible to the center for reports of progress and outcome as requested.

Progress reports have been requested of therapists every three to four months for cases involving weekly individual therapy for children and families, and every six to nine months for children and families placed in group therapy programs, which are usually planned to run through a school year. Thus, periodic administrative and clinical reviews of treatment are made by Dr. Vaughan and when the treatment has been longstanding he must, not solely because of any theoretical persuasion but also because of financial considerations, intervene. Intervention has consisted of case reviews with therapists involved, requests for consultation with another practitioner, full-scale clinical conferences held at the center, attended occasionally not only by therapists and center personnel but also by school personnel, probation officers, and so on. (This review procedure is being changed in view of the development of the departmental psychotherapy review committee.)

Within a year the center had found a sizable number of severely disturbed families. Parents and children frequently end up in individual and/or group therapy, with the parents not infrequently requiring one or more periods of inpatient care or partial hospitalization.

Such disorganized families seem invariably to be eligible for full financial coverage under Short-Doyle, and thus account for a considerable part of the Short-Doyle reimbursement. They will be the subject of a special outcome study by the center.

The practitioners obviously differ from one to another in treatment methods, style, and preferences. Some may see the children alone and the parents separately, some may choose to work conjointly with the identified patient and the parents, and some have special training, interest, and experience in working conjointly with the entire family. Thirty percent of the eighty to ninety children and adolescents in inpatient therapy in the spring of 1971 were in group therapy programs. One senior privately practicing social worker has a large well-established program of activity group therapy. A number of therapists conduct groups for adolescents, both for the younger high school children and for the older high school students and college-age youth.

The largest group of both children and adolescents is referred by the schools—just under half of the children (44 percent) and just over half of the adolescents (53 percent). The other referral sources for children are other hospitals and mental health facilities (20 percent), the parents themselves (16 percent), and family physicians and privately practicing mental health professionals (nine percent each). For the adolescents, 18 percent are referred by the courts; seven percent by family physicians; seven percent on the initiative of their parents; and seven percent are self-referred. A number of adolescents are referred by another hospital or mental health facility and by privately practicing mental health professionals.

During 1970, case records were opened for 222 children and adolescents. About 35 percent were seen only once or twice, another 25 percent were seen from three to six times, and 40 percent were seen more than six times.

For the cases closed in 1970, the therapists rated outcomes as follows. For individual therapy: "markedly beneficial," 20 percent; "moderately beneficial," 78 percent; "of no benefit," one percent; for group therapy: "markedly beneficial," three percent; "moderately beneficial," 79 percent; "of no benefit," 18 percent; for family services: "markedly beneficial," 16 percent; "moderately beneficial," 69 percent; and "of no benefit," 14 percent.

More than two thirds of both children and adolescents are diagnosed as having adjustment reactions. For Short-Doyle admissions during the first six months of 1970, the diagnoses were as follows:

Children

Adjustment reactions of childhood	67%
Behavior disorders of childhood	22
Schizophrenia	4
Special symptoms	4
Chronic brain syndromes	2

Adolescents

Adjustment reactions of adolescence	69%
Behavior disorders of adolescence	9
Drug dependence	9
Neuroses	9
Schizophrenia	2
Other psychoses	2

Outpatient services. The initial step in the referral process is almost always to a private practitioner, in a private office in the catchment area or in an adjoining community. The standard initial authorization has been for six diagnostic and therapeutic sessions by which time definitive diagnostic formulation and recommendation for further therapy, if indicated, has been required.

Initially, substantially all recommendations and requests for expenditure of Short-Doyle funds were approved. Now, as explained above, this function is being taken over by the peer psychotherapy review committee.

Day treatment. The private practitioner who sees the child or adolescent as an outpatient may, if he thinks it appropriate, prescribe that his patient also attend one of the programs operated by the center itself. In such a case, the private practitioner remains the primary therapist, although he may lessen the frequency of the office visits.

One such program is a summer day-treatment program for children from ages five through fourteen. It operates five hours per day, four days a week for a seven-week period. In the summer of 1970 there were 63 children enrolled for at least three weeks. The patients were divided into eight groups, primarily by age. Each group had a paid leader who was a college or graduate student with experience in working with disturbed children. Each leader had as assistants a paid counselor who was a college student experienced in working with children and "several enthusiastic high school and college volunteers." In addition, five students from the Western Interstate Commission for Higher Education's summer work-study program worked with the program. At most times, there were as many staff members (including volunteers) as children. The children need not have been previously in treatment through the auspices of the mental health center; indeed, a fair number had not, but rather were new referrals from schools, pediatricians, and various agencies. In such cases, it is the practice to assign the child to one of the private practitioners so that a specified person will have continuing psychiatric and other medical responsibility.

The children under care in the day-treatment program fall in the main into four diagnostic categories: overanxious reaction of childhood, unsocialized aggressive reaction of childhood, chronic brain syndrome, and childhood schizophrenia.

The camp program uses the facilities of two schools located near the center, one of which has a large swimming pool. The day begins with a thirty- to sixty-minute group meeting, followed by sports, games, and lunch. On two days a week there is swimming for an hour. The afternoon is spent in a variety of group projects. One day a week the entire group goes on an all-day outing to the beach or a park.

The eight treatment teams meet every morning for forty to sixty minutes prior to arrival of children to plan for each child's day. The child's day ends at two to two thirty. Following this the teams clean up, write daily notes, and discuss group activities and experiences with individual children.

Special lectures and discussions on pertinent clinical topics are planned for the staff each week, scheduled in late afternoon.

During the seven weeks of the day-treatment camp, there are three evening sessions between staff and parents, and there are also individual conferences between the senior staff and the parents.

Asked to characterize the camp's principal contribution to its children, the director, a privately practicing social worker who contracts the necessary time to head up the camp, described it as "a positive growth experience that puts the child back in orbit." It differs from a special summer recreation program for handicapped children, in that a careful diagnostic assessment of the emotional and mental disorder of each child is made at the outset, with the social milieu then utilized to provide corrective experiences. The staff, thus, are the therapeutic instruments. A number of general and specific therapeutic goals are identified for each child, and are modified as indicated during the course of each child's participation in the program. General goals include "reducing anxiety" and "increasing self-esteem," while specific goals might include such areas as reality testing, response to direction, and limit setting.

A few months prior to our visit the center had established its adolescent day program. Some patients come at 11 a.m., but in order to allow others to attend regular classes, the program for most does not begin until midafternoon. It continues until 7 or 8 p.m., depending on the activities for the particular day. Adolescents on the inpatient service usually participate in the group. Headed by Dr. Bilmes, the staff consists of three nurses and a "mental health worker" who has completed a limited amount of college. Inpatient nurses assigned to specific inpatient adolescents also help out.

The program at the time of our visit took place in a large group room on one of the floors designated for the mental health center. The stated capacity is twenty, but the highest census had been nineteen; at the time of our visit there were fifteen.

Adolescents are admitted for a variety of reasons. Some have been in state hospitals, and the program hopes that it can provide the support to keep them out. Some are in the day program because of the fear that without this intensity of support they will have to become institutionalized for the first time. Some are intensely lonely and isolated, and "if it weren't for this program they'd go to school and then go home and sit alone in their rooms." Said the nurse, "We have kids in that group who can't even get on a city bus and ride down the street without having anxiety attacks." A number of youths, especially older adolescents, have had serious drug-related problems. Heroin users in particular were found to be very disruptive and had to be removed from the program.

Not all of the young people are scheduled to come every day; the program particularly allows schedule flexibility for children who may want to stay at their schools to take part in extracurricular activities.

As for program, three days of the week are left partially unplanned, and on Mondays the young people and the staff decide together how they will spend these unscheduled days. Group therapy sessions are held every day. Often the decision is to go to an old country property, a former sawmill, about twenty miles away (at which this adolescent program operates full time for the summer months), where they hike, do simple construction jobs, and so on. A typical afternoon would consist of a group therapy session, at which the young people talk about problems at home and school "and tell each other how they feel about each other." This is followed by a period in the center's recreation room, and then dinner, which is sent up on trays for both patients and staff. Then would come a woodworking or tie-dyeing session, for example, or a dramatic reading. On the unplanned afternoons there are various excursions, to museums and shops or into San Francisco to see a play. The program has two automobiles at its disposal; following an outing, the nurse and the mental health worker often drive the children home and sometimes go in to spend some time with the rest of the family.

The director describes the program as "a living experience with adults and youngsters who together create a therapeutic approach." He is looking forward to the day when it will be possible to move to the new facility because he thinks the hospital atmosphere is not the most desirable setting for adolescents.

The program was much too new to have any outcome data.

Other center-operated activities to which the private practitioners may make referrals are an activity group for children and family art therapy. Both are led by the social worker with special training in art therapy. At the time of our visit she was seeing one group of eight- to ten-year-olds and was planning to start other groups for both younger and older children. They come to the center once a week to engage in various expressive activities, such as drawing to music and then telling how they felt as they drew. She also leads a kind of diagnostic family art session in which she has the family members collaborate on a drawing, first silently and individually, then, later, in various combinations. Afterward the family talks about the drawing, and she uses this discussion as a diagnostic medium.

Emergency services. Children and adolescents in emergency situations are served through the generic emergency service of the center, which in turn operates through the regular emergency room of Peninsula Hospital. Staff from the adolescent service may participate when available in the emergency service when an adolescent is involved. At any given time, some particular member of the psychiatric inpatient nursing staff is designated the person on emergency call, and when an emergency that appears to be psychiatric is brought to the emergency room, this person is sent for. She develops as much information as possible, then telephones the psychiatrist on backup call for that day. With time, the percentage of admissions has decreased, and now the psychiatrist must come to the hospital to admit the patient or send him to another facility in fewer than half of the emergencies.

Very few psychiatric emergencies involve young children. During the 12 months ending mid-1971, six children age 11 to 13 were seen eight times in the emergency room (two of them twice). No children below 11 were seen. On the other hand, there were over 100 adolescents age 14 through 18. It was estimated that at least 50 adolescent emergencies per year are admitted to the inpatient ward for at least an overnight stay.

Inpatient service. We have mentioned that inpatient service is limited to adolescents, who have at times comprised a kind of subunit within the adult psychiatric service. Over 120 adolescents were admitted to the inpatient service during the year ending mid-1971. Many of these were admitted as emergencies, often a drug "bad trip" or an intentional overdose. (If the overdose is such as to require emergency medical treatment, this takes place on the medical ward and the young patient is subsequently transferred to the psychiatric ward for evaluation.) Other reasons for admission include severe withdrawing behavior of psychotic proportions and depressions.

We have mentioned that adolescent inpatients ordinarily spend their afternoons participating in the adolescent day program. Occupational therapy and the recreation room are favorite spots for adolescent inpatients at other times. The weekend program for each inpatient adolescent is set by his private attending therapist. Most like to have patients on trial visits home or elsewhere if possible. There is no special adolescent group program on weekends.

The length of inpatient stay for adolescents is relatively brief. During a recent six-month period, about thirty percent stayed less than one week, another sixty percent stayed between one and four weeks, and only ten percent stayed longer than four weeks.

While in the hospital, they are under the care of a private psychiatrist, or a private psychologist or social worker along with a physician. The private therapist continues, if necessary, to see the young person in his office following discharge. The Short-Doyle cases are presented to the psychotherapy review committee for review and treatment authorization.

Very few children under age fourteen are admitted for inpatient treatment. In dire emergencies emotionally disturbed young children are admitted to the pediatrics ward. At the time of our visit there was one seriously disturbed eleven-year-old boy hospitalized on the inpatient service. He had recently been admitted through the emergency room following a beating at home.

Consultation and other community services

As we will describe, the interaction between the mental health center and the agencies that refer children and adolescents seems to be cooperative and congenial. At the present state of financing and development, however, the relationships to a large extent consist of "case consultations" concerning the needs of and plans for particular individuals being considered for treatment. This is especially true regarding certain elementary school system relationships.

The center would particularly like to expand such interaction to include what is customarily known as program or agency consultation, with the goal of improving the activities of these agencies as they go about serving children and adolescents. Dr. Vaughan articulates a twofold purpose of the center. Beyond a first goal of developing good clinical services, he would like

to place child psychiatry and our total mental health service in a public health/mental health context. In terms of theoretical background, this is probably the most important thing.

The center had not fully realized this goal, for three important reasons. The most significant of these is perhaps the financial crisis that confronted the program, with significant cutbacks in the state funds that are required to keep the program operating. The second is the staffing pattern, with few people on the center's payroll and a heavy reliance on solo private practitioners who might be considered unlikely candidates to perform the kind of social interventions which Dr. Vaughan describes. The third is the mere lack of time, since the center had been operating a relatively short period.

There were, however, some interesting beginnings. Various individuals from the staff of the center itself were devoting some time to agency and program consultation in several different ways, aggregating the equivalent of about one full-time person.[3]

Schools. It would probably be fair to say that in terms of its short period of operation the small staff of the center had had a successful impact on a small portion of the schools in its catchment area. We talked with several school personnel who had a highly favorable opinion of the mental health center staff and the services they had provided.

Much of this service, as we have said, centered at the outset on the particular student identified as needing help, but sometimes in unusual ways. For example, one school superintendent told us that occasionally when a disturbed adolescent has flatly refused to have anything to do with a mental health institution, arrangements have been made for a psychiatrist or other clinical staff professional to come to the school and see the child in a vacant classroom, or the nurse's office.

The program consultation activities provided by the center at the time of our visit consisted of the following:

• The senior staff social worker makes weekly or biweekly visits to seven of 33 public elementary schools, plus two parochial schools and a nursery school. She meets with groups of teachers to discuss child development, classroom management, and problem behavior. The schools she visits are those which have indicated their interest in consultation, and she believes that the teachers view the contribution she makes as one of increasing their knowledge of psychodynamics, therefore enabling them to look at particular children "in an increasingly broadened perspective."

---

[3] Drs. Shapiro and Vaughan plan to involve the private attending and affiliate staff in community consultation work starting late in 1971.

• The psychologist-director of the adolescent services meets with nineteen high school guidance counselors once a week for two hours throughout the academic year, in the interest of training them in the use of group techniques in guidance. The high school district purchases this inservice training program from the center.

• The Spanish-speaking psychologist visits weekly with personnel from schools that have a significant number of children from Latin-American families.

• One of the privately practicing child psychiatrists spends a day each week consulting to the special education program of an elementary school district of 4600 students. Her services are paid for by the school district directly.

• The new art therapist-social worker has conducted seminars in use of the art media to enhance communication, expression, and awareness of feelings by children in one school system.

• A biweekly seminar for the clergy has been started in collaboration with the hospital chaplain. Over a dozen have attended.

• Monthly luncheon meetings have been held with school psychologists and guidance personnel and with chiefs of police.

• The mental health center staff meets quarterly with the department of pediatrics to report on program developments, answer questions, and to solicit their participation in such new center developments as the day-treatment programs.

Only two complaints were voiced to us by the school personnel. There was concern that the fee schedule set by the county mental health department assessed fees beyond the financial means of some families needing service. And there was some feeling that the center should strive to provide more of the clinical services actually within the schools.

All consultation provided to the schools, whether clinical or program, is reimbursed by Short-Doyle funds, with two exceptions mentioned above.

The courts. Program consultation for the courts and the probation department was still in the planning stage. The county probation department operates a detention facility in another part of the county which receives delinquent children in need of protective custody; this facility has a psychiatric unit supplied by the county mental health services, and there is some referral of cases between it and the Peninsula center.

A probation officer whose area includes about half of the center's catchment area said that he considers the center his "best resource for family counseling and individual and group therapy." This area is one of low juvenile crime but one of high truancy and illicit drug use. From his caseload of about sixty adolescents, about twelve are in treatment for emotional problems at a given time, and about half of these are patients at the Peninsula center.

Mental retardation services

The summer day-treatment program has had occasional retarded children, "with usually gratifying results—less anxiety, improved social functioning and motor skills, and so on." The center has also helped occasionally with the family casework study of retarded children from its catchment area who are referred by the center's referral service to the county's centralized developmental evaluation unit. This unit, located at San Mateo County's H.D. Chope Community Hospital, takes referrals from all four county regions for intensive psychological, educational, psychiatric, neurological, and social work study. The unit sees a large number of preschool children with developmental abnormalities, and serves as the central agency to mobilize community resources to aid these children and their families.

Research

No formal research projects had been undertaken. The center compiles outcome statistics on all patients, private and Medi-Cal as well as Short-Doyle supported. Private therapists complete a seven-point rating scale at termination of treatment.

The center had made plans to submit a proposal for an extensive evaluation project focusing on fiscal, clinical, and organizational effectiveness and on the impact of the center on patients, professionals, the hospital, and community.

Training

Residency training for first-year residents in the San Mateo County residency training program began in 1970, with two residents at a time spending a four-month period at Peninsula Hospital. These men see adolescents in the emergency room and as inpatients during their stay at the center, are supervised by attending staff, and participate in daily group therapy. They have limited continued clinical work with adolescents under supervision.

A new Graduate School for Professional Psychology was opened in the Bay Area in 1970. Several students come to Peninsula Hospital for field experience and to explore possibilities of gaining access to material suitable for a research project and dissertation.

Financing

The center depends for financial support on a variety of private and public sources. Those who do not fall within the eligibility limits of the Short-Doyle and Medi-Cal programs either pay the fees from their own funds or from health insurance. Except for some group major medical contracts, health insurance by and large will not cover outpatient psychiatric care.

For Short-Doyle patients the Peninsula Hospital acts as financial inter-mediary. The private practitioner bills the center, which, in turn, bills the County of San Mateo. The county then remits (ninety percent of the funds coming from the state under its community mental health law, the other ten percent from county tax revenues) to the hospital, which in turn remits to the private practitioner. No charges are levied for this billing and collection service. The fees are those "usual, customary, and reason-able" for the area, based on the California Medical Association 1969 Relative Value Study and on surveys of privately practicing psychologists and social workers in San Mateo County. For individual psychotherapy they are $20 per hour for social workers, $25 per hour for psychologists, $30 per hour for psychiatrists; for group therapy, $12 per patient per session for psychiatrists and $10 per patient per session for social workers and psychologists.

The center has an NIMH grant covering 8.5 full-time-equivalent posi-tions; the matching money comes largely from the reserves of Peninsula Hospital. The grant began its third year in September 1971.

At the time of our visit the program was in the throes of a severe financial crisis, owing to cutbacks in funds for both the Short-Doyle and the Medi-Cal programs. The Short-Doyle limitations, consisting of a county-wide reduction of one million dollars in a six-month period, were anticipated to curtail the number of low-income families who could be referred for treatment. Substantial limitations of eligibility for Medi-Cal, cutting back service to cases where severe disability or death seemed likely if treatment were not provided within ninety days, had virtually eliminated any psychiatric services to children. However, some adoles-cents from foster homes and welfare families who appeared in the emer-gency room as acutely disturbed, suicidal, or in critical danger of 24-hour hospitalization were approved for day treatment and individual or group psychotherapy sessions under these restricted guidelines. These emer-gency guidelines were removed temporarily from the Medi-Cal program in July 1971 pending new legislation to restore them in large measure.

Philosophy of Service

A PART FROM THE SERVICE FOR CHILDREN patterned after Project Re-ED, we did not investigate the theoretical and philosophical approaches of the centers prior to selecting them for inclusion in this study. Rather, we sought diversity in such characteristics as urban vs. rural vs. suburban setting, socioeconomic characteristics of the catchment area, and special program emphases (for example, a day-treatment program for adolescents or a component for children of preschool age). Consequently, we were impressed with the very considerable similarities in theory and philosophy among these eight centers. As we listened to the directors and staff members of one facility after another set forth the beliefs and principles that underlie their approach to serving children, we realized that in many important respects these independently developed centers share the same rationale. It therefore becomes surprisingly easy to develop a composite description of their values and viewpoints. While the description that follows does not hold entirely for any one of the centers, the considerable majority of it can be said to apply to all of them.

A N APPROPRIATE STARTING POINT would be the premise that children should be retained insofar as possible in their normative settings—living with their parents and attending classes in the regular schools. Generally speaking, the better the quality of the home life and the classroom, the greater the number of children who can remain in these normal situations; thus, the ultimate goal of the mental health center would be to promote emotional well-being by exercising a positive influence over the way children are reared and educated. To do so in a definitive way is beyond the present resources and perhaps techniques of any community mental health center. With a limited number of staff and in most cases budget problems, the centers are doing what they can in a partial and tentative way to bring a positive influence to bear.

For the foreseeable future, there will be a certain number of young people whose situation calls for clinical intervention—either because their prospects for developing into adequate adults are imperiled, or because their behavior threatens the capability of their family unit to

227

continue to cope, or both. Provided the parents or some other responsible agents recognize the need for outside help, they will turn to one of various potential resources. A number of them will apply to the community mental health center serving the area where they live.

The center should make an immediate response, even if it is taxed to the point that some temporary makeshift arrangement is necessary, in preference to having the applying family go on a waiting list. One or more staff members will assess the circumstances, and if treatment seems indicated will then recommend a plan that involves the lowest intensity of care consistent with the situation. A few children will be so massively and manifestly disturbed that the treatment of choice will be a residential program of fairly long duration—provided one is available. As a general principle, however, the first choice would be outpatient therapy involving both the child and his parents, with the child continuing to live at home and go to school. This would be preferable to day treatment at the mental health center, which would remove the child from school; day treatment would be preferable to brief inpatient treatment; and brief inpatient treatment would be preferable to longer-term residential treatment.

Because of the present limitations of diagnosis and evaluation, some treatment plans will prove insufficient to the need, in which case it should be readily possible to substitute a different plan.

In many, perhaps most, cases the treatment effort can be characterized as "crisis intervention," intended to provide special support to the family at a time when its ability to function is threatened. The intention is to work through the problem in as little as a month, but rarely longer than two or three months, although some individual cases may require longer-term intervention. The centers use a variety of other approaches and techniques, but they rarely attempt, either for the child or the parents, to use long-term "depth" approaches that aim at restructuring the personality. Efforts are often directed specifically toward symptomatic behaviors that distress the family and get in the way of the child's functioning in his normal setting; for example, with an enuretic or encopretic child, the principal goal of treatment may be precisely to bring about an end to the enuresis or encopresis.

Implicit throughout the treatment effort is the goal of relieving psychic distress; the centers believe that it is both appropriate and worthy to attempt to bring about relief from emotional pain, just as in physical medicine it is considered a good thing to relieve physical pain.

The centers consider it important that some, if not all, of the treatment staff have training in working with children. If it should be necessary to use as therapists persons who do not have this training, then there should be ample supervision of their work by people who do have the training, so that they can learn what they need to know about young people. There are several reasons for requiring trained staff, and the unifying one is the need to understand the process of development in young people. In contrast to the view of an earlier age that children are merely miniature adults, it is now accepted that approximately the first two decades of life are a period of *becoming,* which is marked not only by distinctions from adulthood but also by important internal distinctions; the twelve-year-old is distinctly different from the six-year-old, and the eighteen-year-old from the twelve-year-old. Unless one knows the behavior and skills that characterize young people at various stages, he is unable to judge in what respects a given individual deviates from the norms, and he is unprepared to develop a realistic set of expectations for his young patient. Because there is a scarcity of well-trained professionals in childhood mental health, programs must sometimes make do with what they can get; child psychiatrists are notably difficult to recruit.

In addition to understanding the developmental process, it is generally useful to understand psychodynamics. Despite the emphasis on brief treatment at the lowest practicable intensity, much of the psychodynamic body of knowledge is useful and applicable. Its conception of the mechanisms through which people maintain their individual equilibrium and sustain their relationships with the outside world constitute the only essentially complete theory of personality.

As is the case in mental health services for adults, a good deal of "role blurring" has occurred in these centers. To whatever extent in the past particular professions—notably psychiatry, psychology, and social work —may have been engaged in specialty activities, that has given way to a situation in which many staff members, irrespective of their formal training, are working as "generalists." Much of the therapy is done by social workers, who are available in greater number (and whose salaries are usually lower than those of psychologists and psychiatrists). Parents are no longer the particular province of the social worker, but may be involved in the treatment plan by any therapist on the staff.

Perhaps the most important manifestation of "role blurring" lies in the departure from the classical "team approach" in evaluating the child and developing a treatment plan for him. Only one of the teams at one of these eight centers uses a team diagnosis and evaluation. While in most cases staff members are assigned to "teams," these do not function in the traditional sense but exist rather as a means of having administrative units small enough for accountability. At only one of the centers is it the practice for each child and adolescent patient to be interviewed by a psychiatrist. In most situations, whatever individual on the staff is assigned the case does a solo diagnosis and evaluation. He or she may, if it seems indicated, then request psychiatric or neurological examinations or psychological tests. At none of the centers is the new patient routinely given a physical examination. Psychological tests, for many years one of the stand-bys in the diagnostic process, are not routinely used at any of these centers; indeed, they are the exception rather than the rule. As in adult psychiatry, psychological tests are considered, in the usual scheme, to be too expensive and time-consuming for their yield.[1]

While many psychotherapists identify for themselves a "school" or theoretical system that they feel they follow in their treatment activities, we have never found it easy to engage them in discussions about these persuasions that underlie their work. In any case, we heard various declarations of allegiance to "behavior modification," "transactional analysis," and so on. What we observed is a rather considerable latitude given to each professional to operate in a style that makes sense to him and gives him satisfaction. When we asked one center director to describe the treatment philosophy of his clinical staff, he replied, "Since we have 45 staff members, we have 45 philosophies."

If one sought a single unifying therapeutic rationale, it would perhaps be the desire to provide the young patient with an opportunity to have a trusting relationship with an appropriate and consistent adult.

Although individual psychotherapy is available at all eight centers, a considerable part of the service is provided through various kinds of groups. The smallest "group" would be the identified patient and his parents. In contrast to the earlier practice of the child being seen by the therapist while his parents were seen by a social worker, family therapy has come to the fore; the child patient and his parents are seen all at the same time by one therapist. In other cases, several sets of parents are seen together in a group, while their children are being seen separately in another group. And in various programs there is "family group therapy," in which two or more entire families are seen together in a group. We found little evidence that group therapy is being used in these programs merely as an expedient to make staff time go further. Rather, we found a high level of enthusiasm for the therapeutic usefulness of the groups, with a belief that they have some unique values and advantages. At the

---

[1] In a Joint Information Service study of personnel at eight community mental health centers, psychologists reported that they spend only eight percent of their time giving psychological tests. R. M. Glasscote and J. E. Gudeman: *The Staff of the Mental Health Center: A Field Study.* Joint Information Service, Washington, D.C., 1969.

same time, individual psychotherapy continued to be highly valued; some children were seen only in this fashion, while in some cases both individual and group treatment were prescribed for the same child.

At several of the day-treatment and residential programs, behavior modification techniques were being used. This is a latter-day manifestation of the conditioning process developed by Pavlov and his associates around the turn of the century. While this work became and remains the underpinning of Soviet psychiatry, it remained visible in the United States mainly in the arena of academic psychology and learning theory, refined along the way by Skinner in his concept of operant conditioning. For some decades it was notably absent from American psychiatry and clinical psychology, which instead went the route of psychodynamics. Eventually, beginning in the 1950's and accelerating in the 1960's, some practitioners and institutions in this country turned to conditioning. To oversimplify somewhat, behavior modification consists of a system of rewards and punishments. Certain behaviors are identified as desirable, others as undesirable. The desired behavior is then rewarded—with attention, with money or a substitute such as a "token," with a recreational privilege, or with "points" or "credits" that may later be exchanged for something one desires. Conversely, undesired behavior is punished either by neglect, by withholding privileges, or by subtracting points that were previously earned. We were interested to learn that some programs which previously extracted penalties for poor performance had stopped doing so; they now give only rewards for good behavior, not punishments for bad behavior.

I F WE WERE TO COMBINE INTO A SINGLE PROGRAM all the services for children and adolescents which were being provided by these eight centers, we would have a very rich model indeed. Viewed individually, each appears to be providing a service which, while more extensive than at many other mental health centers, is still meeting only a fraction of the demand. Even in these carefully chosen programs, there are considerable gaps—for example, there may be a day program for children but not for adolescents, and vice versa; a short-term inpatient capability, but no provision for longer-term residential treatment, and vice versa; services deployed into the schools, but no day-treatment program for young people too disarrayed to attend the regular school. Beyond this, there is the problem of the disparity between supply and demand. While the centers in almost all cases do a good job of making an immediate response to those who come to them, their efforts to "casefind" the young people who might benefit from treatment have been limited. To promote the use of the service would be self-defeating, since it would identify more cases than the center has the capacity to treat. Only enough casefinding is done to provide patients up to the present capacity; largely because of limited funds, the centers would find it impossible to expand staff and facilities so as to provide a definitive service to all the young people in the catchment area.

A Composite Program

EACH OF THE EIGHT CENTERS included in this study was providing some imaginative and creative services for young people. At the same time, no one of them constituted a complete model. However, if we catalog their various activities and combine them into a single hypothetical program, we come up with a very rich model—richer, we feel confident, than presently exists in any community in the United States. Let us consider what such a program would provide.

Family life education. Young people should be reared in environments that promote and support healthy growth. Since for most children the parents are by far the most important influence during the first several years, it is self-evident that parents should be well informed about the process of healthy development in children, including a knowledge of age-appropriate behavior and signs and symptoms that suggest difficulties.

Several of the eight centers studied here, and more than a score of the centers responding to our earlier questionnaire survey, are providing to some extent educational programs concerning child development and rearing. Some take the form of general courses in family life, child development and rearing, sex education, "marital enrichment," and so on. Others are more specifically slanted to special groups, such as expectant mothers, mothers of newborn children, and pregnant unmarried girls. This last group might benefit particularly from interventions intended to help them deal with their feelings about their special circumstances, to help them make an informed decision about whether to keep the child or place it for adoption, and what precautions to take to avoid future out-of-wedlock pregnancies.

Because the substantial majority of high school students go on to get married and have children, we believe that such a course should be routinely available in the high schools—perhaps required rather than elective. The numbers of young people in a mental health center catchment area are too great to expect that most centers will be able to expand their efforts to provide such instruction for all young people. Consequently, the center probably serves its area best by taking the initiative

233

to develop pilot programs as an example for the schools, which can then be encouraged to develop such courses under their own auspices.

Relationships with schools. All eight of these centers—and evidently the substantial majority of all mental health centers—invest amounts of time in the schools ranging from moderate to extensive. Perhaps the major effort is to help classroom teachers to feel comfortable with their students and to make them aware of particular behaviors which, although irksome, may be quite appropriate to children at particular stages of growth.

As far as we know, there is not yet a single mental health center catchment area where the center is providing consultation to all of the classroom teachers. We have already mentioned some of the logistical and financial problems. The ultimate solution, if there is to be one, surely lies in improving the nature of teacher training so that graduates understand child behavior and development better than now seems to be the case.

But even if this should come to pass, consultation from the mental health center would probably continue to be beneficial, because of the many special problems and circumstances that arise. One promising arrangement is that accomplished by the Alger-Delta-Marquette Community Mental Health Center, which provides consultation services to all the elementary schools in Marquette, Michigan, under a contract providing for payment at a modest per capita fee.

Services to the juvenile court. Three of our eight centers are located in communities where the juvenile courts have developed their own clinical resources by recruiting people trained in mental health disciplines to operate a "court clinic." In other cases, the mental health center provides a diagnostic evaluation of young offenders referred by the courts on the suspicion that they may have an emotional disorder.

Interagency caretaker group. One center, Alger-Delta-Marquette Community Mental Health Center, had established an "interagency caretaker group" in a town whose population was too small to have most of the customary agency resources. In this case, ministers, school personnel, a representative from the court, another from the welfare department, and so on, meet weekly to "discuss our jobs, our clients, ourselves, and how to serve the community more effectively."

Referral to private practice. In areas that have a considerable supply of private practitioners, it may be desirable to refer some young people and their parents for private treatment. In some cases, as with Peninsula Hospital Community Mental Health Center, funding arrangements make it possible for the mental health center to reimburse the private practitioner for center patients at his regular fee. In other cases, as at Arapahoe Mental Health Center, the referral may be appropriate because the family income is such as to require a clinic fee approaching the cost of private treatment; through the referral, the center thus reserves its time for those unable to afford private care. On the other hand, if the budget of the center relies on payments from patients, the center may particularly need to hold on to those who have the income to pay most or all of the fee. With a rapid growth in recent years in voluntary health insurance benefits for psychiatric treatment, the center may want particularly to see whether the applying family is covered, and, if so, whether it would not be appropriate to make a referral to private practice.

Emergency service. All eight centers receive high marks for their arrangements for handling emergencies. While none provides mental health personnel actually on the spot around the clock, all have a reasonable provision either for psychiatric emergencies involving children and adolescents to be handled through the general emergency room or by a telephone answering service. In those cases where the personnel are not mental health professionals, they are "backed up" by mental health professionals. In general, there appear to be relatively few emergencies involving young people.

"Urgencies." A larger number of calls concern families whose circumstances, although not really representing an emergency, are extremely distressing and painful. Two of the centers maintain one open appointment each day so that families having problems of such nature can be seen with a minimum of delay.

Advance information forms. The Arapahoe center has developed an extensive advance information form which is provided to the parents of each family applying for service. Among other purposes, it represents a fairly complete social and medical history and thus conserves a considerable amount of professional time that would otherwise be required in taking these histories.

Screening clinic or *crisis unit.* All eight centers see themselves as containing their young patients within a "crisis intervention" mode of treatment when that will serve. Some, such as Peninsula and Convalescent Hospital for Children, actually stipulate the number of sessions by which it is hoped that the crisis having brought the family to the facility will have been resolved (specifically, six and three sessions respectively). Others, such as the Western Missouri Mental Health Center, have particular personnel designated for this "first order" intervention. In all cases, those who do not respond within this time frame can, of course, be provided with an arrangement for continuing care; but in any event certain of the facilities see it as useful to stipulate a specific, and brief, time within which the staff member anticipates a resolution of the crisis.

Evaluation by child psychiatrist. Only at Kedren Community Mental Health Center are all young patients examined by a child psychiatrist in the course of entering the program. (At Convalescent Hospital for Children a psychiatrist interviews all children going into the *day* program or the *inpatient* service.) At all of the others, examination by a child psychiatrist is available on request. This leaves to a nonmedical staff member the decision concerning the need for examination by a person with medical training. The authors and consultants believe that every child and adolescent being evaluated for treatment need should be examined by a child psychiatrist. We realize that to do so would pose problems of *a*) financing, since it would represent an additional expense, and *b*) availability, since many mental health centers have experienced considerable difficulty in recruiting child psychiatrists. Nonetheless, because behavioral and emotional problems may have significant somatic implications, we believe that the child psychiatrist, with his training in medicine, should see each young patient in the course of developing a treatment plan.

Psychological tests, neurological and physical examinations. At all of these programs having an inpatient service, each child or adolescent receives a physical examination as part of his admission as an inpatient. Otherwise, physical and neurological examinations and psychological testing are not done routinely at any of these centers. Rather, the staff member who processes the young patient into the program asks for such tests only when there seems to be particular indication of need.

Evaluation in the schools. Certain of the centers do some or much of certain evaluations within the school, for various reasons. Peninsula Hospital sends a mental health professional to the school on those occasions when a young person is unwilling to come to a mental health facility. The Cambridge program sends a staff member to the school in the case of most children who are being evaluated for treatment, for the purpose of observing the child in class and of obtaining pertinent information from the schoolteacher. As is detailed in the description of its program, Arapahoe Mental Health Center provides a great deal of its services within a number of the schools in its catchment area.

Satellite clinics. Five of these centers, on the premise that the territory covered by its catchment area is too large to be served conveniently from a single locus, have deployed staff to "outposts" or "satellites." These are particularly characterized by locations in lower-income neighborhoods, whose residents are believed to be more reticent than others about traveling out of their neighborhoods to obtain helping services. Typically the satellites provide intake, outpatient, and sometimes day programs and are "backed up" by the parent facility for more specialized services.

Individual psychotherapy. Despite a very marked interest in the use of groups as not only a viable but in some cases preferable approach to treating young people, there remains an important interest in and use of individual psychotherapy. The major training emphasis for perhaps the considerable majority of present-day practitioners continues to be individual treatment, with relatively few having had formal training in group therapy and scarcely any in family therapy; thus, for some professionals there is a greater familiarity with and sense of comfort in individual treatment. Among these eight programs there is a distinct tendency to reserve individual psychotherapy to senior members of the professional staff.

Family therapy. As the focus on working only with the parents changed, in the 1930's, to seeing the child and his parents separately, perhaps it was inevitable that in time families would be treated together as a system or social unit. Family therapy has come to play an important part in the treatment efforts of the eight programs in this study, sometimes involving only the parents and the child identified as patient, sometimes involving siblings as well, with an emphasis in most cases on dealing with the current disequilibrium that caused the family to seek help. Family therapy conserves professional time in contrast to the practice of having one staff member see the parents while another sees the child.

Although a technology of family treatment has been formulated in recent years, it seems safe to say that most of the staff working in these eight programs who are engaged in family therapy learned on the job. Formal training in family therapy techniques remains rare. The child psychiatry training program associated with one of these eight centers continues to make family therapy an elective rather than a required course.

Group treatments. A variety of kinds of groups are in use at these eight centers. Some involve only the young persons identified as the patients. Others involve only the parents of the identified patients. Some consist of special groups such as mothers and daughters, or mothers only. The flavor and character of the groups varies widely. Some may be "time limited," more or less didactic, and "closed" in the sense that the membership remains the same. Others may focus almost entirely on the exploration of feelings, may continue indefinitely, and may be "open ended" in the sense that the patients and/or their collaterals may enter and leave in accordance with individual need while the identity of the group continues. The group may be led by one, two, or sometimes even more staff members, who may either all be professionally trained or may be an intermix of mental health professionals and "paraprofessionals."

The group sessions are posited on the belief that the transactions within the group and among its members can in themselves be beneficial—that individuals and families can take strength from knowing that the problems confronting them are experienced by others as well, that they can help one another to formulate ways of dealing with emotional troubles, that they can assist one another in increasing understanding of their behavior.

One of the more recent manifestations of the group approach is *family group treatment,* in which two or more complete families meet together with a therapist to deal with their problems.

Among these eight centers are a number of personnel, notably social workers, who have been trained to lead group therapy. A number of others with no formal training have been taught, through supervision, on the job.

In addition to the therapeutic usefulness as such of the groups, they conserve professional staff time.

Treatment in the schools. The Arapahoe center provides a certain amount of treatment in the schools themselves. In some cases this occurs during school hours, mostly in the form of group activities designed to enhance the socialization of children who have problems in relating and behaving appropriately and acceptably. These children are not considered patients or clients, and no clinical records are kept for them. The purpose of such groups during school hours is to deal *in situ* with children who have milder pathology or whose parents are resistant to bringing them to the clinic and participating in the treatment themselves. Other groups take place within the schools, but after school hours, for children who for a variety of reasons would have difficulty coming to the mental health center.

Preschool day program. The Cambridge program is notable for a day program for about one hundred preschool children, many of whom have been extruded as "unmanageable" from Headstart programs. Children with emotional disturbance and with mental deficiency are intermixed, in the belief that both forms of deficit need and will respond to the same kind of intervention. The children are seen in small groups which meet for half days two or more times a week, in several locations in the catchment area, to engage in a variety of therapeutically oriented activities and play. Results have been dramatic.

Relatively little is being done by the other centers for preschool children (Kedren is involved in an extensive Headstart operation, but not specifically for children identified as having emotional problems). As we have seen, very few such children are presented for treatment. We heard again and again in our visits of instances in which both organic and functional problems had been overlooked or unrecognized until the child reached school age, by which time remediation efforts might be less successful. The directors of these centers gave us mixed reports about pediatricians; in some cases these child specialists were said to astutely detect and recommend treatment for emotional problems; in other cases they were said to be either indifferent to or disdainful of such difficulties.

One interesting suggestion put forth by several center directors was an experimental program that would start all children in school, for half days, at about the age of three (not just those from deprived backgrounds as are presently served in Headstart programs). It was their belief that such an arrangement would lead to the earlier identification of deficits of various kinds that might respond well to early treatment; and in the bargain it might be beneficial to the emotional well-being of the mother to have a few hours a day to herself. If such an experiment were undertaken, it should of course be designed with a control group, in order to determine what advantages may have accrued specifically from the earlier exposure to an educational program.

Children's day treatment. The majority of these eight centers were providing a day-treatment program for children of elementary school age, for the most part serving children either from schools that have no special education classes or children whose behavior is too disruptive even for the special education class. A particularly interesting program is that run by the Aurora satellite clinic of the Arapahoe Mental Health Center. Focused entirely on eight- and nine-year-olds, this service accepts moderately and seriously disturbed children who have been excluded from regular classes and engages them in a combined didactic-activity schedule involving three staff members and an average of twelve children. As they improve in behavior—and most do—they are "phased back" to regular classes, for a time spending part of the day in the special program, part of the day in the regular classroom. In most cases the children are able, at the end of the school year, to return to their regular studies.

Day treatment for adolescents. Kedren and Peninsula were both operating day-treatment programs for adolescents, under an interesting arrangement whereby the patients attend their regular classes at school and then come into the mental health center in midafternoon for a program that lasts until after dinner. Despite the quite different socioeconomic backgrounds—lower to lower-middle class at Kedren, middle to upper-middle class at Peninsula—these were young people who, in most cases, had been such gross behavior problems in school that they would doubtless have been excluded had the mental health center program not been available.

The Kedren program meets two afternoons a week, the Peninsula program five afternoons. There time is divided between group sessions that explore feelings and problems and a broad variety of activities. The young patients have an important voice in deciding how they will spend their time. The full-time staff who have the most interaction with these adolescents consist mainly of younger people with a moderate amount of training (some college work), who are open, warm, and empathic but demanding. In most cases the behavior of these day patients has improved dramatically, allowing them to remain in their regular classrooms and to make some academic progress.

The advantages of such an "after school" day-treatment program are obvious; it allows the young person to continue his education in a regular classroom, and it spares the mental health center the expensive and difficult task of mounting a formal educational program.

At Kedren the parents are encouraged to attend one of the two weekly day-hospital sessions, but only about half do so.

Summer camps. Cambridge, Convalescent Hospital, Arapahoe, and Peninsula Hospital mental health centers have all conducted summer camps for children and/or adolescents. These have helped to provide structure which some of these young people need at all times (not just during the school year), and they have helped to reduce anxiety within the family by removing the identified patient for a portion of the day.

Short-term inpatient service. Western Missouri Mental Health Center is alone among these eight facilities in having a short-stay inpatient facility for children and adolescents. The majority of the others can arrange brief hospitalization of young children on the pediatric service of some local hospital, and brief hospitalization of adolescents on an adult psychiatric ward. All the programs—including Western Missouri—tend to be appropriately conservative about hospitalizing young people, feeling that one should do so only as a last resort. It does appear that the great majority of children and adolescents with emotional problems can be handled satisfactorily without resort to hospitalization, which should be considered justifiable, perhaps, only in the case of children who present the kind of risks to themselves or others that require a controlled environment, or who are grossly disorganized and need the protection of a medical setting in which to reconstitute.

The centers are wary of the tendency to use hospital beds simply because they are available; for example, at Western Missouri there is some feeling that the court mandates inpatient evaluation of a number of adolescents who might be perfectly well evaluated as outpatients, with considerably less traumatization of the adolescent and at a fraction of the cost. Some situations requiring protection or custody might be adequately handled in short-term nonmedical facilities, if these were available (see below). Whether a given community should encourage the development of separate children's and adolescents' psychiatric services will depend on the quality and availability of placements in pediatrics for children and on general hospital adult psychiatric wards for adolescents; the location, quality, and availability of existing children's and adolescents' services serving the catchment area; the availability of the specialized staff required for such units; and so on.

Residential treatment. Only two of the eight centers were operating residential facilities intended to provide intermediate- and long-term care for children either too disturbed to remain in their homes, or from homes too chaotic for the children's well-being. The utilization was strikingly different. The 27-bed residential facility at Convalescent Hospital was full at all times, with a waiting list that entailed a wait of many months. The more recently established residential center at the Alger-Delta-Marquette Community Mental Health Center had not come very close to its present capacity of twelve. The respective catchment area population of the two facilities may account for most of this discrepant experience: Convalescent Hospital's residential component receives children from the entire metropolitan Rochester area, with several hundred thousand people; the Marquette facility was, initially, limited to about 100,000 persons in its catchment area.

It seems probable that only a limited number of young people are so severely ill in a psychiatric sense as to require placement for a year or longer in a special residential facility. The pity is that even so the number of such resources is remarkably small. In the Boston area, for example, the wait for placement in the state hospital unit serving young people can be a matter, literally, of years. In some cases the state will pay for out-of-state placement in a residential facility, but this too can be a cumbersome process requiring months and sometimes years. In other areas, such as Greenville, the state hospital simply will not accept children or adolescents under any circumstances, with the result that massively ill young people, unless their parents are well-to-do and can afford private care, may receive no treatment at all.

Some special aspects of service. At least two of these eight centers make visits to the homes of their young patients in certain circumstances. The Cambridge center, when it receives an urgent application, is almost always able to arrange an appointment not later than the following day; in the event the appointment is not kept, some member of the staff goes to the home to ascertain why, and to discuss what help might be available. At the Peninsula Hospital, the staff of the adolescent day program often transport these young patients home in hospital cars after having attended various activities in the community; it is common for the staff member to come in with the adolescent and have a visit with the family.

Because of widespread reports in the daily press in the recent past concerning "overmedication" of young people, we particularly inquired into the practices of these eight programs regarding the use of prescribed drugs. The information furnished suggests that the programs use medication in an appropriately conservative manner. For both children and adolescents, antianxiety drugs are used in cases where the anxiety level is so high as to interfere with attending school or participating in a treatment program. With children so hyperactive as to be unable to sit still or concentrate on their work for any length of time, amphetamines are sometimes used. If anything, we found an antidrug orientation among some of these programs, on the basis that it was important for the young patient to externalize his "true" feelings so that they might be dealt with in a psychotherapeutic fashion.

Although none of the eight centers had such a facility available to it, the majority expressed the need for a "transitional home" where young people who urgently require removal from their families could be placed, informally, without red tape or delay, in a nonmedical setting that would insofar as possible simulate a "homelike" atmosphere.

THUS, THROUGH AN AMALGAM OF ALL EIGHT PROGRAMS, we have an admirably comprehensive range of services to young people and their families. Some of the more imaginative components and approaches grew out of the experience and the perception of need of particular clinicians. Others were developed in response to particular requests from the community and its agencies, still others were fortuitous, and others developed out of expediency.

In the absence of hard statistical data, there is much empirical evidence to suggest the usefulness of these various services, in terms of helping young people thwarted in their development to move ahead, in terms of relieving pain and distress within family constellations, and in terms of obviating antisocial behavior threatening to the community. We asked at each of the centers to interview parents of young people in treatment. While we had anticipated that the centers would choose for us cases with a successful outcome, it was nonetheless gratifying to hear parents tell of remarkable changes that had occurred in their children in a relatively brief time. Several mothers told us of children so alienated, mute, and unresponsive as to be entirely unapproachable, who, after six or eight months in a special treatment setting, had made remarkable strides toward reaching the socialization level appropriate to the chronological age. In other cases we heard of adolescents, once a source of much grief to their families and mischief to the community, who had shed their anti-social activities and had made up a significant amount of the deficit in their schoolwork.

Orientation Questionnaire to Community Mental Health Centers

NOTE: A number of questions ask for separate data for children and for adolescents, because some centers operate separate services. If you operate a single, combined service for children and adolescents, please reply accordingly. *Also,* we have asked for data in a number of places for the period January-June (inclusive) 1970. If you do not have data readily available for this period, but do have for some other period, such as a recent year, please use the data already collected but indicate that you have done so.

1. Briefly describe the geographic boundaries and the socioeconomic characteristics of the catchment area served by your mental health center.
2. List the other principal treatment resources for mentally ill children and adolescents in your catchment area.
3. Please indicate the administrative categories you use to subdivide your services to clients or patients under the age of 21, and specify the age limits for each category. (Examples: "children, 0-16," "pre-school, 0-6," "adolescents, 12-18.")

Category   *Age limits*

_____

_____

_____

4. Please check which of the following services you presently provide for children and adolescents.

	As a *separate* service within the center itself	*Children* As part of the *general* services of the center itself	Outside the center through affiliation agreement
Outpatient service	_____	_____	_____
Inpatient service	_____	_____	_____
Emergency service	_____	_____	_____
Partial hospitalization service	_____	_____	_____
Consultation & education service	_____	_____	_____

| | *Adolescents* | | |
	As a *separate* service within the center itself	As part of the *general* services of the center itself	Outside the center through affiliation agreement
Outpatient service			
Inpatient service			
Emergency service			
Partial hospitalization service			
Consultation & education service			

5. In what month and year did your community mental health center become operational as a facility funded in part by the federal program?

6. In what month and year did your community mental health center or its predecessor agencies begin to provide the following services for children and adolescents?

	Children	*Adolescents*
Outpatient service		
Short-term inpatient treatment		
Residential treatment center		
Day program		
Emergency service		
Consultation to schools		
Other consultation		
Community education		

7. Describe the administrative structure of the children's and adolescents' service(s), including lines of authority and reporting.

8. Is the length of time a child or adolescent may remain in treatment limited either by custom or by policy?   Yes _____   No _____
   If "Yes," please describe.

9. What are the hours and days of operation for outpatient services and the day program for children?
   For adolescents?

10. On what legal bases do you accept children and adolescents for treatment?

	Children	*Adolescents*
Informal, without written application		
Voluntary under statutes		
Court commitment		
Any other (specify):		

11. During the period January through June 1970, how many referrals did you receive from the following sources?

	Children	Adolescents
Self-referred	_____	_____
Family	_____	_____
Schools	_____	_____
Courts	_____	_____
Welfare	_____	_____
Family physicians	_____	_____
Other (specify)	_____	_____

Does your method of tabulating "referrals" include
    a. All *applicants* for service _____
    or
    b. Only those on whom a
    case record was opened _____

12. Discuss the waiting list(s) for the various components of service, as of the present time and during the past year.

13. Describe your intake procedure, including (a) the way in which the applicant is evaluated and diagnosed, (b) the criteria by which it is decided whether to accept him or not, (c) if he is accepted, how it is determined to which service and staff member(s) he will be assigned. Particularly, who makes these various decisions?
    a. *For children:*
    b. *For adolescents:*

14a. In practice, are there any categories of children or adolescents who are excluded from or rarely accepted by your center?

14b. Indicate the number and percentage of all children and adolescents seen by the center from January through June 1970 who fall into the following categories (no case should be included in more than one category).

	Children		Adolescents	
	Number	Percent	Number	Percent
One screening interview only	_____	_____	_____	_____
Screening interview, plus community contacts (but no further in-person interviews at the center)	_____	_____	_____	_____
Evaluation only (in addition to screening)				
By psychiatric interview only	_____	_____	_____	_____
By psychological testing only	_____	_____	_____	_____

	Children		Adolescents	
	Number	*Percent*	*Number*	*Percent*
By psychiatric interview, plus psychological testing	_____	_____	_____	_____
Screening interview plus outpatient treatment (without other evaluation)				
For one or two interviews beyond screening interview	_____	_____	_____	_____
For three to eight interviews beyond screening interview	_____	_____	_____	_____
For more than eight interviews beyond screening interview	_____	_____	_____	_____
Evaluation plus outpatient treatment				
Evaluation plus one or two interviews	_____	_____	_____	_____
Evaluation plus three to eight interviews	_____	_____	_____	_____
Evaluation plus more than eight interviews	_____	_____	_____	_____
Inpatient service				
Total stay less than one week	_____	_____	_____	_____
One- to four-week stay	_____	_____	_____	_____
Five- to 12-week stay	_____	_____	_____	_____
Longer than 12-week stay	_____	_____	_____	_____
For how many of the above were there				
Neurological evaluations	_____	_____	_____	_____
Educational evaluations	_____	_____	_____	_____

15a. What were the most frequent diagnoses among children admitted for service from January through June 1970?

Diagnosis	*Number of cases*	*Percentage of children admitted*
_____	_____	_____
_____	_____	_____
_____	_____	_____
_____	_____	_____

15b. What were the most frequent diagnoses among adolescents admitted for service from January through June 1970?

Diagnosis	Number of cases	Percentage of adolescents admitted
_____	____	____
_____	____	____
_____	____	____
_____	____	____

15c. On July 1, 1970, how many children and adolescents were being seen in each of the following kinds of outpatient treatment? (Each case should be entered in one category only.)

	Children		Adolescents	
	Number	Percent	Number	Percent
Individual therapy	____	____	____	____
Family therapy	____	____	____	____
Group therapy with other children or adolescents	____	____	____	____
Family group therapy	____	____	____	____
Combinations of the above	____	____	____	____

16. Please provide a description of the relationship of your services for children and adolescents with the following agencies. *This should include specific information regarding these matters: the number of referrals from and to each agency; the frequency of contacts with each, including the personnel involved and the matters discussed; any pooling of staff time; any "lending" or "borrowing" of staff; accessibility on either side to records and files; and formal or informal collaboration worked out for the benefit of patients.*

   a. Local health departments
   b. General practitioners
   c. Psychiatrists in private practice
   d. Pediatricians
   e. The welfare department
   f. The courts
   g. The police
   h. The schools
   i. The clergy

j. The recreation department

k. OEO programs

l. Well-baby clinics

m. The mental health association

17. Describe the extent of your activities in the following "special" areas:

a. Mental retardation

b. Juvenile delinquency

c. Drug abuse

d. Primary prevention

18a. Indicate the staffing arrangement for services for *children.*

Job title	Percent of time worked in children's services	Any special training or experience in working with children

18b. Indicate the staffing arrangement for services for *adolescents.*

Job title	Percent of time worked on adolescent services	Any special training or experience in working with children

19a. Please check which of the following are used in your treatment program for *children*. (Please check EACH line.)

	In all cases	In most cases	In some cases	In few cases	Not at all
Psychological testing					
Individual psychotherapy with child					
Individual psychotherapy with parent(s)					
Family therapy					
Collateral work with parents					
Group therapy					
Medications					
Formal educational program					
Remedial/correctional experiences (specify)					
Other (specify)					

19b. Please check which of the following are used in your treatment program for *adolescents*. (Please check EACH line.)

	In all cases	In most cases	In some cases	In few cases	Not at all
Psychological testing					
Individual psychotherapy with child					
Individual psychotherapy with parent(s)					
Family therapy					
Collateral work with parents					
Group therapy					
Medications					
Formal educational program					
Remedial/correctional experiences (specify)					
Other (specify)					

20. Describe the system used for maintaining records, including the means by which the record follows the patient through the program's various components.

21. Describe your system of fees for various types of services provided for children and adolescents; include how the system was developed, revisions that have been made, and how it is applied.

22. In each applicable category, describe the funding for the children's and adolescents' services from:
    a. The federal government
    b. State government
    c. Local government
    d. Health insurance
    e. Patients' fees
    f. Medicaid
    g. Welfare
    h. Other consequential sources

23. Describe how you recruit staff for the children and adolescent services, including particularly any problems you have had.

24. Discuss turnover of personnel, indicating the specific reasons for resignations and dismissals.

25. Discuss the use of volunteers on the children and adolescent services, including their functions, training, supervision, and numbers of persons and hours of service per week at present and in the recent past.

25a. Discuss the nature and content of inservice training programs
    For nonprofessionals (aides, ward attendants, mental health workers, etc.)
    For professionals to prepare them for service for which they were not previously trained.

26. Discuss how the various components of services for children and adolescents are coordinated, including the means for providing continuity of care.

27. Indicate what communication takes place between the children's and adolescent service and the referring agency during treatment, at time of discharge, and following discharge.

28. Indicate service in terms of the maximum number of children and adolescents who can be served at one time.

	Children	Adolescents
Short-term inpatient service	_____	_____
Residential treatment	_____	_____
Day program	_____	_____
Outpatient service	_____	_____

29. Comment on the suitability and adequacy of the physical facilities available to the children's and adolescents' service(s).
30. Discuss the psychoactive medications used with children and adolescents and the conditions and circumstances under which they are commonly used.
31a. If you have a day-treatment program for children, describe the content of a typical day.
31b. If you have a day-treatment program for adolescents, describe the content of a typical day.
32a. If you provide inpatient treatment for children, describe the content of a typical day.
32b. If you provide inpatient treatment for adolescents, describe the content of a typical day.
33. For children and adolescents terminated from your program during the period January through June 1970, indicate the numbers falling into the following categories at time of discharge.

	Children	Adolescents
In remission		
Improved		
Unimproved		
Against advice		

34. For children and adolescents terminated from your program during the period January through June 1970, indicate how many were:

	Children	Adolescents
Discharged as requiring no further service		
Transferred to the state hospital		
Referred to some other treating agency		
Referred to some other agency for nonpsychiatric services		
Other (specify)		

35. Describe the training activities in which the children's and adolescents' service(s) are engaged.
36. Describe the research activities being undertaken by or on behalf of the children's and adolescents' service(s), including particularly your efforts to obtain data on the outcome of treatment.
37. What are your plans and/or aspirations for the future for your service(s) for children and adolescents?

APPENDIX II

Identifying Questionnaire to Community Mental Health Centers

1. Within the federal definition of a program offering at least the five "essential services," when did your community mental health center become operational (month and year)?

2. Please indicate the administrative categories you use to subdivide your services to clients or patients under the age of 21, and specify the age limits for each category. (Examples: "children, 0-16," "preschool, 0-6," "adolescents, 12-18.")

Category	Age limits	Category	Age limits

3. Please check which of the following services you presently provide for children and adolescents.

	Children		Adolescents	
	As a *separate* service within the center itself	As part of the *general* services of the center itself	Outside the center through affiliation agreement	As a *separate* service within the center itself	As part of the *general* services of the center itself	Outside the center through affiliation agreement
Outpatient service	___	___	___	___	___	___
Inpatient service	___	___	___	___	___	___
Emergency service	___	___	___	___	___	___
Partial hospitalization service	___	___	___	___	___	___
Consultation and education service	___	___	___	___	___	___

4. Of the total current active caseload of your community mental health center, what *percentages* fall in the following categories?

	Children	Adolescents	Adults	
Outpatient service	____	____	____	(=100%)
Inpatient service	____	____	____	(=100%)
Emergency service	____	____	____	(=100%)
Partial hospitalization service	____	____	____	(=100%)
Consultation and education service	____	____	____	(=100%)

5. What were the principal sources of referrals of children and adolescents from January 1 - May 31, 1970?

	Children	Adolescents
	%	%
Parents	____	____
Self-referred	____	____
Family physicians	____	____
Psychiatrists in private practice	____	____
Schools	____	____
Courts, police, probation, etc.	____	____
Welfare department	____	____
Ministers	____	____
Unknown	____	____
Other sources (specify)	____	____
	(=100%)	(=100%)

6. Please check which of the following are used in your treatment program for children and adolescents (please check every line.)

	Children			Adolescents		
	In most or all cases	In some cases	In few or no cases	In most or all cases	In some cases	In few or no cases
Psychological testing	___	___	___	___	___	___
Individual psychotherapy with child or adolescent	___	___	___	___	___	___
Individual psychotherapy with parent(s)	___	___	___	___	___	___
Family therapy	___	___	___	___	___	___
Collateral work with parents	___	___	___	___	___	___
Group therapy	___	___	___	___	___	___
Medications	___	___	___	___	___	___
Formal educational program	___	___	___	___	___	___
Remedial/correctional experiences (specify)	___	___	___	___	___	___
Other (specify)	___	___	___	___	___	___

7. Please describe the extent and nature of your relationships with the following:
   A. Schools
   B. Juvenile authorities (courts, detention and receiving homes, police, probation officers, etc.)
   C. General health resources (well-baby clinics, pediatricians, etc.)
   D. The welfare department

8. Please describe any preventive activities such as educational programs for parents, expectant mothers, mothers of newborn babies, etc.

9. Please indicate the staff members presently assigned to services for children and adolescents.

Job title	Hours/week spent with children and adolescents or collaterals	Highest degree	Indicate any special training for serving children and adolescents
_____	_____	_____	_____
_____	_____	_____	_____
_____	_____	_____	_____
_____	_____	_____	_____
_____	_____	_____	_____

(use reverse side if more space is needed)

10. In what ways do you feel that your services to children and adolescents need to be intensified or augmented, in order to meet the needs of your catchment area?

11. What do you see as the most significant problems in attempting to provide adequate services to children and adolescents?

WASHBURN CHILD GUIDANCE CENTER
2430 Nicollet Avenue South
Minneapolis, Minnesota 55404